D1478489

89019850

Ahead of His Time

Michel T. Halbouty
Speaks to the People

AHEAD
OF HIS TIME

Michel T. Halbouty Speaks to the People

Edited by James A. Clark

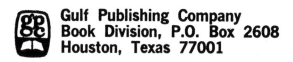

Gulf Publishing Company
Book Division, P.O. Box 2608
Houston, Texas 77001

Library of Congress Catalog Card No. 73-187217.
ISBN 0-87201-024-4.

Contents

Biographical Summary of Michel T. Halbouty

Michel T. Halbouty is internationally recognized as one of the most outstanding geologists and petroleum engineers in the world. He is a renowned authority on the geological and engineering problems of the Gulf Coast of Texas and Louisiana, and is rated as one of the top experts on the geology of Salt Domes. He is also most active as an oil operator and producer—producing and operating in many oil and gas fields.

He is a graduate of Texas A&M University, having received his Bachelor of Science Degree in 1930 and his Master of Science Degree from that institution in 1931 in Geology and Petroleum Engineering. In May, 1956 he received the Professional Degree in Geological Engineering from Texas A&M University. (The first to be conferred by the University.) In June, 1966, the Degree of Doctor of Engineering, honoris causa, was conferred upon him by the Montana College of Mineral Science and Technology.

He joined the Yount-Lee Oil Company at Beaumont, Texas (then the world's largest independent oil producer) as Geologist and Petroleum Engineer, in July 1931, and a year and half later was promoted to Chief Geologist and Petroleum Engineer. He remained with Yount-Lee Oil Company in the latter position until the company was sold to Stanolind Oil and Gas Company in 1935. During the period with the Yount-Lee Oil Company his recommendations resulted in the discovery of several major oil fields in the Texas-Louisiana Gulf Coast.

Following the sale of Yount-Lee Company, Halbouty joined Glenn H. McCarthy, Inc. as Chief Geologist and Petroleum Engineer, Vice President and General Manager. He left McCarthy in

1937 to enter the private practice of his professions as a Consulting Geologist and Petroleum Engineer in Houston, Texas. However, while he was with McCarthy, his recommendations resulted in the discovery of several oil fields in the Texas Gulf Coast.

Halbouty practiced his profession until February, 1942, when he was called to active duty in the Army as a Captain in the Infantry. Prior to entering the Army, Halbouty was geologically responsible for the discovery of nine new oil fields and extensions in the Texas-Louisiana Gulf Coast. After fourteen months of training at the famed Infantry School at Fort Benning, Georgia, he was transferred from the Infantry to serve on the Army-Navy Petroleum Board under the Joint Chiefs of Staff, as geologist and engineer in charge of domestic and foreign allied production. He was detached from the Army in September, 1945, with the rank of Lieutenant Colonel while serving as Chief of the Petroleum Production Section of the Army and Navy Petroleum Board.

Halbouty re-entered the consulting business and soon thereafter also began to drill his own wells as an operator. His first discovery was the Ashland Oil Field in Natchitoches Parish, Louisiana, on January 1, 1946, and since then he has been drilling wells as an independent oil operator throughout the United States. He is responsible for discovering many new oil and gas fields.

Halbouty has written and published over 175 papers, mainly on petroleum geology and petroleum engineering; one book entitled *Petrographic and Physical Characteristics of Sands from Seven Gulf Coast Producing Horizons* and another entitled *Salt Domes— Gulf Region, United States and Mexico* (the only such single volume on this subject in the world's scientific literature); co-author of the best seller, *Spindletop*, Random House, 1952, and is currently engaged as co-author in the writing of two new books, one on the East Texas giant oil field, which will be entitled *The Last Boom*, and the other entitled *The Book of Oil*.

He is a member of many world-wide professional and technical societies, including the American Association of Petroleum Geologists; the Geological Society of America; the American Institute of Mining & Metallurgical Engineers; the Society of Petroleum Engineers of AIME; the American Association for the Advancement of Science; the Society of Economic Paleontologists and Mineralogists of America; the Society of Exploration Geophysicists; the Seismological Society of America; the American Institute of Professional Geologists; The Institute of Petroleum, London, England; International Association of Sedimentologists; the Asociacion Mexicana de Geologos Petroleros. He has served on many important committees and as an officer of the various societies.

He is also a member of the National Energy Study Committee and a member of the Executive Committee of the Division of Earth Sciences, National Academy of Sciences, National Research Council.

Halbouty, also, is president and chairman of the Board of the Halbouty Alaska Oil Company. The company is referred to as Halasko, and owns leases on acreage in Alaska. The company has so far discovered a gas field in this new State and is the first gas discovered by an Independent in Alaska.

In addition to his oil and gas operations Halbouty owns extensive banking interests. He is Chairman of the Board of the following banks: North Side State Bank in Houston, Texas; First National Bank in San Angelo, Texas; West Side National Bank in San Angelo, Texas; the First National Bank in Paris, Texas; and the First National Bank of Deport, Texas; and a Director of the Bank of Texas, Houston, Texas.

Halbouty takes a most active part in community and civic leadership. He is Chairman of the Board of Trustees of the Geosciences and Petroleum Engineering Foundation of Texas A&M University; he is a member of the Board of Trustees of St. Luke's Episcopal Hospital, the Texas Heart Institute, and Texas Children's Hospital, in Houston, Texas; he is President of the Sponsors' Club of the Houston Pin Oak Charity Horse Show, and serves on many other civic projects. In 1964 he was appointed Civil Defense Director for Houston at $1.00 per year salary and has served continuously since his appointment.

In October, 1965, Halbouty received the Texas Mid-Continent Oil and Gas Association's Distinguished Service Award for 1965, presented to an independent for outstanding services and contributions to his industry and profession. In February, 1968, he was named Engineer of the Year by the Texas Society of Professional Engineers and the Engineer's Council of Houston. He was also awarded the Texas A&M University's Distinguished Alumni Award in May, 1968. In April 1969, Mr. Halbouty was awarded Honorary Membership in the American Association of Petroleum Geologists. In June, 1970, he was conferred a Honorary Membership in the Houston Geological Society. In 1969, the Wisdom Society for the Advancement of Knowledge, Learning and Research in Education presented Mr. Halbouty with the Wisdom Award of Honor and elected him to the Wisdom Hall of Fame. In February, 1971, he received the DeGolyer Distinguished Service Medal of the Society of Petroleum Engineers of AIME.

In the Fall of 1964 and Spring of 1965, he was a Distinguished Lecturer for the Society of Petroleum Engineers of AIME and in the Fall of 1965 and Spring of 1966 he was a Distinguished Lecturer for the American Association of Petroleum Geologists.

He served as president of the world's largest organization of earth scientists, The American Association of Petroleum Geologists, for the 1966-67 term.

James A. Clark
Editor
December 29, 1971

Foreword

This book is a selection of speeches on a very complex and vital subject—petroleum—written and delivered by one of the most articulate spokesmen for the American petroleum industry.

These are only part of the hundreds of speeches Michel T. Halbouty has made in the past 40 years. In the same period he delivered many papers on geology and petroleum engineering, all of which have been published.

Although he started appearing before audiences in the early-30's, the earliest of the speeches contained herein was in the mid-50's when the first signs of the energy crisis of the '70's began to surface.

Mr. Halbouty has devoted untold hours preparing for, traveling to and delivering these addresses; all at his own expense, with the singular view of informing those within and those outside of petroleum about issues confronting the industry as they affect the public interest.

He has traveled to virtually every state in the union, and to many foreign countries. For each invitation he has been able to accept, his office has received a score.

The selection of these speeches has been made on the basis of not only their wide appeal, but also on their *prophetic* nature. In many instances, Mr. Halbouty has uncannily foretold important events and the potential harmful consequences to the industry and the public welfare.

He has been criticized as a controversial figure within the industry. Yet the passing of time has frequently converted critics into supporters of his viewpoints.

Mr. Halbouty pulls no punches. He has spoken out against anything that he considered detrimental to his industry, his country, or his professions.

No one who has ever heard Mr. Halbouty deliver a speech will deny that he is one of the most dramatic orators of our day.

He has a rule. He will not insult an audience by making a speech without saying something important. Many of the speeches in this anthology have been made on other occasions with slight variations. He is constantly updating, improving, and enlarging his remarks. He can make the same speech on consecutive nights and those hearing both will find new drama and information in the second speech. In this regard he is much like a professional actor who improvises, constantly changing his lines in an effort to fuse the exact meaning of the word within the rhythm of the phrase.

It was at my suggestion that Mr. Halbouty agreed to have what I considered the most important of his speeches put in book form in order that they might be made available to those interested in the industry, as well as to public and institutional libraries. There is no question in my mind that these speeches will someday have historical significance.

I believe that these speeches capture the spirit and attitude of Mr. Halbouty and indicate his unusual knowledge of the field of energy and especially petroleum controversy.

Mr. Halbouty is one of the world's foremost geologists and petroleum engineers, practicing both professions in his role as one of the nation's most active independent oil and gas explorers and producers.

His advantage over most corporate or political speakers is that he has only to account to himself and his own judgment. He has no boss, no stockholders, and no board of directors to look over his shoulder and censure him. Through his independence he has been able to create the basis of new thinking and new approaches to problems and subjects. Once out in the open these ideas become unrestricted, and are often adopted and expressed by others. He breaks the ice on an approach to a subject. Almost all of his utterances contain some essence of controversy because they are outside the realm of the ordinary, accepted stands on subjects. In fact, it is this controversial nature of his speeches which creates the demand for his appearances and attracts the media to comment.

Throughout these speeches a careful reader will be able to detect Halbouty's iconoclastic attitudes. The most frequent subjects of his attacks have been on policies of those in his own industry, especially the integrated companies. But he has also been highly critical at times of his fellow independent oilmen, geologists, and engineers. Almost single-handed he attacked the sacrosanct Texas Railroad Commission at the very time his friend, General Ernest O. Thompson, probably the most powerful member in the history of that commission, was the most dominant influence in the petroleum industry. Yet neither man ever lost his deep respect for the other. They simply disagreed on the interpretation of the ancient rule of capture as it applied to conservation and especially to correlative rights. In the end of this long and bitter legal battle, Halbouty's views were upheld by the Supreme Court of Texas.

His most pointed attacks on the major companies had to do with their shortcomings in the field of foreign oil imports, but there were other issues. Among these were their shortsightedness in dismissing an army of highly experienced exploratory specialists at the very time company spokesmen were anticipating future serious shortages of domestic gas and oil. He also challenged them on the issue of pitting geologists and geophysicists against each other when they, in his opinion, should have been unifying the two scientific disciplines for the good of joint exploration.

Mr. Halbouty took both independents and majors to task for their frequent hostile attitudes toward each other. In one speech he advocated a forum wherein they could meet to iron out most of their differences without airing their dirty linen in public and adding unnecessarily to the arsenal of ammunition used by the dedicated enemies of the industry.

The federal government is not immune from the barbs of Mr. Halbouty's oratory. In all administrations, Democratic and Republican, he criticized the government's shortsighted attitude toward taxes, pricing and import policies, among other subjects.

His fellow independents frequently felt his wrath. For instance, the Independent Petroleum Association of America proposed legislation to place mandatory import controls under statute rather than executive order. He warned that this would play into the hands of those who favored federal control of the industry, and thereby brought on a major hassle. Immediately,

many sound independents fell in line with the Halbouty viewpoint and in rather short time the association project was apparently scrubbed. And this while Halbouty was serving as a director and member of the executive committee of the organization.

One of Mr. Halbouty's most effective campaigns, this one for total conservation, took him on a one-man sojourn across Texas for better conservation laws. The result of this action was the organization of a statewide committee of independent and major company oilmen which eventually succeeded in placing a mandatory pooling law on the statutes in Texas. The most important fall-out of this was the virtual elimination of the iniquitous rule of capture interpretation which had caused the drilling of hundreds of thousands of unnecessary, expensive and reservoir damaging wells on town lots and other small tracts of land exempt from ordinary field rules.

But probably the most significant campaign in Mr. Halbouty's career started in the late fifties when he warned the industry and the nation about a coming energy crisis and the danger of dependence on foreign sources for oil and gas. The thrust of his warning was that the Soviet Union could gain domination of Middle East and African oil for the purpose of imposing its political influence and theories on western Europe and eventually the entire Western Hemisphere, including the Unitd Stats. Very few, if any people, paid any attention to him then, but, today, petroleum company executives, state governors and legislators, influential members of Congress and even the White House are sounding off on the "imminent energy crisis." It is uncanny that their present concern is exactly what Halbouty said over 12 years ago.

On various occasions and in parts of speeches on other subjects he kept hammering this subject home to his audiences. In 1968, in Dallas at the 8th Annual Institute on Exploration and Economics of the Petroleum Industry, he lit heavily on the subject in a talk that traced the history of U.S. foreign oil development. The speech was one which softened his fellow independents' criticism of oil importers by his lucid explanation of facts leading up to that policy. This speech was repeated on other occasions, as most of his speeches are. But the climax to this subject came in 1970 in Los Angeles when he addressed the American Association of Petroleum Landmen in a speech titled "Mr. Scripps Said It." He went all the way, warning that the Soviet Union was using the Arab-Israeli conflict to gain control over the vast stores of oil in the Middle East and African countries in order to become economic masters of the world without firing a shot.

This was the most publicized of all Halbouty speeches. It was placed in the Congressional Record, reprinted in VITAL SPEECHES OF THE DAY, commented on and editoralized about in both the industrial and general press. Then, most other oil leaders began to pick up the chant, as did spokesmen for the government, among others.

Incidentally, it was also in this speech that Mr. Halbouty reached the high point in his criticism of petroleum industry communications. He was critical of management rather than the professional communicators. He once again accused the industry of "talking to itself", a phrase he had invented a dozen years earlier in a statement to a trade journal. He said the industry talked endlessly about its problems, seldom considering the problems of others and never taking its breath to listen to a question, an attitude or another viewpoint. This talk stirred the industry into action to improve its image and its communications. But he warned that an approach through public relations, advertising and associations alone would never succeed until a method of reaching the general public, "the taxpayer, the voter and the consumer," had been adopted. He suggested a public educational and charitable foundation that would serve the public instead of the industry, and then proceeded to join in the organization of one.

This was a typical approach to a subject for Mr. Halbouty. He never criticizes a statement, an action or a situation without also offering an alternative or a suggestion for a solution.

The secret of Mr. Halbouty's excellence as a spokesman on petroleum lies not only in his ability to articulate, but in his profound knowledge of and sincere fascination with his subject. Often it seems that he has been endowed with a special sense of the future.

His speeches are thoroughly done. First he considers the issue and then he researches it right down to the point where he is convinced his accuracy cannot be challenged. He seeks thought-provoking, even irritating points to pique the interest of his audience. Mr. Halbouty is long on stories, anecdotes or jokes, but his speeches are sufficiently colorful and enlightening to hold his audiences without such additives.

It is obvious to anyone who hears Mr. Halbouty that he actually enjoys public speaking. At heart he is a teacher. Public speaking, statements to the press, and interviews provide him a platform from which to teach.

In this work it has been my pleasure to work with Mickey Herskowitz, one of the nation's most gifted writers, who has written the section and chapter introductions. Mrs. Fred King has edited the manuscripts and the galleys and Stanley K. Young was engaged in various phases of drafting and outlining. The late Harry E. Walton was responsible for the organization of material and the researching of factual information. These people combined their efforts with mine to present some of the viewpoints of a man who is a legend in his time.

James A. Clark
Editor
December 29, 1971

Introduction

In the Foreword of this book I have stressed the rare prescience of Michel T. Halbouty in his writings and speeches. This book is going to press immediately and I could not resist adding this page because the excerpts from the following two speeches exemplify the entire tone and title of this book, *Ahead of His Time.*

Address by Michel T. Halbouty, President-Elect of the American Association of Petroleum Geologists, before the 41st Annual Meeting of the American Association of Petroleum Geologists, Society of Exploration Geophysicists and Society of Economic Paleontologists and Mineralogists, in Long Beach, California, on March 24, 1966.

"This brings to my mind that we are depending more and more on foreign oil. This is not good for the security and welfare of this nation and its people. Communist influence is spreading everywhere. We must now guard ourselves against greater dependence on these unstable foreign sources.

"I think I can safely say that we should look to our neighbor to the north, Canada, for a permanent energy alliance because it is a free country like ours without communist threat and where there is a very high energy supply potential. For this reason, it has remained a mystery to me that the United States and Canada have not, long ago, reached a firm petroleum international policy which later can be expanded into a petroleum hemispheric policy. In fact, the policies between these two great neighbors should include all forms of energy."

Address by U.S. Senator Henry M. Jackson, Chairman, Senate Interior and Insular Affairs Committee, before the American Petroleum Institute Annual Meeting, San Francisco, California, November 16, 1971.

"The notorious instability of some of the major producing areas of the world is well known. The possibility that this instability will be exploited by others to the detriment of the United States is always present.

"The situation elsewhere in the world makes it all the more important that we secure our energy supplies by utilizing to the fullest the resources of the North American continent. In this connection, I am convinced that our relationship with our Canadian neighbors on energy matters must be strengthened. I believe we should be working toward the development of a broad North American energy policy. It may be desirable to establish a Joint Canadian-U. S. Energy Board to develop such a policy and to deal with problems of mutual concern and to exploit opportunities for mutual benefit in the energy field."

This is a precise example of Mr. Halbouty's insight. There could have been included in the book dozens of other examples of ideas and even full paragraphs of his speeches used by many industry leaders, governmental leaders, and others where his utterances were repeated months and years later. When these examples (which formed the basis for my suggestion that this book be published) were pointed out to Mr. Halbouty when the material was first researched over a year ago, he was reluctant to have them included. Senator Jackson's remarks in San Francisco last month, however, constitute such a clear illustration of the title of this book that, as editor, I insisted that this example be included.

James A. Clark
Editor
December 29, 1971

Ahead of His Time

Michel T. Halbouty
Speaks to the People

1
PETROLEUM
AND THE PUBLIC

Social Responsibility of the Petroleum
  Professional
Geology for Human Needs
Oil and the Communications Gap
Petroleum—Civilization's Lifeblood
The Impact of Natural Resources on Society

Introduction

Perhaps no other uniquely American enterprise has contributed more, and is understood less, than the oil and gas industry. In ways too plentiful to count it has improved the quality of American life.

That central fact became the basis for this section of speeches by Michel T. Halbouty, delivered to audiences across the land, in the years between 1963 and 1968.

The thread that joins them can be reduced to one word: communications. How to reach the right target, with the right message, at the right time. An industry can paper the country with press releases, but sheer volume is no more effective a form of communication than junk mail.

His speeches hammer at the dangers of a public uninformed about our country's needs and problems and policies regarding natural resources. Years ago, Mike Halbouty sensed that the public would listen to those who provided special knowledge for public benefit, but it would not listen to trade agencies and industry executives who appeared to speak from self-seeking platforms.

These pages reflect a scientist's instinct for truth and the larger view. Halbouty believes it the duty of the petroleum professional to speak out when the public welfare is threatened. In cities such as Los Angeles and Chicago and San Antonio and Washington, before professional and lay groups, he repeated these essential points:

• The public is entitled to the truth. It cannot reach them if oilmen talk only to each other. The story of oil and gas must be told to the people, in words and ideas that the people can understand.

• The American oil and gas industry, rocked by political and economic changes, can no longer tolerate the sort of recklessness that characterized the early days of the petroleum era.

• The country must maintain a strong, independent domestic industry. We are drifting away from it today, a danger not yet fully recognized by the government or the petroleum interests.

• Foreign imports represent a kind of Russian roulette. Ultimately, the Soviets intend to control oil in the Middle East, in spite of the industry's attempts to maintain a foothold there.

• Ignorance, politics and selfishness have for years blocked efforts to conserve petroleum in this country, and these attitudes have brought us dangerously close to a shortage of domestic oil and gas.

• Today, conservation laws are antiquated and unrealistic, and in many areas create the economic waste they were originally designed to prevent.

As he traveled the country Halbouty appeared in the role of a scientist, and not as a special pleader for an industry in which he has been highly successful. His speeches contained a call for the best that man is capable of, and soon others were responding and echoing his words.

Within months after Halbouty had gone on record, the Oil and Gas Journal chided the industry for failing to inform the public. Sen. Hart of Michigan called for a federal commission to serve the interests of the consumers. And Dr. Charles Jones, the then president of Humble Oil, warned that the next decade would provide a test of "social responsibility."

Others supported his plea for more inter-action between our natural resources and the free enterprise system, and shared his concern over the threat posed by imported foreign oil.

In this section, Halbouty urges the industry to make clear its positions on depletion and import controls and other matters vital to its survival. Then, and only then, can the public evaluate its own stake in a strong and healthy petroleum industry.

Social Responsibility of the Petroleum Professional

"The petroleum industry has a language of its own, and it confines most of its talking to itself."

June 28, 1963

We live today in a volatile world. Many world-wide and domestic problems which drastically affect our lives are political. These problems, whether small or large, will be resolved by politicians who are either controlled by the people in a democracy or dictated to by totalitarian rulers.

The United States has a people's government based on the freedom of the individual. Our way of life will exist *only* as long as the people participate in political action which, in turn, insures that our government at all levels will perform its role efficiently and effectively for the welfare of the people.

Political events that shape our lives do not just accidentally occur. They are maneuvered and regulated by those who participate in political activities.

Consequently, many political events occur from time to time that leave us with a sense of dismay that such "things" can happen—and we begin to wonder how these ever began and why they were not stopped before it was too late? As individuals, we complain of the results of these events, but in the final analysis we can only blame ourselves because we have participated too little in proper public affairs. We let the "other fellow" do the thinking for us, and this other fellow usually belongs to a group organized for the sole purpose of gaining a selfish motive.

These selfish-interest groups are assassins without guns; they poison uninformed minds, connive to obtain their selfish purposes, and slowly achieve the assassin's results by killing what is right through propaganda and demagogic procedures. Those who believe differently do very little, if anything at all, to instigate counter measures.

What about the role of professional societies and associations in public affairs? What should professional engineers, geologists, geophysicists, attorneys, accountants, landmen, scouts—all these professionals and a host of others—do to help the petroleum industry and, in turn, help their state, their nation, and above all, the public?

The answer lies in one basic philosophy: to participate more in public affairs.

The public is entitled to the views of those educated and trained in the professions in any field. It is necessary for professional men and women to participate in all areas and levels of politics from the precinct to national conventions.

Petroleum professionals have created a destructive vacuum by their ivory-tower attitude toward public affairs. That vacuum has been filled by "ward-heelers," special interest groups, the so-called minority groups, political hacks, and others who have their own particular interests, as opposed to the public interest, in mind.

Not everyone who participates in political action or public affairs does so with a selfish motive, but those who do not have a selfish motive and are genuinely interested in politics have a more difficult time achieving results because they lack sufficient support. Most professional men are among those who should be helping, but are not.

Occasionally professional men do step out and express themselves, but they usually wait until only a crash program of public relations or participation can forestall a disaster that has been building for years right under their noses.

It is especially important for professional men to be active in public affairs in a democracy such as ours. Obviously a professional man would not bother with taking the time and money to work in public affairs in a monarchy. The king and his ministers take care of all political decisions in such countries.

It would be suicidal, probably, for a professional man, unless he were part of the governing clique, to participate in public affairs in a dictatorship. That would be an unwelcome expression of a nonexistent freedom.

But, in America, it is the duty of professional men to participate in government. The more educated and highly trained a person is, the more his obligation to participate. In this way he can offer leadership, and he can provide an example.

This country is crying for leadership today at all levels of government, but those who possess leadership qualities, including professional people, are too timid or too aloof to become active.

Any professional man owes it to the public to use his stature, his intelligence, and his prestige in public affairs.

Public affairs include precinct, county, state, and national political activity and the obligation to speak out. This obligation is greater on a subject in which an individual has special knowledge.

Petroleum professionals should speak out in volume and not permit the expressions of a few to represent the opinions of a whole profession. For instance, a few misguided (if not, downright subversive) atomic scientists spoke out recently in every way possible to project an idea that might impair our national defense or security.

Amazingly, other professional men in the same field remained silent, even though they were aware of misleading information being showered on the public or their misguided colleagues. They took the attitude that controversy was not their obligation. They let a few men speak out so that the public accepted their views as a concensus of all scientists. Fortunately, a few did belatedly speak out, even though in most cases they were less articulate. Consequently, the public was confused.

How different it could have been if all scientists had spoken out in unison, preferably through appropriate societies, or at least as individuals. It would have been a tremendous public service. In fact, it was an unfulfilled obligation.

Geologists and petroleum engineers have also neglected to perform as they should in public affairs.

For example, geologists have long known that overdrilling of wells, especially the drilling of unnecessary wells, is an imposition on the laws of nature, as well as the public. The general public cannot understand these complex matters if petroleum professionals, who are supposed to know, refuse to speak out publicly when these matters arise for public consideration. The oil industry has been derelict in its duty in many conservation matters. As early as 1933, Dr. Frederic H. Lahee warned of the dangers of overdrilling reservoirs and the shortsightedness of the industry in failing to practice every means of sound and total conservation of petroleum resources.[1]

His paper emphasized that geologists have always been interested in total conservation; in correlative rights—the rights of landowners, royalty owners, and operators; and in the public rights—the rights of consumers to the prevention of waste of a valuable and useful natural resource, such as oil or gas.

Dr. Lahee also recognized the responsibility of geologists to inform the public about the industry. He said:

I submit that, as a group of technical men and women, we should consider it a duty and a privilege to take every reasonable opportunity of informing the public on the simple facts of oil and gas occurrence.[2]

The unfortunate truth is that geologists, who learned so much so early on petroleum production, have said little outside the profession. Other professions in our industry are just as guilty of talking only to themselves.

The public is entitled to information in a language that can be understood. Such important knowledge should not be confined to a technical paper in the records of a professional society.

Dr. Lahee was not a politician or an oil operator. He was a professional man who believed it his duty to speak up, not in a vacuum, but in a public forum. He spoke out when he saw that politicians, operators, and oil companies were ignoring the laws of nature and the rights of the average citizen.

But Dr. Lahee is not the only geologist who should publicly have waved the red flag. Every petroleum geologist in the country should have spoken up—even if his employer or his client or his regulator looked upon his honesty and frankness with disfavor. To have spoken out would have benefited the general public and the cause of total conservation. But more so, oil professional associations should have backed their members in the release of public statements. The public was entitled to such treatment from a professional body of men.

Harry C. Simrall, a professional engineer and the dean of the Engineering Extension Service at Mississippi State University, commented on participation in public affairs in an article, "The Civic Responsibility of the Professional Engineer," (The American Engineer, May, 1963). He said:

> Engineers say that taking part in politics, in community affairs, and in public service is just asking for trouble. It is a thankless job. It is true that if one takes part in politics and other civic affairs, one must learn to suffer criticism—even insults. This is just part of being a public servant, and one must accept such criticisms and insults without becoming bitter about them. The chance of being criticized is no reason to back away from civic responsibility; for, if one is right, the general public will come to accept this fact in the end. Any professional engineer is willing to defend with all the facilities at his command a technical decision. Therefore, should he not be willing to defend his actions in political and civic matters with the same vigor and forthrightness?

How can petro-professionals complain of irresponsible and damaging statutes, rules, and regulations imposed on our industry if we do nothing to contribute knowledge and practical, technical judgment to correct the wrong-doing?

As a geologist and petroleum engineer, I have been engaged over the past several years in a program to bring about total conservation in Texas. As an operator, I have also been interested in conservation to prevent the physical waste by production practices resulting from antiquated rules and regulations still in force.

My identity with this program, which has included some criticism of not only state laws, but the state regulatory body, has resulted in no small amount of criticism of me.

Some of this criticism has been fair, and a great deal of it has not. I have no objection to anyone having a different opinion on conservation, and particularly proper spacing and proper allocation, as long as such criticism is honest and based on scientific and technological fact. But there has been very little of this.

For the most part, the criticism was based on misinformation or self-serving interest. At least, this kind of criticism proves that somebody is listening and is worried over efforts by a few to do something constructive in the public interest.

During the past year, this effort resulted in an organized attempt by a group of well-intentioned Texas oilmen to get an equitable pooling bill through the legislature. We failed in the first round, but we will be back in the 1965 legislature to try again, and I believe we will be successful.

This bill is an example of what concerned professional men could have done to help. The majority of engineers and geologists favored the bill; probably not a single reputable professional technologist or scientist opposed it.

But it was almost impossible to get a professional man to speak out on the issue. Members of the House and Senate committees, as well as all members of the Texas Legislature, would have listened respectfully if the learned societies and some of the specialized associations had appeared or even sent resolutions on the subject. There were none.

Petro-professionals missed an opportunity to be of service, to dispel a cloud of misinformation, to give guidance to honest members of the legislature who did not know who was telling the truth.

On occasions such as this, professional men must have the courage to speak out and to act in the future. They cannot afford to permit a misrepresentation to spread without counteraction. If they do, not only is their profession going to suffer, but they as individuals will be subject to public censure for neglect which could place our country or its resources in serious jeopardy.

Organizations such as the American Petroleum Institute, the Independent Petroleum Association of America, Texas Independent Producers and Royalty Owners Association, and the Texas Mid-Continent Oil and Gas Association are not enough. They are trade associations. Even CEDOT, the special Committee for Equitable Development of Texas Oil & Gas Resources, is not enough.

Such organizations as these may provide funds and communication facilities as well as research and manpower. But they really have little or no standing with the public from a technological standpoint. Most of them are considered associations dedicated to some commercial or industrial project in the best interests of their membership, and, in fact, they are. So, they are expected to be biased on almost any subject affecting their membership.

But this bias is not expected of professional men or professional organizations unless it is bias in favor of truth. The average citizen respects the high ethics of technical professional societies and will listen when professional men express themselves on important issues, especially in their specialized fields. The public needs their advice, leadership, and courage.

Therefore, when any important piece of legislation develops, such as the bill on pooling or on pollution or on proper conservation, technical professional societies should speak up. Local chapters, after approval of the majority of their memberships, should pass resolutions on the subject.

Trade associations, companies, and even individual operators carry far less weight with the public than technical professional societies or individual professional men speaking as professionals. For example, the Society of Petroleum Engineers of the American Institute of Mining Engineers could be most effective if it advocated any piece of legislation based on sound engineering principles and facts. The public would not only welcome this kind of backing, but would see to it that the legislation was passed.

Of course, such expressions should be made so as to be informative and not as an attempt to sway people. The public is entitled to the viewpoint of the professional man. And these views should be given with decorum and dignity, but without equivocation, without fear, and without the source appearing aloof.

In this nation, the public has reached the sophistication where it now welcomes the viewpoint and the expressions of experts and specialists. The public is hungry for direction from authoritative sources.

Who is better qualified to meet this need than professional men?

The petroleum industry has a language of its own, and it confines most of its talking to itself. It seems afraid that the public will not understand or will misunderstand its complexities.

I give the public far more credit than that. In my state-wide conservation campaign in 1960, I found the public response warm. The legislature and the judiciary respond to public opinion, as they should. The speeches I made and publicized wherever I could gave the people of this state information on a controversial subject that they never had before, and they seemed relieved to know the situation.

About 2,400 years ago, Pericles told the citizens of Athens:
An Athenian citizen does not neglect the state because he takes care of his own household. We alone regard a man who takes no interest in public affairs, not as a harmless, but as a useless character.

Under Pericles, Athens rose to her highest glory. Indeed, that period of history has never been equalled in many respects before or since. Yet, when Athens began to ignore this basic philosophy, she was destroyed by Sparta, which was a Communist police state.

So, we must not ever underestimate the influence of an individual or a single organization in public affairs. It is the professional's duty to speak out whenever he thinks the welfare of his industry and the public is at stake. He then will be doing a service to his company, his community, his state, and his nation. He will also preserve the future and assure the security of a healthy, growing industry and a strong democratic government.

REFERENCES
[1] Lahee, Frederic H., presidential address, AAPG annual meeting, Houston, Texas, March 23, 1933, "Petroleum Geology," Bulletin of American Association of Petroleum Geologists, Vol. 17, No. 5 (May, 1933), pp. 548-557.
[2] Ibid., p. 556.

Geology for Human Needs

"A spiritual enrichment comes to those who are able to converse with the earth. Then, the earth becomes more alive and vibrant, and its many mysteries become challenges to solve."   September 17, 1965

Today, as the human race stretches its curiosity into outer space to probe the moon, Mars, Venus, and untold planets of the future; digs deeper into the earth; and explores the mysteries of the seas, one of the most important sciences covering all of these exciting activities is—geology!

So what is geology? Simply, it is the science which deals with the earth, its constitution and its structure, the agencies and processes continually altering it, and the utilization of earth's material by man. Geology deals with the history of the earth and all living things—past and present.

Our science is based on the ancient studies of astronomy, biology, chemistry, mathematics, and physics.

Among other things, geology deals with the weather and the climates; natural resources; the origin and development of animals, plants, minerals, rocks, and gems; and even the origin of man.

Geology is a curious and fascinating mixture of many sciences; yet, it is a definite and enchanting science distinct from all others.

Geologists have made tremendous contributions to the knowledge and well-being of man, but more startling and captivating contributions are yet to come. Time is the only barrier between greater contributions to mankind.

Although some of the greatest geological contributions have been made in this country, I have the firm impression that the advances that will result from such projects as our space and sea programs and many other less publicized endeavors will write remarkable new pages in the history of geology.

I cannot overemphasize that there is no factor vital to the human race which geology does not explore or participate in to some extent, however remote.

It has been our responsibility to explore for all types of minerals, metals, precious stones and gems, and to examine and evaluate the waters and soils of the earth.

In the field of energy supply, our profession is responsible for the discoveries of the raw energy fuels which have been so important in the progress and prosperity of this nation and, more recently, most of the remainder of the world.

In nuclear energy, based on the results of geological exploration for fissionable materials such as uranium, a whole new age of human progress has been opened.

The space program, the newest field of science, will lean more and more on geology as it progresses. We are becoming more involved in the studies of the other planets of the universe and recently astronaut-geologists have been selected as members of the space exploration teams of the near future.

Civilization is spreading as communications improve, thus creating innumerable new contacts between once isolated communities. If the American standard of living should spread to only half the world in the next century, it is certain that raw materials now known would be used up far more rapidly than they could be found, and it is possible that all of the scientific know-how potential now in sight could hardly meet the demand of finding the required new mineral reserves.

This is why we are gradually turning to the seas. We all agree that the seas make up one of this planet's richest ecological units and consist of a scarcely touched reservoir of resources that will absorb increasing proportions of man's research and development energies.

These untold stores of minerals and life are already creating far-reaching challenges to geologists, biologists, and oceanographers.

In association with the paleontologists, we have recorded the age of man and developed a fascinating story of the evolution of all living things; and, working with the archaeologists, geologists have made invaluable contributions to the culture of the entire world.

We have also been responsible, along with engineers, for the development of major building and construction programs such as changing the courses of rivers; locating dams, harbors, high-rise structures, housing developments, railroads, highways, sites for new cities; and numerous other taken-for-granted activities in the advancement of human progress.

Although there are many examples of construction undertaken without geological advice, which had tragic consequences, large industrial sites, new cities, housing developments, and other structures are still built without geological consultation. *To us geologists, this is unthinkable.*

The tremendous losses suffered by people when homes fall into ravines, or reservoirs break and wash entire communities into a mass of debris and take the lives of innocent home dwellers should be enough warning to the public to seek such geological advice *before* construction—and certainly not after the catastrophe.

Geologists and seismologists are currently involved in studies of past earthquakes and are seeking criteria for the possible prediction of earthquakes. This includes the study of the areas more vulnerable to earthquakes and could result in recommendations for the actual removal of major cities or portions of them to other locations where the likelihood of earthquakes would be negligible.

A most vital human need demanding much of our attention is the world-wide water shortage. Lack of sufficient water limits economic growth, undermines and lowers living standards, jeopardizes the security of nations, and, above all, endangers the health of the people.

Answers must be found for this baffling and seemingly impossible problem, or we face the certainty of watching the world's multiplying population steadily perish for lack of this vital natural resource. The water shortage, I would say, is one of our profession's most serious challenges in meeting human needs.

Modern geology has even penetrated into the field of medicine. Recently, in Montreal, a symposium on "Medical Geology and Geography" was sponsored by the American Association for the Advancement of Science and the Geo-Chemical Society. This symposium revealed that a relation between trace elements and human health may be much more than a fascinating hypothesis. I am confident that research will expand these findings and enable our science to add to its many fields that of "biomedical geology."

While abandoning none of the old goals, our science is being called on each day to meet new objectives and to participate in new projects to help meet the ever-growing needs of mankind.

Demands on geologists will increase as human needs increase. The great task for our profession today is to see that there are enough geologists—good and brilliant geologists—to meet this growing demand.

These new geologists must be found, trained, and put to work.

In the field of minerals alone, the challenge to our profession is beyond comprehension.

With world population doubling every 35 years and per capita consumption of almost every raw material mounting with the progress of civilization, the nations of the world are faced with a great problem. This situation challenges all world scientists and technologists, but especially geologists and those associated with the earth sciences.

In the more civilized areas of the earth, geologists have already tapped the most obvious rich sources of raw materials. For example, the easiest oil and gas to find has been found. The same is true of all other minerals which are now being mined and produced. Now we will have to start finding the more difficult and less obvious deposits, and, as geologists, we will find these hidden reserves by employing unrelenting enthusiasm, bold geological deduction and imagination!

Geologists must continuously plan for the world's increasing multitude of people. *Whether the public is aware of it or not, our science of geology is among the most important in the future welfare of the world's people.*

Today the challenges to geologists are far greater than ever before, *but so are the opportunities.* The type of civilization we enjoy in America today will be demanded soon by the people of all nations. This is the age of science, research, exploration, and development.

Solving the mysteries of space and finding the hidden treasures of the seas will demand the service of hundreds of new geologists.

The growth of geologic aerial photographic interpretation is amazing as new techniques are developed in this field alone. Micropaleontology and sedimentology are finding new applications.

Geologists are needed in the new fields of waste disposal, pollution control, land development, and dam construction aimed at providing new sources of water supply.

Petroleum geologists will be needed to explore for the estimated 700 billion barrels of petroleum that are waiting to be found only along the continental shelves of the world. And that is only a fraction of the oil that will be needed to meet the demand that seems to have no end.

So, there can be no doubt about the future requirements for thousands of new geologists to fill these vital assignments in so many diversified areas of scientific endeavors. Yet the enrollment of students taking geology in our universities throughout the nation is far less than the demand—not only for now, but for the next 10 years.

Every parent who has a child that is scientifically inclined or highly imaginative should give every consideration to leading—yes, even pushing—his son or daughter into the study of geology.

I belong to a family of geologists. I have a brother who is a geologist, a nephew who is a geologist, a cousin who is a geologist, a son who is a geologist, and I have a 17½-year-old daughter I am subtly trying to maneuver into taking geology.

There is no finer or more rewarding profession.

Ours is one of the most vital and essential sciences on earth. It is also one of the most attractive and fascinating.

Our profession is not a closed union. We are an army of scientists reaching far out for knowledge. We need the help of every brilliant mind we can attract. The more we learn and the better men we attract to geology, the more effective our science will become.

And the more qualified we will be to meet the growing challenges of human needs through geology.

People almost universally are imbued with a strong desire to travel and see other places in our nation, other countries, and remote lands.

People are impressed with the wonders of nature; yet they do not understand how these wonders came about. Have you ever asked yourself:

How are glaciers, geysers, caves, deserts, petrified forests, mountains, valleys, rivers, and canyons formed?

What causes earthquakes, tidal waves, volcanic eruptions, mud slides, landslides, and sandstorms?

Where do diamonds, gold, copper, salt, sulphur, uranium, aluminum, oil, gas, and coal come from?

What made the seas?

What made and shaped the land?

All of us should become better acquainted with our natural surroundings. We should be eager to understand the world in which we live. In short, we should become familiar with the science of geology. By understanding the ways of nature, a landscape becomes far more interesting. Through geology you will appreciate the miracle of nature's long creative processes.

Earth, as we see it today, is one frame of a moving picture that has been running for billions of years and will run for billions of years more. Wherever we are, all around us, the ages-long story of erosion, of lands rising and falling, of volcanoes erupting and glaciers forming, of rocks and minerals being created is in the making. Within one's own life span, the changes may seem infinitesimally small, but in geology a thousand years are as a day.

When we look at a mountain or a desert, a valley or a sea, it seems that they must always have been as they are now. Man can cut down a forest or blast a small hill away, but who can build a mountain or set the boundaries of an ocean? No wonder people use such expressions as "the everlasting hills" and "the eternal seas."

Actually, the earth is constantly being transformed. Some of the changes on this planet are sudden and exciting. When a volcano blows its top, a great river floods over its banks, or an earthquake shakes the land, we take notice. But mostly the changes are slow: 5,000 to 10,000 years to make a desert, 100,000 years to cut a small valley, 10,000,000 years to build a mountain range. That is how the earth uses time.

Think of some of the ways in which the earth is, at this very moment, changing:

All the mountains of the world are being destroyed. Frost, gravity, running water—such forces are wearing them down, grain by grain. Some day the highest mountains will be no more.

Sea bottoms in some regions are rising. Ages from now they will be peaks among the clouds. The rate of rising may be only an inch per year, but the earth has time.

There are places where the sea is creeping in over the land. Some day in those places fish and crabs will swim where cities were.

As recently as 10,000 years ago, great ice sheets covered most of North America and northern Europe. The ice has now melted back all the way to Greenland and other arctic regions. But the climate could get warmer still. In another 10,000 years all Greenland could be as warm as Florida today.

A spiritual enrichment comes to those who are able to converse with the earth. Then, the earth becomes more alive and vibrant, and its many mysteries become challenges to solve.

Every person should take a simple, easy, and most interesting course in physical geology. If you do not have time to enroll for this study, buy a textbook on the subject. In any event, insist that your children take the course before they complete high school.

The appreciation of the beauty of nature to be gained by studying an elementary course in geology will be a great source of satisfaction throughout the remainder of your and your children's lives.

If only a half dozen of you follow this simple suggestion, not only will your lives be enhanced by a new understanding of nature and the earth upon which you live, but possibly one of your children may become a great scientist, having been awakened by the knowledge obtained through this primary study of the fascinating science of geology.

Oil and the Communications Gap

*"If we do not learn how to reach the public
mind, we may as well get ready for the government eventually to take over the energy
industry, with public approval."*   November 15, 1967

Communications—both ways—between our industry and the general public is the most pressing problem of the petroleum industry today. And the general public includes most employees of the industry.

We seem to have excellent communications between oil and gas companies and oilmen individually. Our communications with the petroleum press, including the trade press and the oil editors of the daily newspapers in the oil country, could hardly be improved. Our communications with the government at all levels seems to be the special target of most industry associations, and these communications are effective.

Where we are weak is in reaching the remainder of the public with our story. Also, we could stand a program that gives us better insight into problems and progress outside our industry, especially outside thinking about us.

Communications is a two-way street—a sending and a receiving of intelligence. We need to listen as well as to talk. Now all we do is talk.

We have failed in our communications with the general public. Any congressman from Minnesota will admit, for instance, that he is forced to oppose percentage depletion because the people in his state oppose it, but they oppose it because they do not understand it. The failure here is largely the failure of the industry to explain the law, its reasons, and its benefits to the general public in Minnesota.

Time spent explaining depletion to members of Congress from states such as Minnesota may never result in a favorable vote on an oil issue, even if they do understand it. If they vote for the law, their constituents will vote for someone else. So, it is the people in Minnesota, and in other such states, who should be educated.

The same process applies to other issues in government which involve our industry. The import problem is one of these. People on the eastern seaboard who use home heating oil to keep warm in extremely cold weather cannot understand our attitude in demanding import controls that result in higher prices for heating fuel. We have not explained our side, at least not sufficiently.

The public is unable to understand why we urge the easing of producer controls on the price of natural gas. We have been depicted as enemies of the public largely through the efforts of uninformed legislators, regulators, and politicians. Still, we do little at the general public level to offset this unfavorable impression.

The general public has the idea that oil companies make excessive profits; that all independent oilmen are high-spending millionaires; that oil-field workers are ignorant, profane ruffians; and that anyone can enter the petroleum business and get rich in a matter of weeks or months.

The public has no conception of the big oil company as a highly complex corporate entity, or the independent oilman as an entrepreneur whose knowledge is, of necessity, a combination of technical, administrative, and scientific skills that must be kept constantly updated and improved to compete. The public would be most unlikely to believe that the oil-field and refinery worker must be a highly skilled and dedicated worker who earns probably the highest hourly wage paid by any industry in the nation.

From the public viewpoint, there is nothing to finding and producing oil except for drilling deep holes in the ground. Few outside the oil industry itself realize that a variety of unusual skills are applied to the drilling of wells and that they cost hundreds of thousands and sometimes millions of dollars. This is because we constantly emphasize the risks we take. Who cares? There is no law forcing us to take these risks.

So here we go merrily down the road to economic destruction in this industry simply because we have not the sense or the skill to convey our story to the public. We do not even tell it to our employees or our stockholders or landowners. These people are all part of the public, and we simply assume they know all about the industry which keeps them alive.

Employees and stockholders, for the most part, do not even agree that depletion is necessary. They have not been told how much they depend on it directly. This is how well the petroleum industry's story has penetrated. And the industry has never had good relations with its ally in depletion—the landowner.

This is not an indictment of oil industry public relations. What public relations this industry has are good. It simply does not have enough. It does not listen to its public relations experts. Both corporations and independent firms are busy with the everyday job of meeting competition or getting the industry story over to a committee in Washington or the state capitol.

The American Petroleum Institute itself practically dismissed public relations some years ago and turned all of its public attention to what it calls public affairs. No association in the industry takes as much interest in relations with the general public as it does in relations with government.

Congressmen are entitled to the educational help the industry can give them with the public. Both the API and the American Gas Association have school programs and make frequent visits to newspaper editors. But these efforts are not enough. New and effective ideas to reach the public as a whole are the most important goal at the moment.

Oil editors outnumber steel, flour, or pharmaceutical editors on daily newspapers, but few people outside the industry ever read the oil pages. In fact, a Houston newspaper's readership survey proves that oil pages are among the most poorly read pages in most newspapers. And Houston is the center of the most oil-oriented metropolitan area in the world.

This lack of readership is not the fault of the oil writers, but of the industry that loads these men with company handouts in which no one is interested except the company that made the release, and ironically, only a few people in the company are interested.

No one helps the oil editor write a readable, controversial, human interest, scientifically interesting, or just plain good news story. Or not enough to make any difference.

Yet the oil editor of most daily newspapers is among the most competent, knowledgeable, and ambitious men in any city room. He needs help from those he wants to help. All he gets is criticism if the composing room puts the wrong cutline under a picture.

Oil desks on daily newspapers are treated like a dumping ground for literary garbage from the petroleum companies in the form of unpaid advertising. And it takes up space that could be used by fresh, readable news about our industry—news that the average reader could find interesting and informative.

Oilmen spend their time making speeches to each other at conventions held by the many associations and societies around the calendar.

It seems that every corporation in the country is rushing its highest executives into this word combat. It does not matter that many of these people have no talent for speaking, that they are all saying the same thing and talking only to oil and gas audiences.

The industry as a whole should develop a supply of excellent speakers, regardless of what company they represent, to address the Rotary, Kiwanis, Lions, and other clubs as well as chambers of commerce, women's organizations, political groups, and labor and technical meetings to spread the story of our industry, its history and accomplishments, and its essential position in our society.

We have a good story. There is nothing about our industry to be ashamed of. There are people in it who can talk about something besides depletion and gas regulations. We need some professional or at least semi-professional speakers to talk to the public outside the industry in person, speakers who can and will answer questions.

If we do not learn how to reach the public mind, we may as well get ready for the government eventually to take over the energy industry, with public approval.

Most oilmen do not realize how low their image is in the country. Let them read newspapers outside their own regions, watch television and motion pictures, read books and magazines if they really want to know their deplorable public standing.

The situation is desperate, but it is not devoid of hope. Many effective means of communication are available to the industry— if it will just take advantage of them. The public and the industry stand only to gain by any breakthrough in communications.

Petroleum—Civilization's Lifeblood

"Our industry is probably the world's worst at communicating with its customers — the people of the nation; yet this is the people's business more than any other in the country." September 11, 1968

Americans are amazingly uninformed about the petroleum industry. Yet, it is their industry. It was conceived, born, and brought up in America, then spread around the world. It is our only native American industry and is packed with the ingredients of the American story—ambition, frustration, opportunity, drama, romance, color, excitement, adventure, struggle, failure, and success.

The men who pioneered this industry are completely fascinating. They were mostly men of unpretentious beginnings who were hungry for success.

They were men like John D. Rockefeller, a poorly paid clerk; or Harry F. Sinclair, the son of a small town druggist; or Frank Phillips, a barber; or Colonel John J. Carter, a soldier with the Medal of Honor; or men such as M. L. Benedum and W. G. Skelly, who started their own small oil companies at 16.

The petroleum industry is one with which Americans can easily identify. The lives of the men in the industry are inspiring stories of individuals who have made outstanding contributions to our way of life. Yet, their only incentives were to make a profit and to make a success of their lives. They saw a way to chase a pot of gold, a way to use our system of competition and freedom to find success.

Most of these men became wealthy. It is part of our national character to ignore or forget a vastly larger army of oilmen who went broke. But they, too, made their contributions.

The oil industry must have been part of America's destiny since the three most important incidents in the history of petroleum were largely accidental and involve men who were certainly unlikely oil pioneers.

The first man was a railroad conductor on sick leave. Edwin L. Drake was persuaded to go to Titusville, Pennsylvania, to drill the first (recorded) well ever successfully drilled for the express purpose of finding oil at its source far below the shallow seeps. Drake was selected because he was an amiable man of high integrity and he had a railroad pass that would take him to and from the proposed drill site.

The well he drilled on the banks of Oil Creek was a total freak. The oil came from a stray sand or small crevice at 69.5 feet below the surface. Although that well started the oil industry, no oil was ever found at the same depth later, and no other successful well was drilled very near the Drake well.

That well gave birth to oil's illumination and lubrication era. It provided the kerosene for lamps at a price anyone could afford at a time when whale oil was becoming scarce and was so expensive that only the wealthy could buy it. It opened a new world of light for the hours after sundown, enabling people to work and study after they left the field or the shop. Oil, therefore, was a boon to education. But it also provided the lubrication that gave impetus to the lagging industrial age and the mass of new machines which required better lubricants.

The next great well in history, the one which opened the liquid fuel age, was the Lucas gusher in Beaumont, Texas. Anthony Francis Lucas was a lieutenant in the Austrian navy when he emigrated to this country and an engineering graduate from the Polytechnic Institute of Gratz. He was also a temperate man who shunned drink, never smoked, and seldom swore.

His predecessor and the man who attracted him to Beaumont was Pattillo Higgins, who had similar personal habits. Higgins tried to promote oil in Beaumont when every expert in the country scoffed at the idea that oil could be found in the unconsolidated sands of the Texas Gulf Coast. All of Higgins' efforts were failures. When he ran out of money, he talked Lucas into resuming the search. Lucas doubted that oil was under the ground at Spindletop, but he thought he could find sulphur. Ironically, although both were mature men, neither had any experience in the oil industry.

Lucas' first well was a mechanical failure, but to his surprise, he encountered oil and was able to save enough to put in a jar to show the skeptics. Later, with the help of the Guffey and Galey oil firm and money from the Mellons of Pittsburgh, he brought in the gusher that changed the world. The date was January 10, 1901—the dawn of a new century.

Before Spindletop, oil was not a fuel. Its supply was too limited for it to replace coal or wood. But the Lucas gusher came in flowing an estimated 100,000 barrels a day. That was more oil than most wells made in a lifetime prior to that.

An impressive well, the Lucas gusher was capable of producing as much oil as 37,000 eastern region wells; twice as much as Pennsylvania, the leading oil state at the time; six times as much as California; or half as much as the entire United States' output. With five such wells, Spindletop would be able to produce more oil than all other wells of the world combined. The field toppled Russia from the rank as the leading oil-producing country and put America in that spot, never to be overtaken to this day.

The world believed this magnificent well represented an inexhaustible supply of cheap oil that could be used as a fuel. It was truly the beginning of the liquid fuel age and the first time there was sufficient oil to justify conversion of industrial boilers from coal to oil.

Here was a fuel available immediately for railroad engines and boilers in sugar cane mills, laundries, breweries, and ships.

No one envisioned the day of the automobile or the airplane. In fact that very year, a leading magazine, the Literary Digest, had said that the automobile would never become as popular as the bicycle. It was the same magazine, incidently, which predicted 35 years later that Landon would beat Roosevelt.

In 1902, Henry Ford organized his company. In 1903, the Wright brothers made their famous flight at Kitty Hawk, North Carolina. Chances are neither would have been practical without Spindletop. California, Oklahoma, Kansas, and Louisiana were also making great oil discoveries.

Spindletop crushed Standard Oil's monopoly far more effectively than the courts did a decade later. It also assailed monopoly in all fields. It even routed the slow growth toward socialism in the country.

In its first months, Spindletop also provided the low-priced fuel to enable Herman Frasch to put his remarkable hot-water sulphur-mining process to work and make America the leading sulphur country in the world.

For the next 30 years, the oil industry was characterized by spasms of shortage and surplus. The price of crude oil fluctuated with each new discovery or potential market. Roving wildcatters, eager to fill the biggest new orders, recklessly drilled wells where they were not needed, gutted precious reservoirs, and filled the land with the stench of oil going to waste. These conditions led to an unstable supply and no assurance that oil would be available in emergencies.

It was normal for most fields to come in with wells gushing, only to go to the pump in a few months, and soon thereafter to salt water, leaving 80 to 90 per cent of the oil unrecoverable.

In spite of this waste, Americans were enjoying a better life. Farmers moved toward mechanization. The machines eliminated child labor and eased the drudgery of the adult worker. No business or industry was without the benefit of liquid fuel energy.

The American way of life became the envy of the world.

Experts warned that we had only a few years' supply of oil, and then someone would bring in another Signal Hill or an El Dorado or Glenn Pool. Then the same experts would cry that we had too much oil.

During these wasteful years, however, the United States became a world power. Productivity in this country—due to a combination of industrial genius, resourceful labor, and cheap energy fuel—put America in the forefront of nations in industrial power, progress, and prosperity.

But something had to be done about avoidable waste. Numerous efforts toward petroleum conservation were thwarted by ignorance, politics, and selfishness. Then came the last boom.

In 1930, Columbus Marion "Dad" Joiner was an experienced oilman, but he was a most unlikely prospector. He was over 70, ill, and drilling on a shoestring in an area where almost every major company in the business had tried unsuccessfully to find oil.

Dad Joiner got the money to drill his wells largely from peanut farmers, small merchants in East Texas, and widows in Dallas. He was a failure as an oilman but a very persuasive promoter. He based his arguments on a geological report written by a man educated as a veterinarian.

In 1930, no one really needed any more oil. There was a domestic surplus, a depression was just gripping the country, and imports of oil from Venezuela and Mexico were flooding the market. So, all Dad Joiner did was discover a field containing six billion barrels of oil. It was the largest oil field in the world, and even after giving up four billion barrels, the largest in the Western Hemisphere. In fact, no other oil field in the United States has produced as much as a billion barrels of oil or is known to have a reserve that large.

East Texas, every wildcatter's dream field, brought chaos to the industry. For months, drilling activities halted in almost every other oil field east of the Rockies. The flow of oil from thousands of wells in the field was uncontrolled. The governor of Texas declared martial law, but the courts overruled him. Eventually proration was put into effect, but that, too, was declared illegal. The field was shut down to test bottom-hole pressures, but still the drilling continued. Oil dropped to a nickel a barrel, and lower.

There was serious talk of federal control over the entire industry. In fact, for a while, under the National Recovery Act, the government did control not only the oil industry but all industry and business as well.

As a result of this tremendous overproduction of oil, workable conservation laws were passed. These laws required proration of production with well allowables based on market demand. California and several other states had fairly good conservation laws even before the East Texas field came in, but refused to join a federally sponsored Interstate Oil Compact Commission.

The basis of conservation was prevention of the waste of gas and oil, both below and above ground. And since it could not be wasted by venting it into the air, a tremendous amount of gas was suddenly available. This abundance led to the development of the natural gas industry.

As a commercial product, natural gas has a much longer history than oil, but it was never a very important fuel until after conservation laws were passed. Immediately after World War II, the natural gas industry came into its own. Trillions of cubic feet of gas were available with no market. So, smart men such as Paul Kayser of El Paso Natural Gas Company, Gardiner Symonds of Tenneco, and a dozen others organized natural gas transmission companies to take gas to markets in the East, the North, the Mid-West, and the West Coast. Of course, most of the West Coast gas dissipated long before it was needed.

Another beneficial result of conservation of natural gas was the full development of the petrochemical and liquid natural gas industries. These now compete with the oil industry in importance; yet they all stem from the oil industry.

Another important step in the petroleum industry was the development of foreign oil and offshore drilling, which started in the late 1890's at Summerland, California. There wells were drilled directionally or off piers into the Santa Barbara Channel. Now the channel is regarded as the most important potential oil reserve on the West Coast. More than $600 million was paid in bonuses alone for federal leases in channel waters in 1968.

Starting with only an idea and backed by a small investment, the Drake well began an industry that has produced more than 120 billion barrels of oil and untold trillions of cubic feet of gas. These products have meant a great difference in the living standards of America and the rest of the world. They have made us strong, progressive, and prosperous far beyond the hopes of our founding fathers.

Oil reduced the average man's working time from 70 to 40 hours a week. And in doing so, it enabled one man working 40 hours to produce as much as three men did in 70 hours in the last century. It has provided the average citizen with goods and services on a working man's salary that few could afford in the old world.

Drake's well was drilled to a total depth of 69.5 feet to find the first oil. In comparison, a well was drilled recently to a record depth of 25,430 feet at a cost of $3 million. It was, incidentally, a dry hole.

The kerosene which helped light American homes a century ago, mixed with liquid oxygen, lifted the Saturn 5 rocket into space in late 1967. This fuel lifted the 36-story-high rocket 38 miles in 1.5 minutes. The rocket consumed 2,300 tons of propellant, which is over 600,000 gallons.

Besides their use as fuels, we all come into contact with some product of oil or natural gas many times daily, either as medicine, cosmetic, building material, clothing, rubber, toys, plastics, or in 2,500 other forms. With only 7 per cent of the world's population, we consume 35 per cent of the oil and about 90 per cent of the natural gas.

The United States exported the oil industry to every part of the world, first the products and then the techniques and tools for exploring, drilling, producing, transporting, and marketing oil. Starting with oil for the lamps of China, the industry has benefited most countries of the world.

In other countries, the problems of the industry have been much smaller than ours. The United States upholds individual and property rights. In other countries, the rights of landowners, titles, royalties, or rights-of-way are negligible since all minerals belong to the state. Therefore, unnecessary wells drilled in this country to accommodate the correlative rights of all landowners concerned are preventable.

Thus, on the average, an American oil well produces 12 or 13 barrels of oil a day while a well in the Middle East produces 10,000 barrels of oil a day. The economics are obvious.

Balancing this apparent inequity is the fact that in America the benefits of oil go to the people. Elsewhere, the benefits of oil go to the state, and the state decides what the people get.

The most distinguishing characteristic of the American petroleum industry is competition. Out of more than 10,000 producing companies in this country, no one corporation controls more than 10 per cent of the market. Of 148 refining companies, the largest controls only 10 per cent of the business. There are more than 1,000 transportation companies, some 12,000 wholesale distributors of oil products, and more than 200,000 retail outlets. Compared with any other major industry—steel, automobiles, coal, railroads, airlines, or others—that is heavy competition.

Yet, today the petroleum industry is in serious trouble. Drilling and exploration are at the lowest point in more than 25 years, even though we are facing almost incredible demand growth in just the next decade or two. New reserves are not keeping pace with consumption.

It is unthinkable that our nation, which depends on oil and gas for three-quarters of our energy requirements and which has been the greatest oil developer in the world, should ever face an oil shortage. But we are surely headed in that direction, and fast.

Some people say, "Let's get what we need from the prolific Middle East." To do this would be suicide. We have found the oil *in* the Arab countries, *for* the Arab countries, but there are few indications that we have really developed mutual understanding with the Arab people. This vast source of oil is undependable as we have twice seen. No free nation—despite its size—can ever depend on it.

It is ironical that we helped develop an area in the shadow of the Soviet Union which contains 60 per cent of the world's oil reserves that the Communists are almost certain to control eventually.

We must realize that our domestic petroleum is the only available, reliable supply. Other sources can be confiscated or otherwise shut off by the whim of foreign rulers, by wars, and by other emergencies.

When the Arabs cut off production to the western nations in the Israeli war, included were some 200,000 barrels daily to allied combat forces in Vietnam. Germany, United Kingdom, and other western powers friendly to the United States were also denied oil until the Arabs felt the pinch of the economic loss. We met the crisis by turning to our own reserves and those of South America.

The idea that Middle East oil is cheaper to produce than domestic oil is erroneous once the cost of hospitals, schools, and living accommodations for American families; the loss of independent explorers and producers from the domestic picture; and the inestimable cost of national security are added to the per-barrel figure. Then, Middle East oil becomes prohibitive in price.

A balanced import-domestic relationship is the only intelligent basis for solving this import problem. The people of the United States must examine the subject before it gets out of hand and we are left at the mercy of foreign powers for our most vital commodity.

In view of our economic dependence on energy, it is amazing that crude oil prices have not increased in five or six years despite growing inflation and higher costs for labor, materials, and services. Gasoline prices are about the same as they were over 40 years ago. Natural gas prices are even lower.

In the absence of incentives to drill more exploratory wells and the rapid development of synthetics such as shale oil or gasoline from coal, we are in serious economic danger.

As soon as the Soviets control Middle East oil—and that is their prime goal in world politics—they will be able to woo our allies in western Europe and Japan with cheap oil, gear their economics to energy, and then control them simply by threatening to turn off the valve.

In the meantime, unless the political attitude in this country changes, the trend toward a weakened domestic oil and gas industry will continue. Today the government nullifies the law of supply and demand with threats to increase imports or to open the valves on federal offshore oil at the slightest mention of price increases demanded by rising costs.

Stifling to any industry, these conditions are especially dangerous to the petroleum industry as it attempts to meet future energy needs.

Today we have 9.3 years' supply of oil in known reserves, the lowest supply we have ever had. We have 16 years' supply of natural gas, the lowest since we entered the modern phase of the gas business. Both figures are based on present rates of consumption.

Due to anticipated population increases and marked growth in per capita consumption, demand for energy in this country by 1980 will be 50 per cent higher than it is today. Unless there is a big breakthrough in synthetics, oil and gas will continue to be responsible for this demand. We probably could meet it easily with imports, but this nation cannot afford to become independent on foreign sources for its most vital product, even disregarding the Soviet threat.

Imagine what would happen to oil prices and to our balance of payments if we should ever be forced into that trap. What would our recourse be? The answer is simple—disaster!

Our industry is probably the world's worst at communicating with its customers—the people of the nation; yet this is the people's business more than any other in the country. We must be aware of threats to the stability and growth of the industry because petroleum is the lifeblood of our republic, our way of life, and our standard of living. Public awareness of these facts is necessary to preserve this most vital American industry.

The Impact of Natural Resources on Society

*"Many predictions are made about what life
will be like in the year 2,000. It could be
pretty dreary compared to today, unless we
meet certain goals."*   September 13, 1968

Minerals are closely associated with man's material and intellectual development, but large-scale application of minerals in human life, with the exception of clay and stones, is relatively recent. In the earliest days of modern civilization, precious stones were emphasized rather than the more practical treasures of the earth's crust.

Scientific study of minerals was hardly known before the nineteenth century. What had been known up to a few centuries before Christ was apparently forgotten. The father of modern minerology was a German who called himself Georgius Aricola, but whose real name was Georg Bauer. He lived from 1494, two years after the discovery of America, until 1555, about the time of the first application of geophysics.

Since then, natural resources have strongly influenced the development of our society, the progress of our country, and the exercise of freedom.

Yet our society—our form of government, the intelligence of our people, their willingness to try something new, and their ability to get the most good from what they have—has had a great impact on the use and supply of raw materials. In turn, those resources, used in the best interests of this country, have brought us to our present standard of living.

When America was founded, with its small population and its vast, undeveloped territory, its natural resources were thought to be unlimited. It was a self-sufficient world. That a people could ever consume the immeasurable bounties of nature here seemed incredible.

Poor, homeless, and unwanted millions streamed onto our shores from every part of the earth, relentlessly pushing westward and populating all of the land we could buy, barter, acquire by treaty, or accept into statehood until we had expanded from Maine to Hawaii and from Florida to Alaska. Gradually we improved the status of our citizens, increased per capita consumption, and provided the American family with not only the necessities and conveniences, but also the comforts and luxuries of life until we are now wondering if our resources can withstand the assault.

Today that question is foremost in the nation's mind. It supersedes questions of war and peace, poverty and crime, because it involves our very existence.

By the end of 1965, the United States had 9 per cent of the free world population and consumed about 35 per cent of its mineral supply.

Forecasters predict that by 1980 our consumption of minerals will increase by at least 50 per cent and possibly will double. By then our share of the world's population will have dropped to 7.7 per cent, but we still will have 29 per cent more people than at the end of 1965. The free world's population, say estimators, will have increased 50 per cent.

Even today we are largely dependent on foreign imports for our mineral supplies. About 75 per cent of 20 important mineral commodities come from overseas, because lower labor costs, lower taxes, lower costs for pollution control, and more abundant, cheap supplies of mineral deposits abroad contribute to an attractive price.

If the trend increases, we will be importing a major portion of our iron, copper, lead, and zinc, thus adding to the list of commodities for which this country depends on foreign sources.

To reverse this trend, if it is indeed possible, we must update our technology in exploration and discovery beyond the outcrops. We must learn to explore the extreme depths, improve our mining technology, learn to recycle scrap and waste more efficiently, and learn to substitute some of our abundant materials for those in short supply. In addition, we must look to the sea for new sources.

This country has enjoyed the highest standard of living in history because of abundant mineral resources.

Besides being an almost exclusively American industry for its first 75 years, petroleum has made the use of other minerals far more effective than they have been elsewhere.

We have been blessed with enough of the essential metals and nonmetal minerals—iron, lead, zinc, copper, pumice, barites and sulphur, potash, and lime—to support both industry and agriculture on a grand scale.

In energy we passed directly from the wood, coal, and kerosene ages into the use of liquid fuel. However, our expansion, progress, and prosperity have been so rapid they could scarcely be called orderly.

To examine the impact of mineral resources on society, we have to look back only a century, whereas most other civilized countries would have to look back at least a millennium.

To maintain this rate of progress, we will have to remain plentiful in all minerals necessary to our existence. And that is where petroleum geologists come in.

This profession has done more to assure self-sufficiency than any other. While a few adjustments in technology and in government's approach to our problems will be necessary, we know we have sufficient deposits in fossil fuels to last far into the future.

Coal is overwhelmingly abundant. Shale oil, while a debatable subject, will soon be available for use. Natural gas and crude oil in their conventional forms exist in unbelievable supply within the continental United States. The billions of barrels of oil recently discovered on the north slope of Alaska are merely an indication of what we have yet to find in new petroleum reserves.

In addition to technological progress in oil and gas exploration, drilling, and production, mine systems engineering must come up with new concepts for all types of mineral needs.

And these systems and technologies are already appearing. Tunneling equipment not even imagined a few years ago is now available and being improved dramatically each day.

New ideas in extraction, mobility, and use already exist in varying stages of development. Fortunately, our system of government and the opportunity to profit by such developments do not make it necessary for all the ideas to be born in this country. The free enterprise system has brought the best minds, inventions, and ideas of the world to our country when it was feared they would founder in other environments.

In the petroleum industry, for example, we are indebted to France for the electrical log, to Germany for the seismograph, to an Englishman for the art of distillation, and to the Chinese for the birth of drilling ideas.

This brain power immigration is still going on, although it has slowed in recent years. One reason could be that America has projected an unfortunate image, whether deserved or not, in many foreign countries. This is a matter that needs considerable attention.

Many other areas require our attention in the immediate future, such as the elimination of numerous social ills and injustices, problems of air and water pollution, and the production of sufficient food, shelter, clothing, and medicine to care for the expanding population.

Conservation itself deserves much thought. With the production of 40 million automobiles each year, our consumption of steel, lead, copper, zinc, and aluminum in this field alone is a staggering amount. The extension of the present seven-year average life of a car to twice that amount would be one easy step. Another, in the same field, would be to salvage and use the above-ground, high-grade metal resources of more than nine million tons annually which are now shamefully wasted.

The natural resource of petroleum is an example of an impact on society. No one even suspected its existence as a commercial product for almost 400 years after the white man first inhabited this continent.

Yet, in less than 110 years since its discovery as a useful industrial product, it has succeeded in supplying each American industrial and agricultural worker with energy that before 1859 would have required the work of 244 men. Petroleum fuel gives each of us the equivalent of 2,000 men to push his automobile along a modern highway. A locomotive engineer controls energy equivalent to that of 100,000 men; and a jet pilot, the equivalent of 700,000 men.

The humblest American enjoys the services of more "slaves" than were once owned by the richest nobles, and he lives better than ancient kings. The average citizen's family in this country has been provided with the equivalent of 33 faithful household helpers, all on duty 24 hours a day, seven days a week, and 365 days a year, plus an additional day in leap years.

For a single natural resource, that is quite an impact on society.

But take all our other resources, such as water, coal, iron, copper, sulphur, and on and on, and see how one after the other has been fitted into our pattern of living.

Petroleum and the other raw materials were here long before we were. They were in other parts of the world in even greater abundance and are still there, but man did little with them even though he was civilized. The Greeks and the Romans, the Persians and the Medes, the philosophers of Cathay and the intellectuals of Great Britain and France and Italy ignored them. Artists, writers, and craftsmen whose works we still admire did nothing with them.

Natural resources remained below the earth's surface, mostly unused, because the impact of the society founded with the Declaration of Independence benefited the remainder of the world only in direct proportion to the freedom, education, and responsibility of individuals in other countries.

Sulphur alone has made a noteworthy contribution to the development of this country and mankind in general.

Little more than a century ago, almost all of the world's sulphur was dug out of the earth by slaves from mines in Sicily.

Then came Herman Frasch with an idea, aided by cheap fuel discovered at Spindletop by Captain Lucas, and the world supply of sulphur was multiplied thousands of times overnight at a price within the reach of everyone.

Consider too the advances we are making in the fields of plastics and other substitutes now in use in construction, manufacturing, agricultural, and commercial fields. Give a little thought to natural gas, an industry that was almost nonexistent until after World War II, and the natural gas liquids industry, both of which have combined with the oil industry to bring about the fabulous petrochemical industry.

Today our advanced society is worried whether it can continue the manner of living to which it has become accustomed. It has seen the end of finding oil, ore, and other mineral resources by surface indications and other simple methods of exploration. In this land of plenty, we have begun to depend on imports from parts of the world where these minerals are now more abundant.

The first reaction of some people to this situation is to turn to the government with a loud "What are you going to do about it?" Then the government starts gnawing away man's freedom; blunting his ingenuity, ambition, and hope in the process; and providing more socialistic answers.

We have almost reached that point. In fact, we might have passed it had not those scientists, with inspiration and determination inherited from their forefathers, become aroused enough to do something about it.

First, they looked to the sea where we now know that natural resources abound. They considered the second layer of the earth and even some of the first layer we were unable to explore before.

Now there is a renaissance of technological ingenuity in this country equivalent to that of the pioneers of the mid-nineteenth century when Drake's first well fired the imagination of common men and the beginning of this century when it was rekindled by the great Lucas gusher.

Between those years, we saw the railroads link up the East and the West, we fought a stupid and destructive war among the states, we saw the industrial revolution spring to life, and we saw mankind advance more in fewer years than had seemed possible.

While we have always depended on technology, never have we done so to the extent we do right now. We need men to develop tools and systems to explore for and produce raw materials in quantities sufficient to propel us into the twenty-first century fully prepared to meet the challenges; to eliminate ignorance, poverty, war, and most health hazards; to supply man with those things he now needs and cannot afford; and to continue to increase his lot on earth and maybe even on other planets and in space.

Many predictions are made about what life will be like in the year 2000. It could be pretty dreary compared to today unless we meet certain goals.

Today we depend on foreign sources for at least half of our 20 most necessary mineral commodities. Unless we reverse this trend, it will grow steadily worse. By 1980 our mineral needs will be 40 per cent greater than they are today, based on projected increases in population and per capita use. At present, we have 6 per cent of the entire world's population and consume some 25 per cent of the world's minerals.

Undoubtedly we are accelerating the depletion of our domestic sources of minerals. Our high-grade reserves of metals and even oil and gas have long been exhausted. Some metals we never had in quantity.

So, today, we need bold new concepts and revolutionary ideas in systems, tools, machinery, and procedures to keep us on the road to Utopia.

The continuation of our progress and prosperity depends on an adequate supply of all essential minerals, including the fuels to energize our power and transportation. We will need sulphur and phosphates to fertilize our tremendous agricultural needs and the steel, copper, aluminum, lead, zinc, and other metals for building. Minerals are the basis of our economy and the multipliers of our gross national product. They are the essentials for full employment, elimination of poverty, advancement of education, and continued development of freedom.

We do not lack the physical resources to continue these aims. But we must have leaders with vision and daring, scientists and technologists who are willing to risk doing something different. We will have to get below the outcrops and into the second layer of mineral treasures where we will undoubtedly find far more than we ever imagined.

Geology, geophysics, geochemistry, and possibly a variety of new sciences will be given new tasks, including underground nuclear explosives, in-situ leaching of copper, stimulation of petroleum production, and new techniques as yet unimagined.

The answers will be found in education and research. The needs of our people are great and growing. This is no time to sit on our hands and dream. It is time to think—time to get up and work.

If we fail, a civilization could die.

2
INFLUENCES
ON DOMESTIC
PRODUCTION

Alaska—Its Oil Potential
Effects of Foreign Imports on Domestic
    Exploration
One Step Toward Survival
Relation of the Independent
    to the Future of the Petroleum Industry
Forecast of Domestic Petroleum Demands
An Independent's Blueprint for Survival
Role and Responsibility of the Independent
    Producers
Future of the Domestic Oil and Gas Industry
International Factors on Domestic Exploration
Shale Oil—Will it Ever Be a Reality?
Mr. Scripps Said It

Introduction

In a more romantic age, before computers and zip codes and government by committee, the future of America belonged to those bold enough to seize it.

This is the theme that connects the 10 speeches of Section 2, a chapter that deals largely with man's own richest resources: his courage and imagination.

The earliest of these speeches was delivered in 1958, at a time when few other oilmen, if any, were addressing themselves to the problems of the nation, or to the industry's own capacity for self-injury.

On these pages, which record his spoken words at literally dozens of conventions, seminars and banquets, Michel Halbouty recreates the history of the independent oilman: Where he came from and what he has become today, his relationship to the major producers, his role here and abroad and in the new frontiers of the energy field.

The speeches begin with his call for a greater dependence on domestic oil, and less on the unstable Middle East reserves. That appeal, first made in 1959, has been echoed in important industry editorials.

As surely as a wet thumb erases a blackboard, Halbouty leaves no doubt as to where he stands on the towering issues of the day. In this collection of major addresses, he covers the field.

In one, he weakens the myth of so-called cheap imports.

The arguments he used in another have been borne out by later developments: the steady decline in explorations, the tightening of risk money, the gradual acceptance of Halbouty's belief that great amounts of hydrocarbon fuels are yet to be found in the North American continent.

What Halbouty was saying about Alaska's oil potential in 1958 can be easily confirmed today, by a glance at the oil page of any daily newspaper. In a speech first prepared that year for an audience in Houston, he lauded Alaska's "textbook" qualities and predicted that what human materials it lacked, including determination, would soon be forthcoming. Of such visions are the reputations of prophets made secure.

On the other hand, his skepticism toward the near-term development of shale oil, voiced in Denver in 1968, appeared to be supported by the general lack of interest when the government later offered limited test leases.

Halbouty is at his descriptive best when he recalls the hard-nosed early days of wildcatting. He views them with the historian's warmth, but without cloggy sentiment. He acknowledges the professional gratitude that, say, today's military would feel toward Andrew Jackson's brave but ragged irregulars.

Inaction infuriates Halbouty. He was able, at one point, to convert an idea he first advanced in 1961 into an enlightened reality. He had proposed, to widespread editorial approval, the creation of an informal forum through which independents and majors could discuss their differences. The speech won him an industry award. Later, as president of AAPG, he succeeded in forming a committee of sixty.

His *blueprint for survival* contained several suggestions that came to pass, such as a unitization bill and a joint undertaking between the independents and majors to study the small tract and unnecessary well problems.

In two speeches that complete this section, Halbouty advanced the novel, and controversial, notion that oilmen ought to stop preaching about the depletion allowance. He points out that the people need facts and information and what the late E. W. Scripps referred to as "light." He suggests that America is unaware its entire economic and social survival depends on energy, and that 75 per cent of that energy comes from the petroleum industry. Nor does the country understand Russia's objective in Vietnam, or the Middle East: in both cases, the ultimate goal is control of the oil supply. In effect, Halbouty offers the petroleum industry the same challenge Mr. Scripps offered his newspapers—to give light.

Alaska—Its Oil Potential

"One of the attractions of Alaska is the chal-lenge. The country is in its swaddling clothes . . ."   September, 1958

A great chapter of the American oil industry is being written in Alaska. The territory has a combination of extensive basins in width and depth, favorable surface structures as large as any in the world, encouraging geophysical surveys in lowland areas where outcroppings of the formations are not present, numerous oil seeps, the discovery of large reserves of oil and gas in the Arctic Slope, and the recent discovery of an apparently substantial oil field in the southern region on the Kenai Peninsula. Alaska has all the textbook requisites for oil and gas except men, materials, and determination which will soon be forthcoming.

The search for oil in Alaska has been going on for many years —long before statehood was even a dream by its natives. The presence of oil and gas in the Cook Inlet Basin was known to Russian explorers before Colonel Drake's epic discovery at Titusville, Pennsylvania, in 1859. Drilling operations were in progress on the Iniskin Peninsula in 1891, even 10 years before the great gusher at Spindletop.

Today, with modern techniques and equipment, the hunt is continued in a climate that ranges from that of Scandinavian winters to Chicago summers. This climate is the kind that has, in other countries, produced some of the most vigorous and enlightened cultures of the world. Alaska is indeed a land of contrasts where the eyes will always see things of extreme interest and where the people are young, determined, and vigorous.

Until recently, 98 per cent of the land and wealth of Alaska has been practically closed to private capital and investment. Its new statehood multiplied its booming prospects a hundredfold.

Alaska, from the standpoint of an independent oil operator, has an opportunity for gains similar to those expected from an offshore operation in the Gulf of Mexico—and without the tremendous expense of competitive bidding for acreage. As long as the new state supports the noncompetitive leasing concept (except in areas that have already been proved capable of producing oil and gas), there will be more exploitation and more oil found.

Onshore operations in the United States involving expenditures of $2.5 million and more are considered good if the anticipated potential is about 10 million barrels of oil. The same amount of money sunk in virgin Alaska may well find 100 million barrels.

More wells could be drilled in the continental United States for less money than in Alaska, with more chances to find the 10 million barrels. An independent could not stand too many dry holes in Alaska; therefore, his success must be early.

Exploration for oil in Alaska is not a guarantee of success, and it never will be. The geographical location of the new state forbids any so-called normal activity. Special plans must be made months in advance to take advantage of seasonal conditions. For an independent, a test well on the Kenai Peninsula cannot be approved in a committee meeting one day and a rig moved on the location the following day, as is normal in most provinces in the United States. Months of planning and investigation must be made in advance for geophysical, geological, and operating procedures.

A record has been set in moving equipment to Alaska that will be hard to beat. Only 17 days after loading all the equipment on a freighter at Long Beach, California, a well was spudded in Alaska. Within this time, the boat landed at Seward and the equipment was trucked 125 miles to the location in the midst of winter conditions. This accomplishment proves what can be done without being hampered by interdepartmental decisions, bottlenecks, and red tape.

Young aggressive men must want to go to Alaska. The desire to accomplish and overcome problems in the unknown wilderness must be paramount in their thinking, or they should stay home where things are easier.

Alaska is a cold, difficult country. The people there now and those going there in the next few years are cut from the same cloth as pioneer Americans. They are people willing to work for an opportunity under the most difficult conditions. These are rare people today. Others simply stay in Texas or California or Ohio where things are more certain. But the Alaskan is willing to make a great personal sacrifice for the opportunity of getting a real stake in life. Any wildcatter who is actually still a wildcatter at heart is bound to feel at home among these people and is apt to derive a great pleasure from building a new state with them.

Despite this pioneering factor, or maybe because of it, Alaska will no doubt attract more independents. Of course, the costs are high, but costs are not low anywhere. The independent will be able to drill his wells cheaper once he finds oil because he will not be hampered by offsets that will require many times as much money as is normally required in Texas, for instance, to protect and develop a property adequately. Chances are that the unit cost of producing oil in Alaska will be considerably lower than in other oil-producing states.

The cost of drilling a hole in Alaska will be at least three times the cost of a well in the continental United States because at present there are few oil-field equipment and supply companies operating in the whole territory. In time, the comparative costs will naturally come down, but in spending three times as much for drilling a well, there is a chance of finding 10 to 15 times as much oil. Therefore, the odds still favor taking such risks in Alaska.

The market for Alaskan oil is already made. There is, for instance, the Far East market which could absorb all the oil that could be found and produced in Alaska in the next 10 or 15 years. Then there is the Pacific Coast market. Oil can actually be produced and shipped to the Pacific Coast from Alaska at a lower price than it can be shipped from Canada.

One of the attractions of Alaska is the challenge. The country is in its swaddling clothes. Vast domains are still unconquered. The rich geological promise of the country matches even that of the Middle East from a petroleum standpoint.

Almost every geologist who has studied the country has predicted great potential. The opposite is usually true. In many areas now known to be productive, early geologists had said there was little chance of success. But here, the best geologists have said the sky is the limit.

Even so, many have unjustly criticized the oil possibilities in Alaska. For instance, rumors say that field operations will be limited to a very few months out of the year. That is preposterous. Investigations have proved that Alaskan operations can be maintained around the calendar and around the clock.

It has been said there are no transportation facilities, but good roads exist already, and the government is planning many more. Heavy equipment and tools may be transported from the United States to several key areas in Alaska over the Alcan Highway. But the absence of roads in all but the more populated areas does create a temporary problem of unloading and transporting supplies.

If obstacles to transportation can be overcome in the swamps of Louisiana or the rugged country of the Four Corners area or the mountains of Colorado or the deserts of North Africa and the Near East or even the Gulf of Mexico, there will be few transportation obstacles in Alaska that will not be overcome. All it will take is someone to find a substantial amount of oil in any part of Alaska. After that, the problems that now seem great will shrink to nothing.

One must bear in mind that Alaska is a virgin area for oil and gas prospects. Nine major basins where exploration for petroleum is warranted place Alaska among the top areas in the Western Hemisphere where new oil and gas reserves may be found. These areas are (from north to south): (1) all of northern Alaska, north of the Brooks Range, (2) the Porcupine region, (3) the Koyukuk region, (4) the Bethel Basin, (5) the Nushagak Basin, (6) the Copper River Basin, (7) the Cook Inlet Basin (sometimes referred to as the Kenai region) which includes the Susitna and Matanuska lowlands, (8) the Alaskan Peninsula region, and (9) the St. Elias-Yakutat coastal region.

To evaluate its petroleum possibilities, Alaska should be divided into three major geologic-physiographic regions: northern, central, and southern.

Northern Alaska includes the Brooks Range and all the region north of it to the Arctic Ocean. The land area involved is approximately 125,000 square miles, although the area north of the drainage divide of Brooks Range constitutes approximately 76,000 square miles.

This promising petroleum province, commonly called the North Slope, is larger than the entire state of Oklahoma and is one of the largest relatively unexplored sedimentary basins in the world. The onshore portion of the Arctic coastal basin, which holds the greatest potential for future commercial oil and gas fields, occupies roughly the north 50,000 square miles of the North Slope.

The federal government recognized the oil possibilities of the area years ago and in 1923 reserved by executive order the Naval Petroleum Reserve No. 4 covering 37,000 square miles. During 1945-1953, some 37 exploratory and development wells were drilled by the United States Navy on selected anticlinal structures at a cost of over $60 million. Three oil fields and six gas fields were discovered.

In the past 10 years, a vast amount of surface geology and geophysics has been conducted on the North Slope in areas outside the boundaries of NPR No. 4. Seven exploratory wells have been drilled which resulted in two gas discoveries; however, the giant oil or gas field necessary to justify exploitation awaits discovery.

The Naval operations, nevertheless, proved that exploration and drilling in this Arctic region can be efficiently and successfully conducted throughout the entire year irrespective of season.

The central geologic-physiographic region of Alaska covers approximately 275,000 square miles extending from the Brooks

Range on the north to as far south as the Alaska Range, and from the Bering Sea on the west to the Canadian border on the east. The Brooks Range forms a huge barrier across northern Alaska separating the Alaskan Arctic from the more temperate and inhabited central region to the south. In this southern region flows the great Yukon River with its broad flood plains and basin. The most promising areas for production in this vast space are (1) the Porcupine region, (2) the Koyukuk region which includes the Norton Basin, (3) the Bethel Basin, and (4) the Nushagak Basin.

In central Alaska, which is larger than the entire state of Texas, only six holes had been drilled by 1959 for the purpose of finding oil and gas. The deepest of these wells was 350 feet. Imagine what the results would have been, or could be in the future, if only a small per cent of the wells drilled in Texas could be drilled in this region.

Very little geologic information is available from the Bethel and Nushagak basins because these areas are covered by Quaternary deposits. It will require extensive geophysical work and core tests to obtain any data on the structures and stratigraphy that are hidden underneath the Quaternary.

The Koyukuk and the Porcupine regions contain sediments which are most interesting and which definitely warrant exploration and drilling.

The formations known to underlie this central region and the large anticlinal structures so evident in the Koyukuk and Porcupine areas indicate that oil and gas possibilities are indeed excellent.

The third and, at present, the most active geologic-physiographic region of Alaska is the southern region. This region includes (1) the Copper River Basin, (2) the Cook Inlet Basin, which includes the Susitna and Matanuska lowlands, (3) the Alaskan Peninsula region, and (4) the St. Elias-Yakutat coastal region.

The Richfield Oil Corporation's Swanson River Unit No. 1, spudded April 5, 1957, was completed as an excellent oil producer and discovery 25 days later for 900 barrels per day from 11,150 feet to 11,215 feet. It triggered an intense interest in all of Alaska, especially the Cook Inlet Basin, and is responsible for the increased activity in leasing and exploration with geophysical and geological crews and surveys. Ten years later, the field, completely developed with 52 wells producing 30,000 barrels a day, had become a model of conservation and proper development.

Numerous oil seeps exist in the southern region in widely scattered localities. These seeps were reported as early as 1853, and actual drilling was conducted near them in the Katalla district in 1901. The Katalla district is located in the extreme western end of the St. Elias-Yakutat coastal region. From 1902 to 1933, the Katalla field produced 154,000 barrels of oil from shallow wells. Yet, with all of the known requisites available for good oil hunting, the first seismograph was not used in southern Alaska until 1954.

This southern area is presently the most interesting to operating companies because of accessibility into the most promising of the basins. In fact, the entire southern region of Alaska is considered to have exceedingly excellent possibilities for large oil fields with reserves that may equal the best fields in the world.

If only a quarter of the amount of time, effort, and money expended in the Middle East were spent in Alaska, the territory would now be a most prolific producer of oil and gas, with refineries and pipelines owned and operated by the American oil industry under our own laws—stable and without fear of losing the reserves and facilities to some foreign power or sheikdom. Irrespective of what has happened in the past, the oil industry will not let Alaska down as the state reaches out for its destiny as a great petroleum empire.

BIBLIOGRAPHY

Kirschner, C. E., "Developments in Alaska in 1957," Bulletin of American Association of Petroleum Geologists, Vol. 42, No. 6 (June, 1958), pp. 1434-1444.
Miller, D. J., T. G. Payne, and George Gryc, "Geology of Possible Petroleum Provinces in Alaska with an Annotated Bibliography of U. S. Geological Survey Publications on Petroleum and Oil Shale in Alaska by Edward H. Cobb, and Map of Mesozoic and Cenozoic Tectonic Elements of Alaska Compiled by Thomas G. Payne and J. Thomas Dutro, Jr.," U. S. Geological Survey open file report.
Reed, John C. (Cdr., USNR), "Exploration of Naval Petroleum Reserve No. 4 and Adjacent Areas Northern Alaska, 1944-53, Part 1, History of the Exploration," Geological Survey professional paper 301, 1958.
Sable, E. G., "New and Redefined Cretaceous Formations in Western Part of Northern Alaska," Bulletin of American Association of Petroleum Geologists, Vol. 40, No. 11 (1956).
Thompson, R. M. and Louis L. Watson, "Geologic and Economic Report on the Oil and Gas Potential of a Portion of the Koyukuk Basin, West Central Alaska," private communications and report, 1956.
Thompson, R. M., "A Reservoir Study of Umiat Oil Field, Arctic Slope, Alaska," private report, 1958.

Effects of Foreign Imports
On Domestic Exploration

"It is in the interest of our country and our freedom that American companies be the dominant producers of petroleum . . ."   November 3, 1960

The petroleum industry has seen some hard days since the glory year of 1956. Since it is an industry raised in the tradition of boom and bust, those who have lived long in the oil harness are not too discouraged by temporary setbacks, especially since the bust part is not as bad as it once was. Our professions, although not as old as the industry, are accustomed to its periods of boom and recession.

Today we are on the tail end of a domestic oil-producing binge that started right after the end of World War II. The lull in production has been caused partially by imports, but they are not the only reason we are in trouble. For instance, we are stealing the energy market from ourselves with underpriced natural gas. There is a sudden nation-wide slowdown in industrial expansion. In the greater producing areas of this country—Texas, Oklahoma, Kansas, Louisiana, and California—petroleum conservation practices are below par.

In light of these conditions, almost all imports seem to be excessive. Under our system of mandatory import controls, the growth of imports has been retarded. But, at the same time, the growth of demand for domestic crude has come to an absolute stop.

Even the most ambitious importer must admit that imports of oil which supplant domestic production are excessive and burden our economy as well as our particular profession. They tend, along with other surplus-causing factors, to discourage exploration and development. Exploration is up slightly this year, and were it not for surplus-breeding factors, exploration would be normal. Development is off by a substantial margin as compared with figures for the past decade.

Between 1949 and 1959, we increased our crude oil production to two million barrels per day. Production of natural gas and gas liquids, expressed in oil equivalents, increased by 3,790,000 barrels a day. Imports of crude and products into the United States increased by 1,115,000 barrels daily.

Today our total available hydrocarbon supply amounts to 15,675,000 barrels daily, which is 6,905,000 barrels over what it was in 1949.

Today domestic crude production is 7,045,000 barrels per day. Gas and liquid production in terms of barrels of oil is 6,870,000 barrels and closing fast. Imports of crude and products amount to 1,760,000 barrels daily.

From these figures you see that today imports, plus gas and gas liquids, exceed domestic crude oil production in total energy supply by more than 1.5 million barrels a day.

From a position of relative dominance 10 years ago when domestic crude production exceeded its two major competitors, imports and gas, by 1,220,000 barrels a day, it has fallen behind them by 1.5 million barrels. This has occurred during the greatest growth in demand for energy in the history of the nation and the world.

But we cannot fairly criticize American oil companies operating in foreign countries for bringing almost two million barrels of their low-priced foreign production into this country every day. It is in the interest of our country and our freedom that American companies be the dominant producers of petroleum in foreign countries.

While the quest for more oil is circling the globe and for the moment concentrating in Africa, we know that the petroleum industry supports the economy of the free world countries which we count among our best friends. For instance, 81 per cent of the national income of Saudi Arabia comes from oil. In Venezuela 60 per cent comes from oil.

Having the market for more than half the oil consumed on earth but having little more than 15 per cent of its reserves, we know we must provide a market for some foreign oil as a matter of good business.

But we are in trouble when we have a surplus of domestic oil and then add 1.75 million barrels of oil imports a day. That amount of imports is in excess of our present reserve production capacity of 1.5 million barrels daily to meet our national defense requirements. In other words, if there were no imports at all, we would be about where we should be relative to crude oil supply in this country.

The net result affects all of us. Independent operators find it increasingly difficult to continue to invest in exploration.

This year we will drill 44,000 wells in the United States, about as many as in 1951. Steel mills, which count heavily on oil-field operations, are cut down to half capacity. Thousands of oil-field and refinery workers are out of jobs, along with steel workers and others directly affected. Naturally, the oil service and supply business is down to the lowest point in history.

And everywhere geologists, geophysicists, paleontologists, and other professional oil explorers are being terminated, retired early, or laid off temporarily. This is an appalling situation and difficult to understand. Instead of retaining explorers for the needs of the future, companies are discharging them.

This policy is not due only to heavy imports, but it is caused partly by unfair price competition of imports. As long as foreign oil enters this country at prices far below comparable domestic crude prices, our chances of recovering from the oil depression are seriously weakened. This price competition is reducing the prospects for firm and realistic prices which would return some form of prosperity for our industry and our professions.

Domestic crude oil has other unfair competition. For instance, crude oil sells at the wellhead for about $3.00 a barrel. An equivalent amount of gas energy costs the average consumer $2.57 at the burner tip. At wellhead prices, the equivalent of a barrel of oil in gas is 68 cents. This is not only unfair price competition between oil and gas, but it shows that prices paid for natural gas as an energy source are much too low.

Producers in states such as Texas have an additional problem caused by the drilling of unnecessary wells, which leads to a constant reduction in either daily allowables or days of production. This places Texas producers at a well-cost disadvantage with their fellow producers in such states as Utah, Arizona, New Mexico, and Colorado, and results in the destruction of good reservoirs which are increasingly hard to come by in these days of sparce risk capital for exploration drilling.

Adding to these troubles is the recent world-wide price cuts. The cuts were ostensibly to meet the competition from the Soviets who are seriously threatening important world markets through the barter system. The small reductions made in prices are not going to bother the Soviets nor woo the customers in India or anywhere else away from them. So, we can look for more reductions in Middle East crude prices. Venezuela, also operating in the world market, will be forced to meet all reductions. Inevitably, those falling prices are going to extend to our shores and widen the already gaping margin between domestic crude and imported crude prices.

So, with importers cutting prices and refiners running more oil to stills than they can sell at the pump, we can expect continued price reductions. None of this, of course, is going to help the independent producer borrow money with which to explore for more oil to glut the market further. The net result is that professional oil finders, along with many others such as oil and steel workers, are going to suffer.

When we have too much gas and gas liquid competition, a static market for domestic crude, a steadily dropping crude oil price, and the disappearance of venture capital, the independent producer is affected—but good!

For the past several years, there has been no growth in the demand for domestic crude. A major contributing factor is the Suez crisis when we increased prices and stepped up production to meet a situation that was over before we were prepared to act. But we were left with a crude surplus that is probably at the very bottom of our worst trouble. Since the Suez crisis, we have also experienced a slowdown in consumption rates.

And things are really not improving. The American Association of Oilwell Drilling Contractors reported that in the first eight months of 1960, imports were 60,000 barrels a day above the average for the same period of 1959 and domestic production was down 77,000 barrels a day. The association suggested that imports be reduced and limited in 1961 to enable domestic producers to regain their share of the United States market lost since the end of the Suez crisis and that hereafter domestic producers be permitted to furnish the major portion of the increase in United States demand. I think this is a most reasonable suggestion.

History has demonstrated through such crises as World War II and Suez that foreign governments by deliberate action can deny the United States the use of foreign oil. It, therefore, is obvious that if we become dependent upon foreign sources, our security and peacetime welfare are at the mercy of action completely beyond our control.

Before World War II, imports amounted to about 5 per cent of domestic production. By 1958, they amounted to 25 per cent. The growing supply of foreign oil seeking even greater markets in the United States made it clear that action had to be taken to halt the trend.

Although government controls of any kind are repugnant to the American system, some kind of action became essential to stabilize the finding and developing of oil resources. The single endeavor of exploration requires an annual investment of over five billion dollars. Excessive imports stifle this important activity.

It is regrettable that federal control had to be applied to imports of crude oil and refined products. Any kind of federal control over any form of business impairs and retards individual initiative. It would have been better if the importing companies had been able to regulate themselves, but the antitrust laws and other impediments made this impractical.

We are constantly under threat that national political action, not state political action, will control the future of the industry. If this happens, the big will get bigger and the small will get smaller, which would mean the eventual elimination of the independent. If that happens, who will drill the wildcat wells in this country, and especially the dry holes?

Independents drill approximately 75 per cent of all wells drilled in the United States and nearly 85 per cent of the exploratory or wildcat wells. Wildcatting has become the domain of the independent. The only incentive that keeps many independents working to drill one wildcat after the other is the hope of finding "the big one." In that regard he is dependent on venture capital from sources outside the industry. This capital is gradually dwindling because of the present status of our industry, so that less wells are being drilled and less new oil is being found.

Today we face a situation similar to that when East Texas oil threatened to destroy the American oil industry. Today that threat presents itself from the prolific fields of the Middle East, North Africa, South America, and Russia, already a large exporter. The oil industry again faces serious problems, only on a world-wide rather than simply a national basis.

Domestic producers and international oilmen need to bring about some type of world-wide understanding to help stabilize the relationship between domestic and foreign oil.

Sir Stephen Gibson, chairman of the World Petroleum Congress and a former president of Iraq Petroleum Company, said recently in Atlantic City that by 1985 we will have consumed all of the now known 275 billion barrels of world oil reserves, and in the meantime we will be forced to find at least that much more oil. He added that no more than 75 billion barrels of that 275 billion barrels of oil would be found in the Persian Gulf area, leaving 200 billion barrels to be found outside of the Persian Gulf area, presently the most productive part of the world.

Another economist has predicted that in the next 10 years, we will be required to find an additional 52 billion barrels of oil in this country if we are to enter the 1970's with our present reserve ratio.

David T. Searls, general counsel of the Gulf Oil Corporation and one of the world's leading figures in natural gas, has said that by 1970 the consumption of natural gas in this country will reach a total of 18 to 21 trillion cubic feet annually, about twice the present consumption.

This would mean the adding of 220 trillion cubic feet of reserves to presently known supplies. He added that not more than 15 trillion cubic feet of that total could possibly be expected to be supplied by Canada and Mexico combined. That leaves, he said, 205 trillion cubic feet of natural gas to be found in this country in the 1960's.

To do this, Searls said, we will be forced to drill a total of 625,000 wells, or an average of 62,500 wells a year. This figure is to be compared with the 44,000 wells of all kinds we expect to drill in this country in 1960 and the 57,110 all-time-high well-drilling record of 1956.

Searls said that is a *minimum* requirement if we are to meet the needs of the consuming public in this country. If we hope to maintain the present reserve ratio of 20 years, it will be necessary to find an additional 100 trillion cubic feet of gas requiring another 300,000 wells in 10 years.

So, Searls predicts we will really need 925,000 wells drilled in this country by 1970, or 92,500 wells of all kinds per year as an average, in order to find in this country 305 trillion cubic feet of gas to meet future requirements. If we can look forward to such a program as that, there is a great deal of exploring for gas to be done in this country, and it should be starting right now.

Most companies operating abroad have more than profit as a motive. They were asked to go overseas by our government, and our government was right in getting these companies to go into foreign production.

They went foreign not to meet the Soviet threat we face today, but to meet the threat of our allies winding up with all the oil in the world. False prophets were saying this country would be completely out of oil by 1950. By the time that dire prediction circulated, the American economy was already geared to petroleum. Our standard of living, our comforts, conveniences, industrial might, and agricultural abundance were all dependent on petroleum. No political leader in this country wanted to see the United States depend on England, France, The Netherlands, or Belgium for petroleum. So, our industry leaders were requested to look into the possibilities of the Middle East and Venezuela.

When the great discoveries started coming in along the Bolivar Coastal field area in Venezuela, no American companies were producing successfully there. In the early days of Middle East production, the British had it all to themselves.

So, Americans went abroad to meet the threat of world oil domination by forces that were friendly but foreign. They have stayed to meet the threat of communism.

There should be no quarrel with American oil importers as long as imports supplement but do not supplant domestic production, but these same companies have failed to recognize our future domestic requirements.

With all of the demand we face in the future in both oil and gas, we all should start now looking for new domestic reserves. We are the oil finders! Without us, there would be no exploration.

But what is happening? Professional explorers are being laid off, retired early, or terminated by the very companies who are most active in importing foreign oil. Yet these same companies will need domestic future reserves if they are to stay in business.

We continuously ask ourselves, "What is it that 10 years from now we will say to ourselves, 'Why didn't we think of that 10 years ago?' " This is a question the large importing companies must be asking themselves today. The self-evident answer is this: We must recognize the obvious facts being presented by men of vision and utilize today's profits from relatively cheap foreign oil to explore for and find the domestic oil and gas we know we will need tomorrow.

The importing companies are composed of men intelligent enough to know that their companies will be successful in direct proportion to their success as domestic oil corporations. In fact, they know that most of them will soon be greater gas producers than oil producers. And they know the markets. A representative of a typical company was the man who said we would need 925,000 wells by 1970 to meet the demand for natural gas in this country alone.

The companies also know that while it is most important to our country and the world for them to find and produce oil overseas, such production is subject to many dangers. Their properties could be expropriated. They could be cut off from communication with the rest of the world as in the Suez crisis. Or they could be overrun by the enemy in time of war.

They also know that should this country ever become dependent on foreign oil to any extent, our standard of living, our economy, geared as it is to petroleum, and the very way of life that we have built for our people would be threatened.

Should importing companies start converting profits from foreign oil into domestic exploration, they could not only stimulate the industry which made them successful corporations, but they could utilize the services, the genius, and the know-how of the men they are terminating.

They should prepare now for the drilling of 62,000 or 92,000 wells annually by finding the places to drill immediately.

Thus they would be serving their country as they have served it by acquiring with great risk the large concessions in the Middle East, South America, Africa, and elsewhere around the globe.

They would save the independent producer, whom they will need in the future as they have needed him in the past. They would inject new blood into a tired economy. They would encourage investors, who are now pouring their venture dollars into more promising fields, to favor petroleum again with their interest. And they would preserve the industry which has meant so much to citizens of this country upon which the free world relies for a future free from tyranny, dictatorship, and atheistic communism.

To me, that is the great opportunity now presented to importers of foreign oil. As these companies respond to their opportunity, the interests of the independent producer, the international producer, the people of this nation, and our friends around the world will be well served.

One Step Toward Survival

"Someone once called it the oil fraternity—a fraternity of men whose purpose is to explore for, produce, move and market a product without which the gears of progress would halt."   January 16, 1961

The oil business is no longer a dog-eat-dog business. Most of the pirates have perished by their own swords. Actually, the goal of the industry is to serve the states, the nation, and the public welfare, as well as to gain personal satisfaction from a challenging and complex industry. Most men in the petroleum business are gradually realizing their public responsibilities as contrasted with the previous single aim of personal gain and the desire to become millionaires.

Somehow we have to realize the seriousness of the situation with which our nation is confronted and contribute whatever possible to the continuing progress of our fellow man and the deterrence of communism, imperialism, and tyranny.

This industry is so vital to the public welfare and the national security that the public will no longer tolerate wasteful, selfish practices which certain companies and individuals participated in when this industry was developing.

Now we have matured. In the old days, waste meant nothing to those scrambling only for wealth. Little was known about the earth and its hydrocarbon resources other than that they existed and could be extracted. Now with the knowledge we lacked in the wild and booming days that climaxed in East Texas and Oklahoma City, there is no longer an excuse for ignorance or selfishness to dictate our actions. We are men of science, technology, and modern business, imbued with the spirit of the pioneers of this industry. All of them did not seek wealth alone. Some of them sought to conquer the unknown. They were born explorers, who only fooled themselves into believing they wanted wealth and security.

Today our challenge should be not only to preserve the industry they created, but to lift it to an even higher level of public service. Instead of the pot of gold, our ultimate goal must be the continued welfare of our fellow man.

I do not advocate the elimination of the small man's desire to get big. This would call for repeal of a law of human nature. We should never get so scientific and so technical that we discourage the daring and ambitious man from seeking to improve himself, or one company or individual from becoming better than another. But this drive must be tempered by squeezing out greed and selfishness and total disregard for others. The industry needs enlightened ambition and drive and competition which regard the public welfare as well as the desire to grow bigger and stronger.

This disregard for others lies at the base of many of the problems of today's oil industry.

Independents drill too many wells on small tracts, but majors also import too much oil.

Some independents ignore good field practices, but majors refine more oil than they can use.

Majors realize that independents are vital and their status, precarious, but do not know how, or if, they can help without jeopardizing their interests.

Perhaps what the oil industry needs is a forum where both majors and independents can let the other side know what they are thinking. The forum should be organized on a regional basis and without staff or set procedures so the actions would not become public property, but the problems of each could be considered, discussed, and possibly dissolved. Ignorance of each other's condition leads to the majority of the misunderstandings between majors and independents which merely aggravate the problems. All of this works contrary to the public interest.

This is not to suggest surrender of principles or the lessening or elimination of competition. The only intention is to lessen and eliminate some of the imponderable problems which, if not removed in time, will ruin us all—majors and independents alike.

The independent oilman is fighting for survival. This is no new experience. It happened when Oklahoma City and East Texas flooded the market with oil at the same time major companies started pouring oil into this country from Venezuela.

During World War II, independents were caught in the squeeze by skyrocketing costs of materials and labor on the one hand and crude prices frozen by the Office of Price Administration on the other hand. A few of the majors felt that strain, too.

Then came the days when markets were begging for crude, and we could not get pipe or drilling equipment.

The industry has had sorry plights before and has come out of them. But never before has it been in quite the mess it is in today. Alvin Hope of the Independent Petroleum Association of America said that by 1971 we must find 45 billion barrels of crude oil in this country. That is more than we have found in the entire history of the industry up to now.

Solar fuel, hydrogen fuel, shale oil, nuclear energy, and dozens of other energy sources constantly threaten to put us out of business in a short time.

So, the present situation could be worse.

But I believe the independent oilman is here to stay. He is vital as long as a demand for petroleum exists. Major companies cannot find, or even afford to explore for, the amount of oil we will need in the future. So some independents must go broke in the future as they have in the past so the oil this country needs can be found.

Everyone who looks for oil does not find it. And everyone who finds it cannot afford what he does find. The majors let the independents do the heavy hunting. In the early years of the industry, Rockefeller set the pattern. He produced only a small part of the total crude, and most of that was production the trust had bought from an independent who had gone broke looking for more oil. Majors are vaguely inclined to explore for oil today, but wildcatting is, and will always be, left largely to the daring independent. It will always be done, too, with the support of major oil contributions, farmouts, transportation, refineries, and market outlets.

So, the oil industry is a team. The problems of one segment are the problems of another. We once called it the oil fraternity composed of men whose purpose was to explore for, produce, move, refine, and market a product without which the gears of progress would halt.

Of course, the most important member of this team is the public because the public consumes the product in ever-increasing quantities. The public includes the manufacturers of automobiles, airplanes, ships, locomotives, farm equipment, and a host of other implements of consumption.

There must be at least 10,000 independent oil operators in this country. Only about one in 100 ever really succeeds.

Most independents are small businessmen with a flare for gambling on going broke or hitting something that will put them on Easy Street. Without the independent, reckless risk-taker, our sources of petroleum would dry up faster than a locust army can wipe out a wheat field.

Independents have drilled at least 85 per cent of this country's exploratory wells. Most of our oil reserves have been discovered by independents. Our major company friends have limited their discoveries to foreign oil and offshore areas. Most of the oil remaining to be found in this country will be found by independents. The majors might produce more, but they will hardly be in a position to find more unless they justify the necessary recklessness to stockholders and board members who include such conservative citizens as operators of refineries, pipelines, and marketing departments and legal and financial experts.

So, the economic health of the petroleum industry depends on the independent. We can never become dependent on foreign oil, as oil supplies 72 per cent of the energy requirements of this country. Once we do, our world leadership will certainly slip. Some say the industry exaggerates the part oil plays in national defense. I think not. As long as we use planes powered by some kind of petroleum and vehicles and weapons propelled or lubricated by oil, petroleum is essential to national security. But we are only a part of the defense and security mechanism. Others justifiably resent our taking too much credit.

Some people accuse that we are competing with ourselves. They say gas and gas liquids are taking away fuel markets. But since we find and produce gas and gas liquids, we are really only expanding our market. Where we are falling down is in permitting the government to exercise a form of utility price control over us. We do not have to tolerate this, but we do. In fact, we provoke it by having a dozen different oil and gas associations pursuing as many different routes for relief with the result that none of them accomplishes anything.

Associations per se are not objectionable; they merely need some direction. They are wasting their effective ammunition on major oil companies, who in turn divert the attacks onto or defend themselves from independents.

A chain of independent-major forums in every oil region in this country should cure this boomerang nonsense. The forums do not have to be a club or an association bound by a constitution or by-laws. They simply have to be a focal point for a friendly gathering where independents and majors can tear each other apart in private and come away with some understanding of the other fellow and his problems. Maybe we would find out that our interpretations of the other fellow are entirely incorrect.

Possibly such an arrangement could generate interest in finding new uses and new markets for oil.

Independents might at least get the majors to join them in an effort to curtail the murder on the highways and thereby restore the confidence of our best customers in automobile travel by saving their lives and property.

One of the greatest shortcomings of the average independent oilman is his preoccupation with his own problems.

Worries are inherent in the oil industry, but one of the scarcest categories in our country is the ex-oilman. Our problems seem overwhelming now, but a hundred economists see future demand figures that actually seem impossible to meet. This country is facing a population growth that will bring on an unimaginable prosperity, particularly in our industry. A new type of independent oilman faces this crisis. Most of them are educated, and many of them are technical or scientific men. Educated men might be inclined to fold quicker than the pioneers of this industry who did not even know how to spell "fear," but perhaps modern intelligence will substitute for courage.

One of our troubles is a gap of misunderstanding between majors and independents. As long as that exists, we have little chance of complete recovery. Previously most major executives came from independent operations, many of them educated on the derrick floor. They understood the problems of the independent and were willing to help him.

In more recent years, many major executives have little understanding of independent oilmen. They do not even know how much they depend on them. Good, capable executives will never know the independent's side of the story unless they hear it across a forum table. And unless majors do understand independents, both will lose in the long run.

An informal seminar need not be a Utopian dream, but can be a realistic turning point in the health of the independent, and indeed in the existence of the domestic oil industry.

Relation of the Independent
To the Future of the Petroleum Industry

"The industry should lament the passing of these big oil gamblers . . . Their day is over because their rugged daring is no longer necessary."
                                        September 22, 1964

The independent producer has been labeled "the vanishing American" by those in and out of the oil industry. Frankly, I am convinced that independent producers are here to stay. Not all of them, maybe, but most of them. As in nature, the fittest will prevail. The independents are going through an evolutionary process and will be better for it—that is, those who survive! And many will survive primarily because the independent is necessary to our free enterprise system.

The character of the independent producer has changed completely in the last decade and will change more as time goes on. He is the backbone of the industry and as necessary to the future of the petroleum industry in America as the supply of our domestic petroleum reserves. If we ever run out of oil and gas, or if foreign imports completely dominate the American market, we will suffer an about-face in our progress and well-being. And if we run out of independent oil producers, the day will soon follow when indigenous reserves will gradually begin to shrink and dry up.

M. J. Rathbone, chairman of the Board of Directors of Standard Oil Company of New Jersey, predicted in 1963 that by 1985 oil and gas will furnish two-thirds of the free world's energy needs which will range from 35 to 40 billion barrels of oil equivalent per year, more than twice the present free-world level of 17 billion.

Rathbone also observed that the United States alone, during that 22-year period, will consume about 115 billion barrels of oil and 500 trillion cubic feet of gas and that the entire free world will consume about 300 billion barrels of oil and 650 trillion cubic feet of gas, more than twice the total production in the entire history of man up to this time.

The latest United States Geological Survey (USGS) report on probable reserves in this country shows that we have so far consumed 70 billion barrels of domestic petroleum in America and have 32 billion barrels of proved known recoverable domestic reserves. An additional 16.3 billion barrels exist in known pools which might be recovered by established methods, plus another 40.2 billion barrels of reserves that might be recovered from existing fields by new secondary recovery methods. Therefore, in the history of petroleum in this country since 1859, we have produced and have available a total of 158.5 billion barrels. Further estimates include undiscovered recoverable resources of 200 billion barrels, plus another 300 billion barrels which are marginal, but not yet discovered.

The USGS has, therefore, estimated a potential total of over 600 billion barrels of domestic oil including past and future. This is contrasted with the very pessimistic estimate of a total of 175 billion barrels from a study for the National Academy of Sciences. The study stated that the rate of discovery in this country reached its maximum in 1956 and that the peak of production was just around the corner.

I am inclined to go along with the more optimistic USGS survey since pessimistic forecasts on this subject have consistently been wrong in the past.

If this nation is ever to have these more optimistic estimates of reserves, the independent will have to continue to find a large portion of it. In the past, he found approximately 85 per cent of the reserves in this country. In the future, he will still find the larger share, but it will take the indispensable support of the major companies to help him do it. His share in the percentage of future discoveries will be less than in the past, but it will continue to be the most important and dramatic part.

Therefore, the independent cannot possibly be discounted. He has to continue to exist, and he must be prepared to take an increasingly important place in the oil picture because demand is increasing, foreign oil is going more and more to world markets outside this country where oil is needed more, and prices for foreign crude can go no other direction than up. The ever-present possibility of shutdowns of foreign fields, or expropriation, or nationalization, or seizure by enemy forces or subversives automatically throws greater burdens and responsibilities on the independent to meet any new crisis.

The emergencies met by the independents in the past may be a picnic compared to what they may face in the future. Russia is now trying to prove to the Europeans that all of Europe must eventually depend on the Soviets for its energy supply. Russia is continually promoting this event through propaganda and other devious means. Even over political conference tables, the Russians make it a point to inform the heads of European countries that their future oil supply is in the hands of the Soviets.

In the past, Europe has always looked to the United States for oil when its supply from other oil-producing countries was cut off, as in the Suez crisis. Yet, Europe is now saying that it wants a diversification of "sources of supply" to insure itself of oil when a crisis arises. This is a smooth way of telling us that Russia now is more than a hole card to them; that now the European countries will trade with Russia; and that their dependence on the United States is over.

Within the next decade or even sooner, Europe must definitely decide whether its dependence for its future oil will rest with the Communists or the free world.

When European planners speak of "other sources," they forget how suddenly the supply from these "other sources" can be choked off. They have evidently forgotten Suez!

They have probably also forgotten that the United States still remains the only real dependable source of petroleum for meeting European emergencies. Over four million barrels a day from this country would be at once available if these "other sources" are interrupted.

In today's volatile world, it is entirely possible for a catastrophe to occur elsewhere which would in turn bring disaster to Europe. Just think what would happen to the European countries if Middle East oil is again blocked at Suez, if the North African supply is stopped by insurrection, if South American oil is held up by Castro and his Communist allies, or if Russia decides to slash Europe's oil supply to teach it a lesson.

Of course, the ace in the hole is the producers in the United States. The independent producer is the backbone of the domestic industry, and without the independents, Europe's demands might not be met by the United States. This inability to meet the demand would lead to just what Russia wants: a chance to pressure the European countries until they come crawling to the Soviets on the terms of the Communists. This outcome is not far-fetched! It is a real possibility that Russia would welcome—yes, even plan—a sudden combined crisis of oil logistics to win another battle in the Cold War.

So, the independent producer is a *must* for the welfare of the industry he serves, and for his country as well. Independents know of their importance, but they are now beginning to realize that no one else does! The public image of the independent is a bad one that pictures them all rich, happy, and greedy.

But the independent of today is not the happy-go-lucky, get-rich-quick phenomenon of an uncontrolled free enterprise of the past. That breed of overnight millionaires met its doom when the people of this country demanded conservation because they despaired of preventable waste of their most precious natural resource. Demands for conservation are increasing instead of diminishing. In fact, the federal government has become most mindful of the need for more conservation and is making greater demands on producing states for sound conservation practices. These demands imply a serious threat of federal control if the states do not act accordingly.

The independent, as well as the industry, must face the fact that there will not be as many independents in the future as there have been in the past. The marginal operator is almost finished, except that he can still find oil and sell out with a good profit.

Even that process now is undergoing a dramatic change. Many of the older, larger operators are either passing on or retiring. These larger operators came mostly from the ranks of the small or marginal operator who thrived on inducements which simply are not present anymore.

The payoffs are not as fast as they once were. Costs are much higher. Risks are far greater. In many cases, land in potential oil country is simply not reasonably available to the independent. But most of all, financing is not possible to an independent until he has established production, largely because his old backers, the supply houses, are no longer able to offer this service. Even when he has established production, financing becomes possible only on a well-to-well basis.

A few years ago, risk capital for drilling exploratory, or wildcat, wells was available through several sources, especially from people with tax dollars to risk. The pressures of overproduction, unnecessary drilling of highly expensive wells, and a general world-wide surplus of oil, plus lower and lower allowables, have dried up much of this money. If adverse tax laws are passed which affect the oil industry, there will not be any tax dollars left for wildcat oil exploration. This will mean the sure but slow extinction of hundreds of independents.

One reason for the withholding of even tax dollars from independent operators has been the failure of investors to investigate those operators with whom money was being spent. In some cases, they were operators with little or no petroleum knowledge who depended too much on luck. In other instances, they were fly-by-night operators with poor discovery averages but with a repertoire of plausible stories on how they could make the investors rich. And to the dismay of so many unsophisticated investors, they turned out to be, not oil operators, but merely glib promoters who had come into the oil country believing that if they could raise the money, they could find oil without experience. In a few rare cases this happened, but the payoff was so meager after the promoter took his "share" that many good investors lost confidence in all oil ventures.

Most independents, of course, prefer to get their money only from risk-wise investors, those who know the odds and are still willing to enter an oil venture. No wildcat proposition can possibly be a cinch. If it were, it would not be classified as a wildcat. The odds against hitting oil in wildcat areas are great. But, those odds are reduced by men of knowledge, experience, and known integrity using every available technique and scientific tool.

The risks in petroleum exploration and development ventures are great even with the best of professional advice. These risks become astronomical when the venturer disregards this advice and associates himself with promoters and unscrupulous operators. With sound business judgment and expert professional assistance from the sciences of geology, geophysics, and petroleum engineering, the risks are substantially reduced to a point where participating in oil and gas prospects can become a most profitable undertaking.

Many good independents today are actually well-trained geologists or engineers or both. All good independents have had much experience in the field, and generally they operate in a province such as the Gulf Coast or West Texas which they know and where they have gained their experience.

Any good oil operator has to be a hard-working man. One simply does not find and produce oil without hard work for long hours at a time, often without regard to week ends or holidays. One certainly cannot find oil around a gin rummy table or a country club golf course. There is not a more trying, frustrating, or difficult business in the world than exploring and drilling for, finding, and producing oil and gas.

The independent oilman of tomorrow is going to have to expand his knowledge. For instance, he will have to learn about salesmanship in marketing his oil and gas. Few, if any, independent producers have a salesman for this express purpose on the staff. They have all permitted proration, arbitrary price-fixing, and ratable take to obliterate this function. The independent producer will soon have to compete with other suppliers for the best available market and employ all facets of good salesmanship to sell his product to the right purchaser for the right and, maybe, negotiated price. This would necessitate his becoming more informed about world, as well as domestic, markets.

Independents without employed or retained geologists will have to correct this omission because geological prospects will have to be analyzed much better than in the past. Exploratory odds today are not conducive to the continued healthy survival of the independent. Every means must be employed by the independent to reduce the odds and the risks. Prospects now cost too much. One deep failure can break even a highly successful man in the present economic climate. This situation calls for more study of all available information on a most knowledgeable basis. It requires the services of more and more professional men, especially outstanding engineers and geologists.

Operating costs must be trimmed at every corner until they come out as round as a dollar. In the past, the above-ground waste in materials, manpower, services, and just plain frills have kept costs far higher than necessary. Cost accountants are as necessary to independent oilmen today as professional tax men.

Texas has seen venture capital dry up largely because present regulations permit unnecessary wells. The result has been continually lower per-well allowables and lengthened payouts which made it almost impossible for independents, who must operate on a short-range basis as compared to long-range operations for majors, to raise money for worthwhile drilling projects.

Now, two recent state Supreme Court decisions have curtailed a considerable amount of the abuse of unnecessary wells. Arbitrary formulas controlling the allocation of production of oil and gas have been eliminated, and in their place, allocation based on acre feet or unit acreage has been instigated. These decisions are landmarks for proper and sound conservation practices in Texas and will help keep the independent around a while longer. More than anything else, these decisions are a prelude to other proper rules to eliminate physical and economic waste.

For example, the Texas Railroad Commission recently ruled a double allowable for Phillips Petroleum Company for doubled well-spacing in Penwell field, Ector County, on the basis of protecting correlative rights. This ruling eliminates the necessity for Phillips to drill an unnecessary well to protect itself and those with land, royalty, and working interest ownerships. This type of ruling will eventually help return to Texas risk capital for exploration and development.

While this is a good ruling, most Texas operators are not satisfied. A committee of operators has prepared a bill to eliminate the possibility of a conflicting ruling being passed in the future by a different commission. This same type of procedure is happening in other states in an attempt to bring about fair and total conservation in the interests of all concerned from landowner to taxpayer.

Texas has gradually gone down in per-well production allowables from 18.5 barrels per day for 230 days per year in 1950, to 12.5 barrels per day for eight days per month, or 96 days per year, for all except exempt wells in 1962. Exempt wells include secondary recovery projects, old marginal fields, salt dome fields, and others which have peculiar geological and production problems which necessitate production on a 30-day-per-month basis to keep the wells "alive."

Secondary recovery is one area in which independents are overlooking their biggest opportunity. This practice involves old fields where knowledge of the industry, good engineering, and geological practices can result in most profitable investments. There are many such opportunities waiting to be exploited in Texas and older producing states.

The biggest threat to the independent oilman today is the constant threat to the tax structure, depletion, intangible charge-offs, and other necessary elements of tax laws as they apply to wasting assets such as oil and gas.

These harassing devices employed by irresponsible and/or misinformed individuals and organizations, a few members of Congress or the national government, and some mass media must be halted.

Periodic surveys of the petroleum industry by Congress and the Treasury Department with a view toward an occasional tax law change are expected, as they are in other industries, but it is unwise and costly to the nation for a continuous, vilifying campaign to be carried on against the oil industry for the apparent sole purpose of getting votes or selling newspapers or magazines.

Congress and the Treasury Department seem to be interested in tax programs which serve the public interest, so they would probably not consider seriously any change in depletion or other elements of oil and gas taxation, which have proven to be sound. However, the threat frightens investors away from oil prospects, and that is certainly contrary to the public interest. This threat serves no one, as it only creates a feeling of instability in the industry and out of it.

Tax laws are written to benefit the whole public and not any particular segment or class of people. The depletion percentage, for instance, serves the people far better than it serves any oilman or oil corporation. It provides the incentive to continue the search for domestic oil and gas reserves necessary to maintain our energy-based economy.

Wildcatting on an over-all basis is a hazardous business. But it can be profitable. For example, Petroleum Outlook magazine reports that in 1962, the industry produced 16.2 barrels of oil per foot drilled, the average cost of drilling was $22.90 per foot, and the estimated discovery-development cost per barrel of liquid hydrocarbons was $1.41. A composite figure showed that the average net income per barrel of oil produced was 82 cents, while the average cost of oil per barrel is approximately $2.50.

These figures tell a discouraging story, but a producer with a successful exploratory record can still make money in the oil industry. Those with poor success records are simply going to be forced out of business.

Before conservation, a producer with a poor record could revive himself with a big discovery after a long string of wildcat failures. Then costs were low, taxes were nominal, depths were shallow, equipment was uncomplicated, and waste was rampant. But a man who had drilled 50 dry holes at a cost of a half million dollars could recover all his money with one new discovery well and a month's production, and sometimes, a week's. Anyone investing in wildcat oil ventures today believing such conditions still exist is 20 to 30 years out of date.

Today small producers are considering selling out as soon as possible, before the threatened changes in the tax laws become a reality. The ABC method of purchasing oil properties is under serious attack. Its elimination would reduce the ability of the independent to negotiate freely for a reasonable consideration for his properties and would in turn place the independent at the mercy of the large purchasers.

Harold Vance, a Houston banker, pointed out recently that present demand for oil and gas reserves has raised prices to what probably are peak levels. He said, however, that most small producers were holding onto their reserves fearing that they would have nothing to do if they sold out and worrying about what they would do with the money received. He predicted that opportunities for the peak prices will fall off because imports will probably not decrease, payoffs will be longer as costs mount in the future, and investors are becoming more difficult to find.

A few years ago, there were 42,000 independent producers and explorers in this country. Today that figure has shrunk to 10,000. The day is not far off when not even that number of independents will be able to stay in business. But those who do will be as important, if not more so, than any other segment of the business because they will continue to find a large proportion of the future oil. Financing oil takes risk capital, and large corporations have their limits in this area.

Admittedly, independents cannot compete with the majors in bidding, exploring, and drilling for offshore oil and gas. But, as far as we know now, offshore oil will never become a serious threat to the prospects on land in volume of discoveries. Furthermore, the prospects offshore are limited even to the largest integrated companies. They certainly cannot get all the available leases in the tidelands. Those that do acquire many large blocks of acreage are the biggest gamblers the petroleum world has ever known. They can make a "killing" or they can come close to bankruptcy. Only the biggest with the greatest cash reserves are able to afford the necessary gambling. Then, on most occasions, companies combine to diversify the risk.

The independent wildcatters and producers who are able to stay in business will do so at far less risk than in the past for the simple reason that they will have become better businessmen and oilmen. Many of these independents will be incorporated, but that status will subject them to the criticism of overcautious stockholders and self-serving directors who may see a quick profit in selling out or merging.

Of course, these independent oil corporations will provide one type of investor with exactly what he wants, but the individual independent who runs his own company; guards the right to make his own decisions; and uses his knowledge, experience, and imagination to the fullest always will and should attract real risk capital. The rate of risk is also going down. While only one wildcat well in 50 turns out to be profitable, the ratio will narrow when the most reckless gamblers, those with the lowest success ratios, are eliminated by the process of self-extermination which is certainly apparent today.

The industry should lament the passing of these big oil gamblers. Their contribution to our world leadership and abundant way of life may never be recognized. They have been maligned and castigated by the press and the politicians. But each of them has made a greater contribution to his country than all of their critics combined.

Certainly they were show-offs. They drank whiskey and spent money and carried on like an army of coal-oil Johnnies. But they were a different breed of men. Most of them were laboring men who had more than the average amount of intelligence and a will to work as hard as they played and were blithely unaware of the odds they faced.

They never disturbed our economy because most of them lost their fortunes as fast as they made them. But in doing this, they were finding the fuel to provide the energy for a new way of life. There is not another breed of men on earth who could have or would have done what they did. My hat has always been off to them, and my head is bowed at their passing.

Their day is over because their rugged daring is no longer necessary. They made their contribution, and they went as far as possible. They fired many with their enthusiasm and boundless optimism.

They were tolerant, and they were helpful. They were generous in passing along their practical, hard-won experience and advice. As little hope as they had for a man with a degree, they went out of their way to try to make something out of a young man in spite of his "disadvantage" of excessive education. Those old-time oilmen were impeccably honest, and their word and handshake were far better than any contract a lawyer could draw up today.

They made modern communications possible by motor vehicle and airplane. They eliminated the horse as transportation and put power in the railroad and the steamship. They removed drudgery from the farm and factory. They made it possible for us to have innumerable conveniences that we enjoy or take for granted because we never lived without them.

Soon we will have only a few thousand independent explorers left. The weeding out of the undesirables is good for the industry. But, in time, we will have lost thousands of the most solid and valuable men in the country. No school can produce an independent oilman. The universities turn out geologists, engineers, lawyers, accountants, and others; and some of these become independent oilmen. But no college or university has a course in intestinal fortitude or hard work or how to recover again and again from one heartbreak after another. And corporations seldom develop such men even with all of their screening, selecting, supervising, and training. The thinking and the make-up of independents place them in a distinctive class.

The American independent oilman is not dying out—not the good one. His present status may seem shaky, and he may need some help. But the most important thing he can do is to *help himself*. The independents who modernize their own operations and update their own thinking are the independents who will survive in the evolutionary weeding-out process. Some of the self-help must be done collectively by the independents. We will see evidence of that soon, not necessarily through any single formal group or geographic area, but through a real grass-roots awakening to the need for collective and unselfish action by a large number of realistic and thoughtful men.

The oilman who stands still will not long remain independent. The times move too rapidly. The independent oilman who adjusts to his environment will gain strength from it. As a survivor in this evolutionary struggle, he will be the independent oilman of tomorrow!

Forecast of Domestic Petroleum Demands

"The learned men were saying we were out of oil when Pattillo Higgins and Anthony Lucas found Spindletop."   November 5, 1964

The availability and pliability of statistics on the oil industry have resulted in a recent rash of long-term supply and demand forecasts. The differences in them, if analyzed closely, lie in the specific interest of the experts and their companies or institutions at the time of their writing.

There are many hidden and unknown factors in forecasts. Who knows what new indicators will appear? What kind of government will we have in the future? To what extent will other energy sources compete with conventional energy sources? War, disease, and even new pills could change the whole picture in population forecasts.

An accurate market demand for 20 years into the future would require a staff of domestic and international experts in the fields of economics, health, population, public safety, transportation, agriculture, chemistry, and world politics who would complete the job in about 20 years.

We are again confronted by several "crystal-ball gazers" with predictions that we will shortly run out of oil and gas and even coal. The latest of these was made in Geneva at the 1964 International Atoms for Peace conference by two atomic scientists from India.

They said the world reserves of oil and coal would be exhausted in 30 years, or in this century. This to me is a completely ridiculous and absurd prognostication.

If these scientists are right, it would certainly mean the greatest demand ever for fossil fuels in the next few years. If they are wrong, they are not the first. Many intellectual forecasters before them have also been wrong.

In 1907, when oil was just beginning to pour out of Texas, Oklahoma, Louisiana, Kansas, and California in far more promising amounts than in the old "oil region," a United States Geological Survey study stated that oil resources in this country would be exhausted by 1935.

That report recommended that oil use be gradually confined to the lubrication of watches, clocks, and other precision instruments and that alcohol from potatoes, grains, and waste products be used for illumination and power in place of gasoline. Natural gas was not given much hope either. In fact, it was considered a nuisance.

A 1925 paper presented before the American Institute of Mining and Metallurgical Engineers again predicted our running out of oil and gas. Some western railroads were at that time contemplating changing certain divisions back from oil fuel to coal.

Part of that paper prepared by learned men of the day read:

> It is . . . indicated that the peak in use of gas and oil as fuel is about reached and that a reduction in the use of these fuels should be expected in the future . . . and will be replaced by coal.

Self-appointed experts, politicians, industrial leaders, and even scientists have been telling us about the end of oil and gas ever since Drake brought in the first oil well in 1859.

In a well-researched paper at the World Petroleum Congress in 1960, Sir Stephen Gibson, chairman of the Congress and a former president of Iraq Petroleum Co., said that in two or three years from that date, the world surplus of oil would begin to disappear. Four years later, there was no evidence of this projection coming true.

In a so-called "platoon system" of forecasting, a group of experts comes up with an indisputable prediction. The platoon is supposed to relegate the individual forecaster into oblivion.

An example of such forecasting is the "Future Supply Committee" which reported recently that we have yet to find 629.5 trillion cubic feet of gas to add to our present-known reserves of 276.15 trillion cubic feet for a total available supply of 905.65 trillion cubic feet.

If this report is true, then we will be out of gas in this country by the year 2000. In fact, some figures show that under proper conditions, we could use up 1,000 trillion cubic feet of gas by 1980.

This, incidentally, is probably the most optimistic gas supply report ever published, even if it did get the committee disassociated from the American Gas Association which created it. AGA apparently did not want to be out of business by 2000.

What these out-of-the-blue figures do insinuate is that there should not be a shortage of a natural gas market in this country before 2000.

Gas is by all odds the most wonderful fuel ever produced by man from the earth. It is safe, clean, convenient, and exceptionally cheap. No fuel yet known can come anywhere near to competing with it. So, the demand will always be high as long as there are a few hundred trillion cubic feet in known reserves available to satisfy the market.

The supply of gas is unlimited under the proper conditions. There is no evidence that gas cannot be found to supply any market as long as the explorer can be compensated for his efforts. He will have to drill more wells, suffer a greater ratio of dry holes, and drill them deeper; and millions will have to be spent on new tools, techniques, and technology. But who knows how many and where great gas fields are to be found?

Hundreds of millions of acres of sedimentary land in this country have never been explored at all. The proven and productive sedimentary basins still have to be explored deeper—even below 25,000 feet.

No man can say with accuracy what the earth holds in the way of hydrocarbons. Too many have tried it, many of them as distinguished and as learned in their day as present prognosticators. They have all goofed.

The learned men were saying we were out of oil when Pattillo Higgins and Anthony Lucas found Spindletop. The experts were stating unconditionally that we would have to depend on oil from Venezuela for future supplies when old Dad Joiner found the great East Texas field.

Who knows where or when or how many fields we might find with great reserves like the King Ranch, Katy, Carthage, or Hastings; or Signal Hill, Kettleman Hills, or even the Panhandle or Hugoton? The geologic conditions in this country do not rule out such possibilities. All that is required is sound scientific exploration.

One major incentive for exploration is a good market. The demand will provide that market. So the amount of oil or gas that can be found in this country is unlimited under incentives and freedoms which encourage exploration.

What predictors should have been saying all these years is simply this: As long as there is a market, there will be a supply of hydrocarbons to meet the demand; demand will create price incentives; and the hope for profit will send men scurrying to new and deeper and more widespread holes in the ground.

Now, I must add one reservation—that we remain free. In fact, we must regain some of our freedoms which have already been taken over by government in the form of gas producer controls.

Gas producers require freedom to explore, or the ratio of reserves to demand will continue to dwindle. The extent of freedom, of course, is up to our government and its leaders and the people who own and operate this country—namely the consumers and the voters.

With the markets which are bound to develop in the next 20 years, the problem we face will not be demand. It will be *supply*.

We will always need to maintain a domestic supply of energy. The best source of domestic supply is oil and gas, the energy and heating fuels we know best. These are the sources which offer the best hope for increased development, particularly in the field of petrochemistry and advanced technology.

Should we fail to come up with adequate supplies of conventional oil and gas, we know that we have at least a century of supply in a trillion barrels of undeveloped shale oil reserves. Shale oil is our hole card, especially until scientists develop a process for waste disposal that will make atomic energy feasible and its cost competitive with, if not cheaper than, hydrocarbons.

My forecast is a summary of worthwhile, well-documented studies and reports such as "Resources in America's Future," (1963); the Texas Eastern Transmission Corporation's 1961 study titled "Energy Fuels in the United States . . . 1947-1980"; "Energy in the American Economy, 1850-1975," (Resources for the Future, Inc., 1960); and the study by T. W. Nelson, senior vice-president of Socony Mobil, in April, 1964.

One basic fact emerges from all these studies: Energy demand is going to increase steadily and, before the end of the next decade, will be controlled almost entirely by those providing the raw materials.

My research indicates that annual demand for oil, including natural gas liquids, by 1970 will average 4.1 billion barrels in this country. By 1980 this figure will have risen to 5.3 billion barrels, and by 1990 demand will have reached 7.2 billion barrels per year, compared with present demand of about 3.3 billion barrels. Between 1980 and 1990, there will be a demand of 62 billion barrels, of which domestic sources will furnish 50 billion barrels.

Imports will probably average about 20 per cent, since anything over that would mean our dependency on outside sources and jeopardizing our entire economic structure.

In the year 1984, the target for my guess today, we will have a market for six billion barrels of oil annually and will have to produce about 4.8 billion barrels of that amount ourselves. This compares with less than three billion barrels of annual domestic production at present.

As for natural gas, we are presently producing more than 14 trillion cubic feet annually. By 1980 this figure will most likely increase to 24.5 trillion and by 1984 to more than 26 trillion cubic feet.

These figures indicate that between now and 1980 we will consume over 400 trillion cubic feet of gas, whereas present known recoverable reserves are about 275 trillion cubic feet. We will need another 500 trillion in reserves just to reach the year 2000, not to consider the reserves needed that year to get along until 2020.

We will also consume, between now and 1984, about 78 million barrels of crude oil, which is more than twice the amount of presently known recoverable reserves in this country. So by 1984, we will have to find about 100 billion barrels of new oil in this country merely to keep our production-reserves ratio in line.

Up to now, production of gas has exceeded consumption each year. But there is one indication of trouble ahead—the life expectancy of existing reserves. The figure is dropping. In 1945 we had 30.8 years' supply. By 1960, when reserves were 116 trillion cubic feet higher than in 1945, the gas in reserve had dropped below 20 years' supply. Today we have less than 17 years of gas supply in present reserves.

Federal controls, imposed by the Supreme Court in the Phillips decision, have eliminated independent competition in gas exploration and production and promoted monopoly in the production of gas. Unless there is a change, we will not find sufficient gas to meet market demand in this country for the next 20 years, and certainly not to the end of the century.

What can be done to supply the growing demand if those controls are removed is anyone's guess. But that decision and the subsequent action of the Federal Power Commission, has already eliminated many good explorers and producers. The damage is so great that, even if the provisions of the Natural Gas Act of 1938 were immediately restored by Congress, it would be difficult to meet the goals of the future.

No one, not even the government, is going to explore for gas at tremendous risks when there is no way of making a reasonable profit even if the search is successful.

If these unnecessary controls are removed, it is possible that we will find the gas to meet market demands far into the future because there is no known limit to the geological potential in this country.

At the present rate of increase in demand, it will be necessary to provide 45 billion barrels of new oil and probably more than 275 trillion cubic feet of gas by 1975. This does not necessarily mean that we will consume this much oil or gas. It does mean however that, to maintain our ratio of reserves to production, we will have to produce that much oil and gas because we will probably use up all the oil and natural gas now known to be recoverable.

In spite of this tremendous short-term future demand forecast, in 1962 and 1963 we found less crude oil than we produced by 60 million barrels each year.

If we are to meet the demand for only the next 10 years, we will have to drill many more exploratory wells than we are now drilling. In 1964 we drilled approximately 11,000 exploratory wells in this country. In addition, there were 34,000 development wells drilled. Development wells add little to the reserve picture. They simply prove up previous or new reserves found by exploratory wells.

Actually we should be drilling a minimum of 60,000 wells per year for the next 10 years if we expect to meet the demands for the next 20 years—and at least 25,000 of those well each year should be exploratory tests.

Development wells can be controlled by proper spacing, thus eliminating unnecessary wells. The savings can be put back into exploration and thereby maintain a level of supply that will help us meet future demands with safety.

We can find all the oil and gas we need within the boundaries of this country if we have the proper incentives, including—but not limited to—market, price, and tax considerations, and the proper tools and equipment.

The crisis now is that we will continue to use our domestic reserves faster than we can replenish them. There is no competition in sight to relieve us from finding more oil and gas. The growth of atomic energy for peaceful purposes will only increase demand for oil world-wide. As demand grows in foreign countries, the supply of foreign oil to us will decrease.

Americans, while consuming more energy per capita than any other people on earth, have only begun to satisfy their desire for energy in all forms. Our whole economy has long been geared to energy, and for the past 20 years, the great majority of that energy has come from the fossil fuels.

Petroleum is still the most important of the world's energy sources. Oil and gas account for three-fourths of all primary energy consumed in the United States. In the foreseeable future, neither nuclear energy nor the other non-conventional energy sources offer any serious competition to oil and gas. For instance, in the United States, nuclear energy is expected to supply only 4 per cent of the energy requirements by 1984, and only 14 per cent by the year 2000.

Although there is now a world surplus of petroleum, the time will come soon when we will have to think more and more about conservation in the production and utilization of hydro-carbons. The process has already started. Today it is painful. Tomorrow it will be a blessing.

Refining processes will be continually and dramatically improved. Petroleum chemistry will play an ever-increasing role in our lives and in our markets as new uses for petroleum appear.

Besides conservation, good communications (or public relations) are essential to the future of the oil and gas industry, as well as to the entire system of individual enterprise. The petroleum industry's present communications are ineffective. Our public image leaves much to be desired.

What can we do to change our image?

First, we must eliminate bickering and bitterness within the industry itself. We have too many do-nothing-but-think-they-do associations, too many trade journals, too many unproductive meetings among ourselves. We should do something about this deplorable situation.

Our public relations people tell us we should project a good image. No one else can create an image for us, and we can reflect only the image that exists. If our image, which we create in everything we do, is productive, then we should do all in our power to project it.

Our industry does have a good image to project—the image of accomplishments which have contributed so much to the development of this country and the abundance enjoyed by its people.

We are wrong to maintain associations within our industry which antagonize and fight each other. The public is confused and bewildered.

We are wrong to preach to the public about such things as depletion. Coming from us, this sounds self-serving, when it is not. After all, the reduction or elimination of depletion would have less effect on the oilmen than it would have on the public. The public would pay higher prices, suffer domestic shortages, subject our nation to dependence on foreign sources for oil, and thereby endanger our economy, our way of life, and our national defense.

But oilmen should not talk about this themselves because, coming from us, the public assumes we have a selfish motive and that anyone will say anything for enough profit. The more we talk about this, the worse the matter becomes. The public concludes that oil producers are trying to protect a good tax "gimmick" that the public cannot equally enjoy. And the public resents our method of defending it.

We should say to the public and to Congress, "If you don't like percentage depletion, do with it what you will! Retain it, reduce it, or eliminate it! It is *your* law enacted for *your* protection. The future of the country will be guided by your actions."

The same reasoning applies to imports and natural gas legislation.

The public and Congress certainly realize that this country must possess sufficient energy resources to sustain our rate of progress. The decisions they make on these matters will mean the success or the failure of our economic future.

I am not implying that this industry should not answer questions and provide data upon which proper decisions can be made, but I do mean to imply that all these matters are more important to the welfare of the public and the continuation of freedom than they are to the individual oil companies and oilmen in this country. This is what we have failed to get the public to understand.

We can easily accomplish this if we take an active part in public affairs, not for the express purpose of gaining a better image, but because we know we should. Thus we can educate the public about our industry in a constructive way.

We must understand as much as we can about what goes on outside the oil industry. After all, everything that happens in the community affects product sales. And product sales create the need for oil and gas, which in turn promotes exploration and production of those natural resources.

Explorers, producers, transporters, and processors must join the marketers in thinking about the consumer, the man who keeps us all in business. We are only as well off as the consumer, no more and no less. In general what is good for the consumer is good for all of us, including the industry's labor force and its professional men.

If we took all the human energy we are now spending on intraindustry warfare and put it to work solving problems instead of creating them, we could write our own ticket regarding demand for oil and gas 20, 30, 40, or 50 years from now.

An Independent's Blueprint for Survival

"Yesterday's oil operator was the so-called practical oilman. His engineering education was gained on the derrick floor, and he learned his geology from cuttings."   May 10, 1966

The status of the independent in the present-day oil industry can be summed up in one word—precarious.

But just to say the independent oil operator is in serious trouble is not saying anything new. Independents, collectively and individually, have told everyone who would listen that their road is full of chug holes and it seems to be leading to oblivion.

Actually the evolutionary process has been at work in the petroleum industry. It is going on gradually every day and by more precipitous spurts every time an upheaval occurs in the industry. It happened after Spindletop, after East Texas, and during the depression. Outmoded practices were discontinued. Weak companies and individuals disappeared. The strong and the adaptable carried on.

Now there are at least 10,000 independent oil operators in the United States. The general public has heard of very few of these, and only the spectacularly successful ones at that. Even people in the oil business forget that this industry is composed of thousands upon thousands of small businessmen.

These independent operators drill three-fourths of all oil wells and more than 85 per cent of the exploratory wells. Without independent operators, wildcatting would not be cut 85 per cent, but exploration for oil in this country would be drastically curtailed.

Most of our nation's oil reserves were discovered by independent oilmen. And most of the reserves yet to be discovered will be found by the independent operator. The health of the oil industry is largely determined by the economic health of this vast army of independents.

Our nation's defense machine runs on petroleum. Our defense capacity is therefore directly related to the activities of the independent operators who will find the oil our nation will need today and tomorrow.

Men in high and responsible places in the oil industry know this. Government men understand it, too. Neither group will allow the independent oil operator to become extinct. They cannot afford to.

But neither is it necessary to mollycoddle him. The oil patch is not a protected playground. It is a tough world and a changing world. Not all the independent operators will survive the evolutionary changes that are now evident. Those who do survive—and they will be the majority, I think—will be those who adapt themselves to present economic conditions.

The economic threat to the independent is coming from several directions. The most obvious current threat is the familiar bugaboo, imports, which has displaced a considerable amount of domestic production. In 1956-1958, the average daily allowable in Texas was cut in half. Few businessmen in any industry could stay in business with half their income cancelled and expenses rising. So far, the independent has been carried by his credit at supply houses and service companies and by a temporarily obliging banker. But the situation cannot last forever.

Another potential economic threat is shale oil. Before long, billions of barrels of petroleum will be unlocked from oil shale at a price competitive with crude.

As far as energy per dollar is concerned, the petroleum industry is even getting into competition with itself! Natural gas has taken markets from fuel oil and will continue to do so until prices are equalized. And for the more distant future, new sources of energy are appearing such as atomic and solar power.

Coal replaced wood because, in the long run, it was cheaper. Oil supplanted coal for many uses because it saved money. Oil lost some markets to gas for the same reason. As soon as another source of energy can do a job cheaper than petroleum, we will lose customers.

Imported oil, shale oil, and new sources of energy all pose a threat to the independent at the dollar level. So, to stay in the race, the independent will have to get more oil per dollar than he is getting today. He will have to do a better job at less cost.

The surviving operator will be the one who takes advantage of every scientific advance because finding and producing oil has become very much a science. Yesterday's oil operator was the so-called practical oilman. His engineering education was gained on the derrick floor, and he learned his geology from cuttings. He came up the hard way and was proud of it. He was long on courage and hunches, and despite his scientific shortcomings, he found a lot of oil. He was inclined to squelch the engineering school boll weevils he hired and frequently ignored the recommendations he was paying for.

Today's oilman is far more likely to be a scientist, an engineer, a geologist, specifically trained and educated for the industry. He will employ every scientific principle that will make his operation more efficient and more effective. Together with specialists in accounting and administration, he will apply the knowledge that will enable him to produce more oil per dollar, oil that will compete with other sources of hydrocarbons and energy.

Besides examining operations to make them more efficient, independents must re-examine some of their pet philosophies to make sure they are not outmoded.

For instance, the independent has historically been against wide spacing. Because he felt he had to have a fast payoff and the quickest way to get more oil was to drill more wells, most independents wanted to drill as many producers as possible on the acreage they held. That concept was financially practical in the days of the $10,000 well, but not today with development wells that frequently cost 10 times that or more. Yet as long as the well factor continues to dominate the formula for setting allowables, we still have to double the number of wells to double our production income. If, however, the allowable formula could be realistically and scientifically adjusted to apportion greater weight to acreage and to reserves, wells could be allowed to produce closer to their most efficient rate. The savings effected are obvious.

By producing his reserves with a reduced investment in a smaller number of wells but at a rate sufficient to make the operation economically feasible, the independent can make more oil per dollar. And he can stay in the economic race.

We are operating today, in most instances, under spacing concepts developed nearly a generation ago. In the meantime, reservoir engineering has made great advances. Independents in the 1930's had reason to mistrust the scientific data, but today more data and more accurate data are available. Even more important, the independent is able to understand and apply it.

To survive, operators must broaden their spacing ideas. Twenty acres may have been wide spacing for 5,000-foot wells, but it can make the development of a 15,000-foot reservoir an economic nightmare when the operator knows he could get just as much oil from an 80-acre pattern at one-fourth the drilling cost.

Surely scientific progress and years of experience can enable the oil industry and the regulatory bodies to develop new spacing concepts which are economically feasible and meet the particular needs of the independents.

This conflict cannot continue between the independents and the majors. This is an issue that the industry as an industry is going to have to solve if we are to keep domestic crude in the dollar race as an energy fuel.

With the wealth of experience and scientific information available, the oil industry can surely solve another complex and often controversial issue, unitization. It is absolutely necessary that we find a solution if we are to stay competitive. To get efficient spacing, to enable operators to institute appropriate money-saving automation techniques, to take full advantage of the scientific advances developed in research labs every day, to make secondary recovery projects possible, to squeeze the cost-per-barrel ratio as small as possible, a revision of unitization practice is mandatory.

This may require compulsory unitization or maybe official encouragement of voluntary unitization through proper incentives. Nevertheless, the survival of the independent depends on making all operations as efficient as possible, and unitization is a vital key for accomplishing that.

Certainly equitable unitization could be applied to new fields as they are discovered. And it is not inconceivable to extend the practice into fields which have already paid out.

The basic problem is to find a unitization system that will protect the rights of all concerned.

Application of the Rule of Capture to oil production dates back to the days when the nature of petroleum reservoirs was completely misunderstood by the oil industry and by the courts. Because they thought rivers of oil ran in torrents beneath the surface of the earth much like rivers of water, the courts applied the same laws to both situations. Confinement within an oil structure was not considered. Universal application of the Rule of Capture to oil production gutted many a field and caused the unnecessary drilling of thousands of wells. Surely in this age of science, we need not base our production rules on the theory that oil is flowing under our leases in a mighty river!

I am hopeful that a movement for intelligent unitization will develop from within the ranks of the independent operators themselves and they will lead the fight for their own survival. If independents wait for the majors to take the lead, it will be that much more difficult to get the support of the majority of independents—for a long time at least.

The independents should form a committee or a group to study this unitization problem in all oil-producing states. From this research could very well come an equitable and workable proposal—perhaps suggested state legislation—which through the Interstate Oil Compact Commission might become widely adopted. This group could also promote the program within the oil industry.

Unitization is not incompatible with the independent's way of doing business. Unitization is coming in one form or another, and a program devised and promoted by thinking independent oilmen is likely to be the program that will protect the independents' interests.

In the Old Ocean unitization program, the land and royalty owners formed a committee to meet with the operators' committee and work out problems in the best interest of all parties. The royalty committee hired trained geological and engineering consultants to advise them on the technical aspects and legal counsel for the contractual aspects. Unitization at Old Ocean has made possible the orderly development of a contrary field complicated by engineering and production problems that might not have been met without solid support of all involved.

The consuming public benefits from efficient methods and money-saving techniques. The consumer profits from the lowest possible prices and from a dependable domestic supply of oil. Present production practices permit the recovery of a large portion of the oil in place to be used for unlimited purposes. Inefficient production practices can leave millions of barrels of oil in the ground lost forever to the landowner, the operator, and the consumer.

The word for the independent oilman today is the same as it always has been—dynamic—connoting energy linked with motion, as opposed to static or stationary energy. The oilman who keeps abreast of, or ahead of, the economic atmosphere will remain independent and, in doing so, will insulate the oil industry against a radical shift in its exploratory effort. The independent must fight for survival within the industry, for without his kind, the industry would succumb to its many economic pressures and competitors.

Role and Responsibility
Of the Independent Producers

"The independent must be the first to recognize that creative geological thinking, based on highly scientific procedures, is the key to discovering these large reserves."   January 15, 1968

The financial plight of the independent oil producer has been blatantly aired recently by producers asking for incentives, handouts, controls, or just about any government action to aid them in their struggle for survival. Unfortunately they do not seem to realize that the more we ask for governmental help, the more liberties we place in jeopardy. Nothing will be given to an industry by the government without something being taken away.

For example, a few years ago, the oil industry had voluntary import controls. The system was not perfect, but at least it was controlled by the industry.

Most of the importers did their best to keep imports as low as possible under constant pressure from the State Department to increase the flow of foreign oil into this country. But independents kept complaining that importers were ruining the domestic oil industry and flocked to Washington in droves, insisting on mandatory import controls.

We finally succeeded in getting mandatory controls. Now we have three times as much foreign oil and products coming into this country as we had under the old voluntary plan—and many new importers. Some say the increases would have come anyway. That may be so, but I doubt it.

Mandatory import controls gave the government the right to control crude oil prices. Independents certainly did not have that in mind when they advocated the abolition of voluntary controls. Today, the influence of variation of supply and demand on oil prices is nullified by the control of imports out of Washington.

So we lost a great deal by asking for help. Evidently we have not learned our lesson. So what are we now about to do?

We were urging Congress to make mandatory import controls statutory instead of by executive proclamation—to lock us in a law from which there is virtually no escape. We were hoodwinked by the idea of passing part of the import allotment on to domestic operators as "drilling incentives." If the government gives an operator drilling money, it can eventually dictate the way wells are drilled, where they are drilled, how and how much oil is produced from them.

So such a law holds the danger of federal control of our industry. I am opposed to it. Many other independents feel the same way.

Statutory import controls contain the threat of final and total federal control of the petroleum industry. Such an action by Congress could be the decisive stroke to what freedom of operations we still enjoy as individuals in the oil industry.

The production of natural gas is under virtual federal control now. Perhaps some of us are growing accustomed to such controls. But I prefer to continue opposition to gas controls rather than support legislation to impose more federal control of oil.

Most domestic oil producers today seem to want Congress to pass a law to take import controls out of the hands of the executive department and put them into the hands of the Congress because they feel the executive agencies have lacked wisdom and resolution. They have been indecisive regarding imports from Canada. They have let certain chemical plants take advantage of loopholes. They have permitted the growth of imports in various ways that are detrimental not only to the domestic producers but to the welfare of the American people.

These actions resulted from pressure applied by certain selfish, shortsighted companies and individuals bolstered by specious arguments which sound convincing until all sides of the issue have been considered.

But even this situation is preferable to total federal control of our industry. As long as we have a trace of freedom left, I will not be a party to any attractive, but ill-conceived plan that will further deny my rights as a citizen without speaking out.

Naturally, I am opposed to any government official or anyone else using import controls to hold down crude oil prices—to offer to open the flood gates of either foreign oil or federally owned offshore oil to deny producers equitable and just prices to offset part of the tremendous rises in costs and risks.

I am opposed to all oil and gas imports which supplant domestic production. Of course, we must always accommodate some imports in order to maintain beneficial relations with other producing countries, to prevent the bulk of the world oil supplies from falling into Communist hands, and to be certain that our free world allies are never forced to depend on communism for oil and gas supplies. The volume of imports, however, should never be so great as to discourage domestic exploration or reach the point where we are dependent on outside sources for so much as a single barrel of oil.

But statutory import controls, as attractive as they may seem at the moment, will require and impose a system of federal control which could utterly bind us. We would forever be at the mercy of a law which could only be changed by another law. If later we found we had made a mistake, as we almost certainly would, we would also discover that it was too late for correction.

Now import controls can be adjusted to meet any stituation or crisis by the simple implementation of an executive order. Occasions may arise when immediate drastic changes in imports

—either up or down—would be needed to safeguard the economy and security of this country.

Statutory controls could bring about—eventually if not immediately—absolute federal control over direct pricing, conservation, drilling, leasing, transportation, marketing, financing, and exploration for oil and gas. In fact, this could be the most important step in the complete nationalization of all mineral and energy industries in this country and the assumption by the government of all mineral rights, royalties, and interests.

The present proposed legislation does not contain such provisions at all. If it did, of course, the very men and associations making the proposal would probably withdraw their support. But statutory controls contain the implied threat.

Ironically, the people who most abhor federal control often promote legislation that can be self-destructive. Yet, in this instance, those who are most often accused of favoring federal control—the bureaucrats—are vigorously opposing this measure. I understand their reasons, and I do not like them. But I am thankful for any reason which prevents the passing of a statutory law.

Many independents are falling into the same trap that most major oil companies and some independents fell into during the Roosevelt administration. In those times of great oil surpluses, most of the integrated oil companies and a few large independents decided that federal control was the only answer to the ineffectiveness of existing state conservation regulations. Even the American Petroleum Institute in November, 1932, endorsed the idea by announcing its support of a federal oil production quota plan.

Such controls probably would have been effected had it not been for the error Secretary of the Interior Ickes made in Dallas in November, 1934, when he openly admitted that the oil industry should become a public utility. That statement changed the attitude of every oilman and company who had ever favored federal controls of their industry. When Ickes "called for strong federal control of the petroleum industry and for a declaration that the industry be held a public utility," the Board of Directors of API, *by a close margin*, reversed its stand and came out against further extension of federal power over the petroleum industry.

The creation of the Interstate Oil Compact Commission in 1935 not only headed off but defeated possible federal control. Yet it was not easy to get the IOCC passed by Congress because many oilmen wanted firmer and more authoritative controls than those the IOCC could offer. In fact, some of the founders of IOCC, including Oklahoma's Governor Marland, wanted the IOCC to make production allocations, dictate prices, and in effect, make the Commission a vehicle to lead the federal control.

Throughout the history of our industry are instances of leaders on all sides and in all segments of the industry favoring legislation or regulation which would have led us into federal control.

In all cases, these pleas have come in times of oversupply, or shortages, or waste, or circumstances that put a temporary pinch on one group or another.

When these crises arise, our first reaction is amazingly that much-traveled path to Washington with the cry, "Pass me a handout," or "Take me over; I'm confused," or "Throw me a life preserver; I'm sinking," or simply, "Please, Uncle Sam, do something for me now and forget the cost."

And not 40 years after Ickes' famous public utility declaration, we are again advocating legislation which could result in the very controls that could destroy the last vestige of our cherished independence.

Yet the history of the threat of federal control of the petroleum industry should be enough warning for us.

It is high time we all studied the facts objectively. We must do so with the well-being of our country and our whole industry in mind—not simply our own personal welfare.

If we had spent as much time, effort, and money explaining how vital our industry is to the public as we have spent trying to convince Washington to legislate and regulate us more, we might be better off today.

As a counter measure to the proposed law, we should attempt to gain representation on a special board—to be appointed by the President—which, for simplicity, could be called the "Petroleum Import Control Board." On this board should be representatives from Congress, the Department of the Interior, independent oil producers, major oil companies, and others who may be concerned with the problem. The board should consist however of a small number so that it may function efficiently.

This board should adopt procedures to provide all interested parties an opportunity to be heard on any proposed change in the policy of imported petroleum. Such a procedure could furnish guidelines to the government in making major decisions on imports. Actually, the Petroleum Import Control Board would be a liaison between government, the industry, and the consumer.

These cooperative measures and the present import control system should suffice and make a law and its unpalatable consequences unnecessary. I strongly urge our associations to consider making immediate recommendations to the President that a Petroleum Import Control Board be established and begin functioning as soon as possible.

Instead of asking for self-defeating incentives, such as federal laws for survival, it is the responsibility of independents to exert all their energies toward convincing the public, and the government, that the exploration for and the development of domestic sources of oil and gas are of the most important economic and strategic value to this nation.

The time has passed when we can coast along with a smug attitude about yesterday's exploration methods. We are faced with finding more reserves in this country immediately. To do this, we must increase our exploration activity.

In the next 10 years, just to maintain an adequate reserve position against increases in demand, the oil industry will need to find 55 billion barrels of oil and 300 trillion cubic feet of gas in this country. With constantly rising costs, sustained low prices paid to producers for oil and gas, and greater risks involved in exploration, the search for petroleum takes on a deeper significance.

If we do not find more and larger reserves now, we may find ourselves dependent on foreign oil to meet our requirements, and if this happens, mandatory or statutory import controls would be irrelevant.

We will not find these new reserves by employing present exploration philosophy and methods. Yet, no good earth scientist will deny that the oil and gas are here to be found.

The independent must be the first to recognize that creative geological thinking, based on highly scientific procedures, is the key to discovering these large reserves.

This creative imagination must be applied to basins and areas which are inadequately explored—for example, the entire eastern seaboard. A dozen dry holes should not be allowed to condemn an area from Maine to the Florida Keys.

In Alaska alone, it is conceivable that a field equal to those in the Middle East may be found. Also tremendous reserves are possible in stratigraphic or paleogeomorphic traps in the continental limits of the United States. The United States could even become an exporter of oil because of the new large reserves which may be found by a concerted exploration effort.

Today, our intelligence in exploration is high, our knowledge is comparatively unlimited, and our tools for drilling and producing are highly sophisticated. We have the advantage of great scientific breakthroughs, advanced technology, computers, atomic science, and other aids unknown even three decades ago. No longer do we drill a dozen unnecessary wells in an area where one well will do the job. Soon we will realize that total field-wide unitization is the only way to set prices based on demand and cost without fear of being drained by uncooperative operators.

There is no reason to fear competition from coal, atomic energy, shale, or tar sands. There is no reason to look upon offshore oil or even foreign oil as ogres of competition. There is no reason to cringe as projects such as Gasbuggy threaten to triple gas or oil supplies available to our country. There is no reason that the electric car, or the fuel cell, or liquid natural gas motor fuel should dampen our enthusiasm.

But if petroleum is to continue its important role in future energy demand, several vital changes are needed now. The government must include independents in its import thinking and decisions. The majors must give up or drill some long-held untouched acreage, give more farmouts on just and equitable terms, encourage independents to drill more wells, and back this encouragement with substantial "bottom hole" dollars instead of with meager "dry hole" support. Independents need to re-establish the old wildcatter's optimism. The industry must resist trends in government control and demand government cooperation with us.

This means that we all need each other. We must work together. We cannot afford to spend our time and expend our strength fighting among ourselves.

We must do everything possible to straighten out the industry's poor image and produce a real understanding with the public. We need to stop shoveling millions of dollars annually down a rat hole of so-called public relations and self-protection which the public either ignores or ridicules.

The independent must play an important role in these activities. The public should be made to realize that without the independent, the industry will fail.

The independent of the future will assume a more vital role in exploration. In addition to finding and drilling his own prospects, he will be sought after to drill major company farm-outs more than ever before. He will be able to expand his operations into new districts and areas—especially by capitalizing on a recent change of exploration policy by many major companies.

In 1948, most major companies suddenly decided that to find petroleum, their explorationists should be located in district areas. The philosophy was very logical. The delineated area could be watched over and worked better, the area prospects submitted could be defended more vigorously by geologists who created them, and a continuous area company representation was more healthy and more informative than management from central offices. Therefore, decentralization began.

Most majors have now concluded that decentralization was a mistake, so district offices are being closed. But because of family ties and personal investments in property, many geologists refuse to move from the area. Consequently, the majors have lost many good oil finders to the consulting and independent segments of the geological profession.

With this loss and the shortage of graduate geologists, the majors will be critically shorthanded in meeting their exploration responsibilities in these vacated areas. This will necessitate the majors' retaining consultants—probably the same geologists who once worked for them and probably at a cost greater than the entire district setup.

This arrangement may prove to be a boon to some consultants in fees, but hopefully the good consultants will turn down such representation to be able to drill prospects of their own without creating a conflict of interest with the majors. These same prospects would probably have been found eventually by majors had the district offices remained open. Therefore, by this major company policy, millions of dollars from new oil and gas reserves will be gained by independents.

What will this change in exploration philosophy mean to independents? They will move into the vacated districts and begin drilling the cream of the prospects worked out by the geologists who remained in the area as consultants or independents. Therefore, the activity of most independents will spread beyond the previously restricted area.

Because the independent is just that—independent—unhampered by a dozen committee decisions and company politics, he has been able to find 85 per cent of onshore domestic reserves.

The same, if not a greater ratio, will still be necessary to meet the nation's petroleum needs.

So, in modern exploration, the independent will assume a more aggressive policy in moving into and drilling new areas, in encouraging the drilling of prospects worked out by new geological concepts, and in working with the majors more than ever before in the over-all exploration effort.

BIBLIOGRAPHY

Clark, James A., "Three Stars for the Colonel," (New York: Random House, 1954), pp. 127-129.
"Conservation on Oil and Gas, A Legal History," Section of Mineral Law of the American Bar Association, 1948, pp. 558-559.

Future of the Domestic Oil and Gas Industry

"We cannot depend on the fat cat—that is,
the wildcatter who has made his fortune and
does not want to take risks anymore."   March 5, 1968

Demand for both oil and gas is climbing rapidly in spite of all the new synthetic types of energy either in production or in prospect.

Our population growth is matched by the expanding per capita demand for petroleum and other energy products; so while the proportion of oil and gas to the total energy supply is dwindling slightly, the amount of petroleum necessary to meet future requirements is steadily increasing.

We will never become dependent on foreign oil and gas for the simple reason that we cannot afford to do so, regardless of how much oil is found outside this country. Very recent events have underscored this resolution.

Several times as much oil and gas remain to be found in this country as we have found and produced since 1859. Our task is simply to find and produce it. The market is here, and adequate prices will follow as soon as the people of this country realize the situation.

Recently hundreds of speeches and forecasts concerning our future petroleum needs have appeared. They have come from major company economists and executives, scientists and technicians in government bureaus, banks, statisticians for oil and gas associations, and many leading independents. In recent weeks, important national magazines, news syndicates, television and radio commentators, and daily newspaper editorial writers have picked up this obviously newsworthy item.

The Middle East war and our plight in Southeast Asia have made these thought leaders aware of the need for our self-reliance in energy sources, particularly liquid hydrocarbons.

For this reason, any oil finder or producer who has survived the lean days of the oil industry since 1957 can rest assured that he is needed now more than ever and that his opportunity is virtually unlimited if he possesses the proper mental tools and courage.

Major company executives admit they still need the independent to be the point man in the battle for new reserves and the front man in the war against federal control or even nationalization of the industry.

Today most independent oilmen are worried by the surplus of crude oil in this country which keeps crude oil prices unrealistically low.

This, of course, is the crux of our present problem. If we can hold off federal control until demand for domestic crude starts putting pressure on supply, the majority of our troubles will be solved.

Most industry leaders are not so concerned with excessive imports or low prices though as with problems of supplying the needed domestic reserves without becoming dependent on foreign sources. Yet, with this concern so evident, exploration at the moment is at a dangerously low level.

The oil industry can meet its petroleum demand based on what we know of potential reserves, but all who call themselves "independent" may not be able to survive until the situation changes.

Consequently, independent oilmen are preoccupied with the problem of imports to the extent that they are turning desperately to Washington demanding a statute that could and probably would force them—as well as the entire industry—into the straight jacket of federal control, a trap from which there is no escape.

If these oilmen would pause in their race to Washington and analyze the facts, they would see that the problem they are trying to solve will evaporate before they can get the proposed statute passed and implemented.

For instance, most major oil importers are shifting their sights back to the United States as they become disenchanted with the multitude of insoluble difficulties and uncertainties of foreign production.

While maintaining their foreign operations, they will give greater attention to domestic exploration than in the past 20 years.

Even before the Middle East crisis, they were finding themselves victims of their own overseas successes. The more reserves they found, the greater the demands of the foreign producing countries.

They faced higher prices, greater shares of the profits, larger royalties, and expropriation of properties by the home country. The trend toward extreme nationalization was growing dramatically.

The Suez crisis in 1956 shook the companies considerably, but the recent Middle East crisis left all more concerned than ever. Now, most American oil companies operating abroad are realizing the tremendous risks involved, in spite of the large reserves to be found. They look back to the United States and yearn for its stability.

They are beginning to recognize that our domestic petroleum is the only available dependable supply. Other sources are subject to nationalization, expropriation, confiscation by exorbitant taxation, the caprice of foreign sovereigns, war, and other emergency disconnections.

Many contend that Middle East oil costs only pennies a barrel to find and produce. This is an illusion, as it does not include the costs of our fleets in the Mediterranean to protect these interests.

It does not include the hospitals, schools, highways, and untold other facilities that we build for these countries. It does not include the international accommodations which are costly to our taxpayers and have to be made at every turn.

It does not include the cost of the tremendous damage to our domestic industry which has seen exploration virtually limited to offshore areas, the disappearance of thousands of independent domestic operators, and the exodus of experienced and needed drilling contractors from the energy picture. It does not include a thousand other untold costs to our economy and our security, including our losses in the balance of payments.

I contend that oil from the Middle East is the most costly commodity we have in the world today!

Furthermore, American international oil companies are wondering if the great reserves overseas, with diminishing returns, are in fact necessary. They see the galloping progress of atomic energy, the feasibility of production from shale deposits and tar sands, and the practical aspects of producing gas and gasoline from coal.

So, the larger oil companies are diversifying into these fields to become real energy companies instead of merely oil and gas companies.

And it is high time they did so.

Dean McGee, chairman of the Board and chief executive officer of Kerr-McGee Oil Industries, Inc., recently told the Gulf Coast Association of Geological Societies that by 1980 total energy demand in the United States is expected to increase by 50 per cent. He said this increase in annual energy demand is equal to the total United States demand for energy in 1950.

As much additional capacity for production of energy must be provided, he said, by 1980 as was developed in America in the 385 years between the time of the first explorer-colonists in 1565 and 1950.[1] This illustrates the remarkable challenge we face in meeting demand for public energy consumption.

As for oil, the Department of the Interior has estimated we will be required to produce 52 billion barrels of domestic oil in the 15-year period between 1965 and 1980. This amount is about 20 billion barrels more crude oil than we now have in known recoverable reserves.

Demand for oil has risen 44 per cent in the past 10 years while proved reserves have gone up only 15 per cent. Obviously, domestic reserves are not commensurate with increase in demand.

Today, the United States consumes more than 12.6 million barrels of oil daily. By 1980, we will be consuming 18 million to 20 million barrels of oil per day.

Even if the right political climate existed and we wanted to get the five million barrel difference plus daily increase in oil needs from foreign sources, I seriously doubt it could be done effectively.

Indeed we are now pulling away from foreign oil rather than depending on it more and more. This withdrawal is being forced by the masterful strategy of the Soviet Union in its attempt to gain at least political control over all of the big reserves in the Middle East. This move is nothing more than unilateral Soviet oil and gas aggression.

We simply cannot afford to depend on the Communists for the lifeblood of our economy, but we might have to if we continue to develop foreign oil and gas to the comparative exclusion of domestic exploration.

The year 1968 has been forecast as the last year in which the new supply of gas will exceed production.

Ten years ago, we had 22.1 years' supply of gas reserves based on the market demand then. In 1967, the ratio of reserves to production was 15.3 to 1. By 1980, domestic production of gas is forecast to be 26.9 trillion cubic feet compared with the present 18 trillion cubic feet. At that time, assuming no drop from the present annual additions to supply (and no increase), we will have less than 10 years' supply based on the growing demand.

Therefore, the additions to supply will have to be increased tremendously, or the natural gas industry will face extinction. The only way reserves can be increased is by a substantial surge in exploration plus the success of such artificial stimulation processes as the Gasbuggy project.

In addition to the pressure of demand that will offer many new opportunities to the domestic producer, especially the independent wildcatter, there are signs of lower costs that provide more incentive.

An illustration is the discovery cost for oil in 1966. Although the discovery cost of 81 cents a barrel was actually 45 cents more than the year before, it was 5 cents a barrel lower than 1963 and 1964. And it was $1.10 lower than the high year of 1957. The low 1965 figure of 36 cents per barrel reflected improved secondary recovery methods which provided 600 million barrels of oil in addition to normally expected discoveries.

Of course, real discovery costs are higher than the reported costs which include development wells, dry holes, and property acquisitions, but not geological, geophysical, general overhead, or administrative costs.

Then, in 1967, refiners' margins were up 6 per cent over 1966 and were at the highest point in 10 years. This is exceptionally good for the industry since producer prices depend to some extent on refinery margins. Crude price increases usually are reflected the following year.

Industry marketing practices have been upgraded, although far too many uncalled-for gasoline price wars and major brand giveaway programs still exist. These excesses are eventually piled on the producer.

Possibly the day will come when producer associations will actively protest these and other practices that are so expensive to their members.

The necessity for higher crude and natural gas prices is shown in an American Petroleum Institute survey of the most important 1967 producer costs compared with those of 1956. Well-casing prices were up 28 per cent, average hourly wages for all industry workers were up 41.2 per cent, and oil-field machinery prices were up 17 per cent. In the same period of time, crude oil prices had gone up 4.3 per cent from $2.79 to $2.91 a barrel.

Today we have only 9.3 years' supply of oil and natural gas liquids for the present rate of consumption. And the rate is going up 4 per cent a year. In 1980, we will be using 2.6 billion barrels more crude oil than we used in 1967.

The pinch on us comes from the fact that while we have only 10.2 per cent of the world's oil reserves, we still produce 24.2 per cent of the oil and consume 35 per cent of it.

Obviously, we must both find and produce more oil, or rely more on imports, or develop synthetic energy sources. The best course is to find more domestic oil and gas as soon as possible because both are available to be found.

The United States Geological Survey estimates quite conservatively that more than 300 billion barrels of natural oil are yet to be found in this country. That is twice the amount produced or in reserves now. We have produced about 81 billion barrels and have 39 billion barrels in reserve, including natural gas liquids, or a total of 120 billion barrels to date.

It was estimated in 1958 that 555 trillion to 1,200 trillion cubic feet of natural gas were still to be found.

But to show how backward or bashful forecasters really are, the highest estimate then indicated that in 1980 demand would be 20 trillion cubic feet. Already authorities estimate we will have 50 per cent more than that by 1980. In fact, we estimate more than 18 trillion cubic feet in 1968.

Estimators hardly ever see things as big as they really are. With a healthy and sustained exploration program, the amount of natural gas to be found in this country is unlimited. In fact, almost all very deep wells today are natural gas-distillate wells. Our future supply of natural gas is in far less danger of exhaustion than the future supply of domestic oil.

One of the hopeful signs today is that major companies seem more willing to cooperate toward domestic exploration for the future. Some of them have reverted to befriending independents with farmouts and substantial cash contributions toward bottom hole and not dry hole wildcat drilling. They realize that the market for domestic oil and gas is overwhelming the industry and that the need has disappeared for holding millions of acres of prospective land under lease. It disappeared, in fact, in Texas when the mineral pooling law was enacted in 1965. Sooner or later, Texas will have a compulsory unitization law which will be even more beneficial economically to all segments of the industry.

More and more large oil company leaseholders in Texas are realizing that the expense of unnecessary wells has been practically eliminated by the pooling law. Since they are not risking vast sums for unnecessary wells, they are selling unnecessary protection acreage.

This excess acreage costs almost as much as the unnecessary wells in rentals, bonuses, taxes, overhead, and personnel expense. It is cheaper to let others bear those expenses, plus the cost of dry holes, and then buy any oil found. Presently, the trend toward farmouts and contributions is accelerating for these very reasons, and it will bring back the day of the hungry wildcatter who, in turn, will find much of the oil and gas of the future. We cannot depend on the "fat cat"—that is, the wildcatter who has made his fortune and does not want to take risks anymore.

There is also some sign that the independent is beginning to see the folly of fighting the majors and crying about imports, prices, and other such matters to the extent that he discourages his most productive source of risk capital—the outside investor.

I have faith that imports will take care of themselves, that the public and Congress will be wise enough to resist tampering with depletion, and that the price of crude will resume its own level as demand rises. I also believe that, in time, the federal government will see the absurdity of its present way of regulating the well-head price of natural gas. In fact, the consuming public will probably see this even before the government does and thereby demand the government to ease the regulations.

We can expect better drilling tools and techniques and important breakthroughs in geology, geophysics, and petroleum engineering.

Many more giant oil and gas fields are here to be found—but they will not be found by our sitting in conference rooms and bemoaning the sad condition of our industry. What we need is more optimism, enthusiasm, and daring in the field of wildcatting. This means we must have the nerve to drill unconventional prospects and to move into areas others fear to enter.

The easiest oil and gas has been found. Now, we must have the courage to drill for the less obvious, subtle traps which are mainly located by the minds of men instead of by transistors, coiled copper wiring, and computers.

Never in the history of the country has the oil industry or the individuals in it faced a brighter future—but also, they face immense responsibilities to make that kind of a future a reality.

Someone is going to search for and find the oil and gas our nation demands. Those companies and individuals will prosper and, in turn, gain a tremendous sense of achievement.

There will be pitfalls, heartaches, frustrations, and failures as there have always been; however, the American know-how and system of free enterprise will prevail.

Irrespective of the many international factors adversely influencing our industry, the future of the domestic oil and gas industry is brighter and more promising than at any time since Drake first brought oil out of the ground in 1859.

REFERENCE

[1] McGee, Dean A., chairman of the Board of Kerr-McGee Oil Industries, Inc., "Energy—Past, Present, and Future," address presented before the Gulf Coast Association of Geological Societies, San Antonio, Texas, October 6, 1967.

International Factors on Domestic Exploration

"The Russians believe today, as they have believed since the establishment of the Soviet Union, that petroleum is the way to conquer the world."   March 6, 1968

"USSR Gets Foothold in Mideast Oil Output by Agreeing to Help Iraq to Develop Resources,"[1] declared a headline in the Wall Street Journal on December 26, 1967.

The story underneath pointed out a Soviet breakthrough in access to Middle East petroleum. The Russians had been given the right to explore and develop two important areas of Iraq, including the 32,000-square-mile Rumaila district of southern Iraq on the Kuwait border.

Before 1960, this area had been held by the Iraq Petroleum Company, owned by a consortium of American, British, French, and Dutch interests.

This agreement was the culmination of a half century of patient, persistent, and determined effort by the Communists. In this effort, their planned program had included the Suez crisis of 1956-1957 and the six-day Arab-Israeli war of 1967.

The Russians have always believed that petroleum is the way to conquer the world. Probably the most challenging question of the atomic age is, "What can the free world do about it?"

It is obvious that eventually the Soviets intend to take over all the Middle East and North African oil holdings through the Arabs. With that control of petroleum, they hope to win most of Western Europe and much of Asia. The ultimate goal, of course, is the world.

Since Colonel Drake brought in his famous well in western Pennsylvania in 1859, international factors have influenced domestic exploration in this country.

The Civil War, which started less than two years after that momentous discovery, is a good example. The Union was able to offset its world cotton trade loss with oil shipments. In fact, exports far exceeded domestic use of oil throughout the war. A $1-per-barrel tax on oil added to northern coffers, and oil helped keep northern industry operating at a high level.

This condition led to constant exploration for petroleum during the Civil War and an accelerated program immediately after the war.

Between 1859 and 1874, this country provided 90 per cent of the world's oil. Between 1874 and 1883, our production was never less than 80 per cent of the world total. In 1884, when the Baku fields in Russia started producing, this dominance began to dwindle. In fact, between 1898 and 1901, Russia was the world's leading oil producer. Spindletop and the fields that followed it in the Southwest returned the United States to oil leadership in 1902. By 1914, the first year of World War I, the United States was producing five times as much oil as Russia.

In the meantime, several international factors had prompted an increased demand for oil exploration in this country. One factor was the dual recognition by the British that (1) oil was necessary to the operation of their navy, and (2) their navy was the backbone of the British empire's world power leadership.

Of course, the United States and other navies of the world, as well as merchant marine units, were also converting to oil. As early as 1916, the president of the Board of Trade in England told the House of Commons that his country had to secure control of the world's supply of oil. In that year, the United States was producing 777,000 barrels of the world's 1,180,000 barrels of oil daily, or approximately 66 per cent.

Because of an unstable domestic supply, foreign countries were unable to rely completely on American oil. British, Dutch, and French companies began to explore in the Middle East, Mexico, Venezuela, Colombia, and the Far East to safeguard their needs.

The seeds of oil policy problems, both national and international, were sown between 1910-1916. American oil companies had started searching for oil on a world-wide basis in order to supplement and protect their foreign markets.

In the early 1910's, American oil companies received a considerable setback when the State Department announced that all American companies in alien countries would have to go on their own. This meant that Americans in countries such as Venezuela were left without government support. Consequently many valuable foreign oil properties passed into the hands of the British and the Dutch. When World War I started in 1914, Americans were producing oil in only two foreign countries—Mexico and Romania. Dependence of other countries on the United States for petroleum kept exploration activities here at a very high level.

World War I, incidentally, created the long prevailing Mid-East problem. The tremendous potential for discovery and development there created a rivalry between the great powers in their search for oil independence.

During 1911-1914, the British first realized that ships could not run at the required 25 knots with any fuel except oil. Therefore, on July 17, 1913, Winston Churchill announced that the British would supply their own oil from sources under British control or influence. The Germans, French, Dutch, and Russians were entertaining similar thoughts. Thus began the departure of other countries from dependence on the United States for petroleum.

An example of the unreliability of the United States' supply occurred in 1912. This country was suffering from one of its oil famines which was ended abruptly by the discovery of Cushing field in Oklahoma. Cushing established Oklahoma as the premier oil state and dropped crude prices from $1.05 to 55 cents per barrel. Within less than a year, Cushing began to decline, and this country dropped into another oil famine which proved Churchill's point. England and other countries had to have their own supplies of petroleum; they just could not depend any longer on supplies from the United States.

By the time we entered World War I in April, 1917, petroleum had become "indispensable" to the world's activities.

Despite its unreliability as a source of supply, this country provided the allies with 90 million barrels of oil, or virtually all of the oil used in land, sea, and air operations in World War I.

During the war, the Petroleum World of London first warned of an impending shortage of petroleum.

The international interest in oil had brought new heights in oil exploration. Demand brought prices which attracted new risk capital in this country. Gasoline, which sold for 13 cents per gallon in 1914, had doubled in price by May, 1917, and there were persistent rumors that these prices would go as high as 40 cents per gallon.

A. C. Bedford, president of Standard Oil Company of New Jersey, was appealing to every oil producer in the country to seek the utmost possible output of crude oil. He called it their patriotic duty, adding, "Frankly, there is no shortage of oil, simply a shortage of effort to get it out of the ground."[2]

As a result of pleas by President Wilson and Bedford, oil production was stepped up by almost 100,000 barrels per day which was a little more than one-tenth of production in that year. After the United States entered the war and the demand for oil became virtually impossible to meet, the price of crude advanced to $2.25 per barrel, up from $1.40, adding great stimulus to exploration.

From 1919 to 1923, severe world-wide oil shortage scares resulted in an increased search for oil in all foreign fields. The United States Secretary of Commerce, Herbert Hoover, told leading oil company executives to "get out and find some oil." He said if we had to depend upon foreign sources, they should be from our own American companies.

Britain and Holland were already strong in Mexico and had the cream of the concessions in Venezuela—thanks to the United States' non-protection policy established just before World War I.

Although the United States was still supplying 72 per cent of the world production, American companies were excluded from oil rights in many countries, notably in the Middle East mandated nations through the San Remo Oil Agreement. The San Remo Agreement was signed on April 24, 1920. Under its terms, the British and French divided all the Middle East oil under their influence and barred the United States from participation.

When this secret pact was exposed, the United States government adopted a h a r d open-door policy on petroleum. Smarting under this snub from its two recent allies, the United States gave a strong shove to American companies to embark on petroleum expeditions all over the world.

American geologists became active in nearly every country believed to be favorable to oil. Much of the knowledge of prospects in many undeveloped regions is contained in major company files as a result of this far-flung activity of the early 1920's.

About this time, Navy Secretary Josephus Daniels panicked, fearing the navy would run out of oil and America's first line of defense would be imperiled. He started a campaign for government control and nationalization of oil, with the Shipping Board and the Department of the Interior supporting his position. These foreign forays, heavy imports from Mexico, and pleas for nationalization temporarily dried up venture capital in this country and caused a drastic decline in exploration activity.

Also, Mexico's famous "golden lane" gushers had started going to salt water, thereby dampening the pleas of independent producers for an oil import tariff.

Suddenly, because of this world-wide oil shortage scare, wildcat activity in this country picked up and again there was overproduction at home. Britain and The Netherlands were increasing production steadily despite the loss of their Russian properties shortly after the war. They were highly active in Western Hemisphere developments. Although Russia had expropriated all foreign oil interests under the new Bolshevik regime, she reached a low of 9.6 per cent of world production.

At home, Dr. Van H. Manning, Director of the Bureau of Mines, was saying that within the next two to five years, the oil fields in this country would reach their maximum production, and from that time on, we would face an ever-increasing decline.

This view caused the Council of National Defense, composed of most of the President's cabinet, to advocate government acquisition of Indian lands for exploration for oil under government control.

George Otis Smith, Director of the Geological Survey, warned that the United States would be out of oil in 18 years and have to depend on foreign sources or use less oil, but the rest of the world would have an ample supply for the next 50 years.

Professor Harold Hibbart of Yale University told the American Chemical Society that our supply of crude oil would be entirely exhausted within 13 years and that no solution was in sight. He said he felt confident, however, that chemists would eventually solve this problem through research. Crystal balls were not much better then than they are today, it seems.

It is likely that a national petroleum company would have succeeded had not Secretary of State Bainbridge Colby warned that foreign nations would refuse to do business with such a company in areas within their jurisdiction.

To impress the British and French with its determination for an open-door policy in the Middle East, the United States government threatened to place an oil embargo on any country discriminating against American oil interests. On January 19, 1921, the Financial Times was able to say:

> It is now clear that the French government, like the British, aims at non-monopoly of the oil business. The policy of the open door is to be adopted, and as a result, the Royal Dutch group will be in a position to obtain concessions from the French government.[3]

This was the first trace of the famous Red Line Agreement[4] which would become official in 1928.

Toward the end of 1922, Sir Edward Mackay Edgar, British financier and industrialist, was telling his people that America's insatiable demand for oil would bring on a world-wide shortage. He speculated:

> As for oil, America has already reached the importing stage. Our business, as Britons, is to sit tight on what we have and export all the oil, cotton, and metal possibilities in the non-American world. In that way, we shall do more than safeguard our position. We shall be able to supply America.[5]

This statement by Sir Edward promoted the so-called John Bull scare. But the John Bull scare was drowned in a flood of oil by November 4, 1923. The ink was hardly dry on Senator Robert M. La Follette's prediction that gasoline would go to $1.00 a gallon when discoveries in the Los Angeles Basin, at Elk Hills, Huntington Beach, and Santa Fe Springs counteracted the decline of Mexico's "golden lane" fields. Added to the discoveries at Hewitt, Tonkawa, and Burbank in Oklahoma; Smackover in Arkansas; and Big Lake in Texas, these pushed the price of crude down from $2.00 per barrel in February to $1.00 in November. At the same time, gasoline fell from 21.5 cents to 13.5 cents a gallon.

These incidents relaxed tensions between this country and its former allies. President Coolidge rescinded the exclusion of Roxana Petroleum Company from Indian lands in the United States. And in 1928, by the Red Line Agreement and through a strong State Department determination to have American companies gain a foothold in the Middle East, the Near East Development Company, composed of five major American companies, gained a 23.75-per-cent interest in the Iraq Petroleum Corporation.

The period 1929-1935 was concerned largely with the Great Depression in this country and efforts to bring about conservation. A phase of this conservation movement was the attempt to establish world-wide proration. The Federal Oil Conservation Board was stressing the international aspect of overproduction, and the American Petroleum Institute's committee on world production and consumption of petroleum worked out a plan on the subject for its board. The whole idea was killed when the Attorney General ruled that Americans could not participate.

Worry over world petroleum supplies temporarily faded into the background with the first giant discoveries in Venezuela and the East Texas field, the world's first billion-barrel fields.

In 1929, the Independent Petroleum Association of America (IPPA) was formed in Colorado Springs for the express purpose of working for a tariff on petroleum imports. The organization credited the new oil surplus in this country to imports from foreign fields.

International companies immediately began to curtail imports voluntarily in fear of the tariff or even a total embargo on foreign oil imports. In June, 1932, an excise tax of 21 cents per barrel on foreign crude and $1.05 per barrel on gasoline went into effect.

As World War II approached, oil enhanced its importance in international affairs. Germany, realizing it would probably be cut off from oil in the war it was planning, started the development of liquid fuel from coal. To a lesser extent, similar experiments were underway in England, France, and Belgium. France developed a process of substituting alcohol for motor fuel through the restriction of petroleum imports and subsidies to grain producers. Romania, which at one time sold oil all over Europe, was confining its markets to German and Italian outlets. By 1938, Mexico had expropriated foreign oil properties as Bolivia had done a year earlier, and other South American countries began to organize government-owned oil companies.

In the United States, domestic oil was flooding the market. In Bahrain, Saudi Arabia, and Kuwait, American oil companies were making sensational strikes.

Despite all of this, when the United States entered World War II on December 7, 1941, petroleum was one of the few American industries prepared for the emergency. The industry was called upon to supply the bulk of the 100-octane gasoline, toluene, aviation lubricants, synthetic rubber materials, and other critical products.

Almost immediately after Pearl Harbor, the transportation bottleneck for petroleum shipments to the East Coast became acute due to intensified German submarine activity. The proposal to build the "Big Inch" and "Little Big Inch" pipelines brought on a genuine shortage scare for petroleum. From the Senate came cries that the British were not making oil available to the United Nations from Middle East sources.

In 1943, the Petroleum Reserve Corporation was formed to put the government in the pipeline business to transport American oil from Saudi Arabia to the Mediterranean coast. The charter of this government corporation provided also for the building of refineries and other activities in foreign countries.

It was again evident that the United States government intended to go directly into the foreign oil business. This action brought immediate and strong protest from the oil industry and precipitated the "great debate" on domestic oil policy. President Wilson's Secretary of State Bainbridge Colby, who attacked the first attempts to nationalize the oil industry, came out of retirement to attack this new attempt.

The Oil Administrator, Secretary Ickes, campaigning for the government-built trans-Arabian pipeline, revived the old campaign declaring, "We are running out of oil." The President, the Joint

Chiefs of Staff, the Secretary of the Navy, and the Secretary of War all joined in the chorus. Eventually, the Petroleum Reserve Corporation project was killed by the National Oil Policy Committee. It is ironic that Ickes had appointed this committee, composed largely of oilmen, to support him in his position.

The next step by Oil Administrator Ickes was an effort to bring about an Anglo-American oil agreement providing for an orderly development of reserves in the Middle East and other foreign countries. The treaty was never ratified by the Senate.

In the meantime, the oil industry was hampered by an Office of Price Administration (OPA) price on oil and products as well as a low priority for steel and steel products. Tremendous oil discoveries were being revealed in the Middle East by the United States Petroleum Mission. Steel had become available for the building of the trans-Arabian pipeline to deliver Texas Company and Standard of California oil to the Mediterranean.

The Anglo-American Treaty fight was to continue until well after the end of the war. In the midst of all of these debates and rationing of oil products and strangulation by OPA, this country was supplying by far the greatest amount of oil to the war effort.

In the closing stages of the war, Russia was already attempting to secure oil concessions in Iran, but was refused on the grounds that the Iranian public would consider that permission had been granted under duress with foreign troops stationed in their country. Since Iran was backed by both the United States and Great Britain, this issue threatened to grow into a Big Three crisis.

The issue was called a proving ground of allied oil policy. The editor of one United States oil trade journal viewed the situation as "a display of pressure politics by the Soviet government against foreign governments, possibly leading to serious activities for American oil companies now operating in the Near East."[6]

From these events sprang the recent troubles in the Middle East which erupted first with the Suez crisis and then with the Arab-Israeli war.

It seems obvious in looking back that the international situations of the domestic oil industry in World War II were serious. The United States government consistently refused to grant crude oil price increases and steel necessary to stimulate seriously needed wildcat drilling. It seems that the government was deliberately trying to keep domestic exploration down while promoting Middle East oil development, despite the relative danger of enemy acquisition.

At the same time, the government was squandering good money promoting a synthetic fuel program—the ill-fated Canol project in Canada—and keeping the lid on the Elk Hills Naval Reserves No. 1. In spite of this, domestic production increased from 3,842,000 barrels per day in 1941 to 4,695,000 barrels per day in 1945.

As World War II ended, it was obvious that the world had for the first time become truly oil-conscious.

Russia, recognizing the strategic importance of oil occupied country after country in Eastern Europe—including Romania, Poland, Hungary, and part of Austria, Yugoslavia, and Czechoslovakia, all oil-producing countries—and perpetrated a gigantic oil grab.

Russia prolonged the stay of her troops in Iran, then the largest oil-producing country in the Middle East, precipitating the first United Nations crisis and launching the Cold War.

In the aftermath of World War II, the Truman Doctrine, the Marshall Plan, the Korean War, and the North Atlantic Treaty Organization were all part of an era of emergency. All these factors involved petroleum supply and refinery, pipeline, and marketing considerations that would sooner or later influence exploration in the United States.

So the United States, immediately after World War II, faced the "Cold War oil scare," which resembled to some extent the John Bull oil scare that followed World War I.

The State Department began attempts to revive the stalemated Anglo-American Oil Treaty, supported by the Joint Chiefs of Staff and members of the Army-Navy Petroleum Board.

Attention was called to the fact that "Russia threatens Middle East oil," and Secretary of the Interior Julias A. Krug revised the old "United States scarcity-foreign plenty" approach.

Although OPA price ceilings were removed late in 1946, crude prices reached a 15-year high, and domestic production and exploration were in high gear, the Marshall Plan backers in Congress suggested a government policy aimed at saving domestic oil and drawing on Middle East oil as much as possible. This plan, of course, would have destroyed our domestic exploration and eliminated the independent.

Postwar demand in this country was little short of phenomenal. The Army-Navy Petroleum Board testified that the military services faced an acute shortage of aviation gasoline.

In spite of this, oil shipments were going to Russia, but eventually criticism caused the Office of International Trade to reinstitute wartime controls on oil exports. Behind all of this was the obvious government promotion of the Anglo-American Treaty which was already doomed.

The Red Line Agreement was quietly dissolved, and the 50-50 profit sharing policy was initiated in Venezuela and spread to the Middle East, both of which were expanding rapidly.

"Sowing the petroleum" was the Venezuelan plan to plow oil royalties and taxes back into public improvements. All of this had a braking effect on domestic exploration.

In 1948, the United States lost its tremendous advantage of being a net oil exporter with the reversal of the historical West-to-East oil flow.

In 1950, the outbreak of the Korean War created a new oil emergency, and exploration picked up with great success.

In 1951, Mossadegh nationalized Iranian oil. This constituted a serious threat to the Korean oil supply, to NATO, and to the success of the Marshall Plan. This act was Soviet-inspired, but the Foreign Petroleum Supply Committee's plan of action averted impending disaster.

Meanwhile, in 1952, the Select Senate Committee on Small Business released a previously classified staff report of the Federal Trade Commission titled "The International Petroleum Cartel," which stirred up dissention and cast new suspicions on the vital oil industry. Huge foreign demand following the European recovery brought on a temporary supply problem.

Two years later, the Iranian oil consortium was formed with the backing of the State Department, as an indication of the importance of Middle East oil to the free world, and Americans moved into other areas of the Middle East, Africa, and South America in what has been described as the greatest search for oil in history.

This search inspired an editorial in one of this country's leading trade journals which indicated that oil may lead to world freedom. The editorial read:

> The rapid, widespread expansion of American free enterprise oil operations over a huge portion of the globe may provide multitudes of people with greatly improved living condi-

tions and thereby build a formidable barrier against the spread of communism.[7]

What the writer did not realize was that communism would be attracted to those areas of development.

On July 26, 1956, one of the momentous international factors in the history of petroleum occurred when Egypt seized and closed the Suez Canal. England and France took steps to force the reopening, but their efforts were thwarted by Russia's offer to send volunteer forces to Egypt, and later, a threat of atomic reprisals against NATO nations. The issue was finally settled by Eisenhower's Middle East Doctrine.

Europe's Middle East oil supply was cut off. The Foreign Supply Committee became the Middle East Emergency Committee, and Soviet policy in the situation was described as an attempt to use Nasser-style Arab nationalism as a dagger to strike at the oil-jugular of the western alliance.

As oil was moved around the Cape to Europe, the Middle East Emergency Committee became the focal point of an intra-industry debate on imports. Independents demanded more pipeline connections. State proration policy, especially in Texas, drew fire when allowables were not raised to meet the crisis.

A 50-cent crude oil price increase stunned Washington and most of the major oil companies except Humble, which instigated the increase. In Washington, a Massachusetts congressman called for an 11-member National Petroleum Commission to take over all phases of the industry in the interest of national security and the economy.

In the over-all picture, the Middle East Emergency Committee provided Europe with sufficient oil to prevent a million-barrel daily shortage.

And when it was all over, our domestic industry was unable to reverse its program quickly enough, and the result was an oil exploration and drilling depression from which we have not yet recovered.

In an address before the Chicago Executive's Club in mid-November, 1965, Howard W. Page, director of Standard of New Jersey, explained the action of the western nations, especially the United States, in the crisis when he said:

> The importance of the Middle East lies in the fact that it is the greatest single reservoir of energy available to supply the growing needs of the entire Eastern Hemisphere outside the Iron Curtain. It is also important because it is the testing ground

for new nations. What happens there profoundly affects not only Europe, but Africa, the Far East, and even Latin America. And what happens in all these places affects America. [8]

As soon as the crisis ended, politicians clamored for investigations, new proposals for federal control of the entire industry, and even for internationalization of the entire western world's petroleum industry.

The Russians sat by silently for a few months getting their first satellite into orbit and then opened a new Middle East campaign, centering on Masqat and Oman, Syria, and Egypt.

Meanwhile, crude oil buyers in this country were putting purchaser proration into effect.

To try to keep things safe in the Middle East, the State Department was pushing the American International Companies toward increased imports of oil into this country, and by October, 1957, Texas was on a 12-day producing schedule, after three successive 13-day months. Domestic producers, many of whom had loans based on twice that many producing days, were facing financial disaster all over the country.

Then came announcements that $60 billion must be invested in the oil industry in the next five years and that at least half of that would be invested abroad if we were to meet world-wide demand. Of course, domestic producers in this country, swimming in a sea of surplus oil, were perplexed.

Now, Russia stepped up the Cold War in the Middle East, and world-wide demand for oil suddenly took a temporary but highly significant downward turn. The Russians, concentrating exclusively on the Middle East, put on a propaganda barrage stressing their military strength and technical superiority as indicated by Sputnik's flashing signals as it orbited the earth.

Again on June 5, 1967, a third of the free world's petroleum supply was suddenly halted as Israeli and Arab guns flashed out in the historical six-day war.

The Soviets' and Arabs' determined efforts to create a European oil famine failed. This country supplied 90 million barrels over and above normal production during the crisis. That, interestingly enough, is exactly the amount of oil the United States had provided to win "the war to end all wars" in Europe between 1914 and 1918.

Throughout the entire crisis, the Soviets were urging the Arabs to use their powerful economic weapon—oil—to punish the United States and other western powers friendly to the Israelis.

Russia also was out in the market place offering to supply Soviet oil to help the unfortunate Europeans. And, as strange as it seems, they found some takers.

Today, they are offering cheaper oil to countries all around the world from Japan to West Germany and England.

The question now is, "What influence will this great new international factor have on domestic exploration in this country?"

Unless the western world, and especially the United States, can come up with a better brand of leadership than we have seen in international oil in the past few decades, it could bring total disaster to us all.

I have dealt here with only the most obvious but probably some of the most significant factors in the history of international petroleum.

This is a subject upon which a book of probably several volumes could and should be written for an industry with virtually no sense of its own history.

Domestic exploration in this country has been influenced by international factors since the 1860's.

Possibly the most important factors were those occurring immediately before and immediately after World War I. They were factors based on poor leadership and the fallacious assumption that the United States had exhausted its sources and supply of domestic oil.

Since then, foreign wars, insurrection, political actions and maneuvers, crises, expropriations, revolutions, and fantastic discoveries in the Middle East, South America, and Africa have had tremendous and often immediate effects on domestic exploration in this country.

These effects will continue, although it is obvious that unless some intelligent, effective action is taken soon, in the industry as well as in the government, the Soviet Union's plan to conquer the world through the control of liquid energy will brush all past factors into a heaping pile of insignificance.

The Soviet's program appears to be one of controlling 90 per cent of the world's liquid hydrocarbon reserves, dumping them on the world market at whatever price it takes to make others dependent on them, and then giving their customers the choice to communize or return to the economy and defense vulnerability of the nineteenth century.

This plan of world control can be stopped, but not as long as western nations ignore the pointers, or as long as our government and our citizens do all in their power to destroy the most vital and important industry in the history of world progress.

REFERENCES

[1] Wall Street Journal, December 26, 1967.
[2] Oil Trade Journal, August, 1917.
[3] Financial Times, January 19, 1921.
[4] Red Line Agreement consummated on July 31, 1928, with the organization of the Turkish Petroleum Company, composed of Anglo-Persian Oil Company, Royal Dutch-Shell Company, Compagnie Francaise des Petroles, and Near East Development Company, each with 23.75-per-cent ownership, and Calouste Gulbenkian with the other 5 per cent. It limited activities of the participants to specific Middle Eastern areas marked out by a red line on the map.
[5] New York American, December 14, 1922.
[6] "World Petroleum Policies," (New York: Mona Palmer Publishing Corp., 1957), edited by Leonard M. Fanning, Part 6, p. 7.
[7] Ibid., Part 7, p. 8.
[8] The Lamp, Winter, 1956.

BIBLIOGRAPHY

"American Petroleum Interests in Foreign Countries," hearings before Senate Committee investigating petroleum resources, 79th Congress, First Session, 1945.
Bacon, Raymond F., and William A. Hamor, "American Petroleum Industry," (New York: McGraw-Hill Book Co., Inc., 1916), Volumes 1 and 2.
Brooks, B. J., "Peace, Plenty and Petroleum," (Lancaster, Pa.: The Jacques Cattlett Press, 1944).
Clark, James A., "The Chronological History of the Petroleum and Natural Gas Industries," (Houston, Texas: Clark Book Co., 1963).
Fanning, Leonard M., "Our Oil Resources," (New York: McGraw-Hill Co., Inc., 1950), second edition.
Fanning, Leonard M., "The Rise of American Oil," (New York: Harper & Brothers, 1936).
Hamilton, Charles W., "Americans and Oil in the Middle East," (Houston, Texas: Gulf Publishing Co., 1962).
"History of Petroleum Engineering," American Petroleum Institute, Division of Production, (Dallas, Texas: The Boyd Printing Co., 1961).
"One Hundred Years of Oil," American Petroleum Institute, 1959.
"Petroleum Facts and Figures," American Petroleum Institute, 1928.
"Petroleum Panorama," (Tulsa, Oklahoma: Oil and Gas Journal, January 28, 1959).
Powell, J. Richard, "The Mexican Petroleum Industry, 1938-1950," (Los Angeles: The University of California Press, 1956).
"Proceedings American Petroleum Institute," annual meetings 1923-1966.
Various issues of Houston Chronicle, The Houston Post, National Petroleum News, New York American, New York Herald Tribune, New York Journal of Commerce, New York Times, Oil and Gas Journal, Petroleum Week, Wall Street Journal, World Oil (Oil Weekly), and World Petroleum.

Shale Oil—Will It Ever Be A Reality?

"Oil shale can best be developed by private enterprise, wherever it is located, whether on public or private lands."   May 2, 1968

Man's progress today is directly related to his ability to utilize energy. Because of our rapid success in harnessing various forms of energy, the United States is one of the most advanced societies in the world.

National productivity is directly related to our energy consumption. The economic security and social welfare of the United States demand that adequate low-cost energy resources be available at all times.

The most abundant energy resources in the United States are hydrocarbon fossil fuels, consisting of oil, gas, oil shale, and coal. Currently the most important of these are crude oil and natural gas. Although our supply of oil and gas is adequate today, we must recognize that they are depletory substances. Within the next few years, the increasing demand for liquid fuels will make it necessary to supplement domestic supplies of energy from crude oil and natural gas with synthetic fuels such as from oil shale.

The over-all energy picture is affected by two factors: an ever-growing population and the rise in per capita consumption of energy. Since 1920, the United States population has jumped from 106 million to more than 200 million. Annual energy use has increased from 20 quadrillion BTU's to more than 57 quadrillion BTU's.

Because of this rapid growth in energy use, the United States is by far the most prosperous nation in the world, with the highest standard of living. With only 7 per cent of the world's population and 6 per cent of its land space, we currently produce about one-third of the world's total output of goods and services. On a per capita basis, we consume oil at a rate that would provide more than 900 gallons a year for every man, woman, and child in this country—about eight times the per capita figure for the rest of the free world.

Oil and gas began to account for one-third of the total energy consumed in this country by the late 1920's. By the mid-1940's, oil and gas were providing half of our energy needs; they account for three-fourths of our energy needs today.

And still the demand goes up. While we now consume petroleum products at a rate of almost 12 million barrels a day, it has been forecast that we shall consume 50 per cent more petroleum by 1980. Eighteen million barrels a day is a lot of oil. If we are to meet the demand, the petroleum industry must come up with more than 75 billion barrels of products between now and 1980—twice the present proved crude oil reserves in the United States. This explains why we have to keep hunting so diligently for new reserves. Even though our supplies are adequate now, consumption too soon will begin to outstrip additions to reserves.

What must we do to keep pace with these mushrooming demands? Three basic ways are open to us—and we may have to use all three. The most important way is to increase domestic exploration for oil and gas. The second is to increase imports. And the third is to develop production of synthetic fuels and coal and nuclear energy as a reserve force of energy fuel supply for the future.

We cannot rely on the first way *alone* to supply our increasing energy needs. Future oil and gas discoveries cannot keep up with demand unless the present exploration program is expanded immediately and is successful in finding large reserves at an accelerated rate. We cannot allow ourselves to become as dependent on foreign oil as increased imports would necessitate, or we will find ourselves paying a great deal more for foreign oil than we pay now—not only in money, but in national prestige and security. So, by far the most attractive and feasible way of supplementing our energy needs is with synthetic fuels such as could be derived from oil shale, in addition to coal and nuclear energy.

Oil shale is abundant and certainly could become a major source of synthetic fuel. Important domestic deposits are in Colorado, Wyoming, and Utah where shale deposits are estimated to contain two trillion barrels of oil. The most important of these areas is the Piceance Basin in northwestern Colorado which includes 1,380 square miles underlaid with potential commercial shale beds—that is, deposits 10 feet thick or greater that yield 25 gallons or more of oil per ton of shale.

The oil shale in Colorado alone has been estimated as high as 1.5 trillion barrels. The minable portion which averages 25 gallons per ton or more is estimated to contain 480 billion barrels of oil, of which 60 per cent or 288 billion barrels might be recovered using current technology. There is a growing public misconception that trillions of barrels can be recovered from oil shale. To recover 288 billion would be phenomenal. Every effort should be made to dispel the "trillions of barrels" rumor that not only the public but unknowledgeable persons in important positions are assuming as a fact.

With the public believing such large figures, it is not surprising that a number of critics of free enterprise rally under the banner of public ownership and federal control and wave red flags of "scandal" and "fear" claiming that fabulous wealth belonging to the people will be given away. For example, former Senator Paul Douglas of Illinois, an honorary chairman of the Public Resources Association headquartered in Denver, said about oil shale deposits on publicly owned lands:

> Every man, woman, and child of our country owns a share of the vast resources of recoverable oil, and the value to each in terms of total sales volume is at least $25,000.[1]

Douglas warned of a possible "giveaway" of a great resource which he says is owned by all the people.

This sounds as if the shale oil has already been developed and sold, and the money set aside in a communal warehouse or deposited in a bank. All each of us has to do, Douglas implies, is write a check or get a shovel and withdraw our personal share.

What nonsense! By similar reasoning, each of us could take an ax into our national forests, mark off our "personal" trees, chop down our share, and put the lumber to our own uses.

The Public Resources Association is staffed and led by men of much the same persuasion as ex-Senator Douglas. Its other honorary co-chairman is Dr. John Kenneth Galbraith of Harvard University, who is determined to see shale oil developed by the government, to "protect the public interest, as opposed to the selfish and speculative interest" of private business. Again what nonsense! Whatever private business does with oil shale accrues to the benefit of the public. The development certainly is not selfish. However, it is speculative; private industry could go bankrupt in this oil shale venture!

One of the more outspoken advocates of government control and development of shale oil is Professor Morris Garnsey of Colorado University. Dr. Garnsey has argued bitterly against what he calls "development of a vast resource by the monopolistic oil interest." He says:

> The oil industry in the United States is so highly monopo-lized, we can't trust the development of this resource to that industry. We must avoid the greatest giveaway in the history of our nation.[2]

In my opinion this is silly. Who else can develop this resource? In the first place, the question still exists if oil from shale will ever be developed by anybody.

Critics favoring government development and control, as op-posed to private development, know how to appeal to the public imagination and influence the public mind. They raise the specter of another "Teapot Dome Scandal"[3] and speak of "stealing a public treasure"[3] and of the "multi-trillion dollar value"[3] of a shale oil industry. This reasoning does not hold up even under grammar school arithmetic. The value of all the land in this country, plus all the surface improvements, is estimated to be no more than $1.5 trillion.

If we could get out two trillion barrels of oil and sell them at $3.00 a barrel, we might have a "multi-trillion dollar industry." But we are not going to get that much oil. We will do well to obtain 288 billion barrels of recoverable oil from an estimated 480 billion barrels in commercial grade shale. This is still a large amount of oil, but nothing to generate a "multi-trillion dollar" value.

Not all leaders in the academic world lack so much basic knowledge of shale oil or distort the facts in an appeal to naive minds. Dr. Orlo Childs, president of the Colorado School of Mines, speaks more knowledgeably and in sounder terms. To Dr. Childs, the view that development of a substantial shale oil production in the United States is unnecessary is

> not only shortsighted as to the oncoming energy require-ments of our citizens but . . . is also dangerous to the military and economic security of our nation.
>
> At this critical time of need for rational decision, it is in-appropriate to fan the emotional fires of fear and endanger long-range values to our national economy. Let's not be be-guiled by those who believe that the government is all-wise and all-seeing and that total administrative regulation of our energy resources is the best answer. Let's not be charmed by those who not only say they can best determine what is in the public interest but also insist on the right to enforce their decisions by direct and indirect control over operations of the market place.[4]

Another authority speaking out for the free enterprise system in developing oil shale is Dr. Charles H. Prien, head of the chemical division, Denver Research Institute of the University of Denver. Dr. Prien is one of the foremost authorities on the advancing technology and economics of the emerging shale oil industry. He is unalterably opposed to those who shout about "giveaways," who say reserves on public lands are not needed now for a viable shale oil industry, and who contend that private industry cannot be trusted with a resource owned by all the people.

Dr. Prien has been active in oil shale research for a quarter of a century. He has written 35 technical papers and portions of books on oil shale technology and has been the advisor on oil shale to the President's Office of Science and Technology. Dr. Prien thus speaks with authority when he says:

> The era for development of our oil shale resource is now, to supplement our natural resources in meeting our burgeoning energy needs. Shale oil will never dominate the energy market or displace conventional petroleum, but will simply take its proper position in the highly competitive total energy mix.
>
> The potential contribution of an oil shale industry to our national economy is enormous—in creating new jobs, new tax sources, new by-product industries, new national wealth. None of these benefits can be realized while the shale deposits remain undeveloped in the ground.[5]

Production of oil from shale will be costly. The per-barrel investment in a commercial mining and retorting operation may be lower than for liquid petroleum, but unit operating costs will be considerably higher. One reason is that shale oil cannot be refined by conventional means. Oil from shale is deficient in hydrogen, and hydrogen will have to be manufactured and added during the refining process. Shale oil also contains relatively large amounts of such elements as sulfur and nitrogen, which will have to be removed during the upgrading process. This process will be especially expensive. Shale oil produced in commercial operations involving mining, crushing, retorting, and processing—and under reasonable royalty and tax provisions—would have about the same rate of return as the national average for mining and manufacturing. The proposed Department of the Interior regulations, however, set forth terms under which these returns would be substantially lower. Nothing in the studies of shale oil operations suggests enormous profits, and shale oil operations are not going to offer any get-rich-quick opportunities. It is most peculiar that critics of the free enterprise system do not know this. They continue to believe the oil from shale will gush forth like the old oil gushers at Spindletop, Signal Hill, and El Dorado at 100,000 barrels per day without any expense.

The ownership and leasing of oil shale lands is unusual. The federal government owns 80 to 90 per cent of these lands so a satisfactory basis for leasing the federal lands must be devised soon.

Oil shale lands should be leased on a competitive bid basis, preferably by public auction, using a bonus system with a moderate, fixed royalty. The bonus system will result in the maximum leasing income to the federal treasury, will preclude political or other forms of favoritism, and will avoid speculation in leasing. Competitive pressures will insure that the lease bonuses reflect the profitability of shale oil operations. Therefore, the royalty should be held to a relatively low, fixed amount so that shale oil will not be at a cost disadvantage compared with competing energy sources.

Bidding for leases should be open to all potential participants on a competitive basis, with no discrimination in respect to firms in any particular industry, size category, or other classification. Unitization of lands into efficient conservation or production units should be permitted. It is not necessary that an extensive amount of acreage be leased currently. Oil shale lands should be researched and developed at once—therefore, leasing procedures should be adopted and the lands leased out for development.

The research and development of shale oil should be the responsibility of private industry. It has repeatedly been proved in this country that private capital investments based on the free enterprise system are most efficient and productive. Our whole nation has prospered under this concept, and anything contrary to it borders on socialism and other "isms" which our people do not desire. It has also been proved that the greater the federal control on operations of this kind, the less the efficiency, the less the productive capacity, and the greater the cost to the taxpayer. The offshore oil and gas operations in federal waters are an excellent example.

The availability of dependable, low-cost energy is basic to national security and welfare. The petroleum industry has established a remarkable record for providing the energy needed at reasonable prices. Gasoline is an excellent case to support this point. The gasoline sold today is not only a higher quality product than gasoline sold in the 1920's, but also cheaper, excluding taxes.

Energy needs are growing so fast that, within the next eight to ten years, energy from conventional hydrocarbons will need to be supplemented with synthetic fuels from shale oil, coal and/or nuclear means. Gasoline from shale oil will require large commitments of technical talent, significant capital expenditures for research and development, and a substantial period of time.

Timely action by government in establishing a framework within which a shale oil industry can function is essential, and given the proper incentives, private industry *may* be able to realize commercial production during the next decade.

In evaluating shale oil development, some points must be considered:

1. *Synthetic liquid fuels* could be needed in the next 10 years, and oil shale could become an important source, provided large-scale operations to recover this oil are begun immediately.

2. *Because of the lead time requirements,* steps should be taken now to encourage the necessary research and development of oil shale, or it will be too late for this source to be of any assistance to us in an emergency.

3. *Private enterprise* can best develop oil shale wherever it is located, whether on public or private lands.

4. *Clear title* to the public domain oil shale lands is essential to such development.

5. *Regulations proposed by the Department of the Interior* do not provide the necessary encouragement and incentives for private enterprise to commit its technical and capital resources to the important task of developing this industry on the public domain.

6. *Revised regulations should be issued* by the Department of the Interior without delay to encourage the research and development by private enterprise so that shale oil can make its proper contribution as a supplemental energy source when the need arises.

7. And, last, but most important is that the *technology for commercial operation of oil from shale is still uncertain and unproved,* and we cannot wait another decade for a definite answer to this question.

Those who oppose private industry's role in the *attempt* to develop oil from shale speak as if the end product were already a commercial reality. There is absolutely no proof that oil can be extracted from shale economically. Experiments and tests which may work in the laboratory or in a small pilot plant may be most difficult to put in large-scale commercial field operation.

Furthermore, I am disgusted with hearing a self-appointed oil shale expert declare, "It should be a comfort to us that domestic oil reserves in shale can supply the deficit of our future needs."

What future? How many years from now? Ten, 20, 50? How much longer do we have to wait?

No one has yet given an exact date for the economic manufacturing of such reserves!

Twenty-five years ago, we were told that oil from shale would be a reality in five years. Twenty years ago, we were told it would be in five years. And for each successive five-year period, it was still five years away. And today, we hear oil from shale will be a reality in the next five years. Some doubt that it will ever be a reality. In fact, if private industry is not given the immediate opportunity to determine whether oil from shale on a large-scale operation is economically feasible, it will turn its efforts to other sources of supply, and the reality of large oil reserves from shale may never occur. And what a great loss this would be to the people of the oil shale states and our nation.

Let us not be lulled into apathy by hopes that shale oil reserves will be readily available to us when we need them, especially in times of an emergency. This is wishful thinking on still *unproved* economics and unproved profitable foundations. Billions of barrels of oil are worthless if it costs one penny per barrel more than its returned sale value.

Until costs of such manufactured oil reserves are reasonably profitable, we should orient our thinking to find the natural petroleum reserves we know still exist and can be found in this vast country of ours. Several times as much oil and gas remain to be found in this country as we have found and produced since 1859. Our task is simply to find and produce it.

Therefore, our current responsibilities are twofold: first, to accelerate by every possible method a daring, imaginative, and greatly expanded program of exploration for natural (conventional) petroleum reserves; and second, to insist that shale oil lands be leased immediately to private industry for research and development to determine whether such shale oil can be produced economically and whether shale oil reserves can be included in estimates for our future energy requirements.

REFERENCES

[1] A "dear friend" broadside, undated letter on the stationery of the Public Resources Association and signed by Senator Paul Douglas.
[2] Denver Post, July 17, 1967; also in report of Senate Subcommittee on Interior and Insular Affairs hearing, April, 1967.
[3] Saturday Evening Post, December 30, 1967.
[4] Denver Post, July 18, 1967; also testimony before the Senate Subcommittee on Interior and Insular Affairs, February, 1967, and September, 1967.
[5] Denver Post interview, July 27, 1967.

Mr. Scripps Said It

"Whoever believes that oil is not today's most important international commodity in either war or peace, either hot or cold, is unaware of the situation. And the American people do not have the necessary information to provide light by which they might find their own way."   June 18, 1970

The late E. W. Scripps, founder of one of the most aggressive and influential chains of newspapers in this country, is best remembered for his strict adherence to a basic journalistic principle —total objectivity in reporting the news.

He incorporated this idea into a slogan of his newspapers, "Give the people light, and they will find their own way."

He did not believe anyone had the privilege to tell other people right from wrong, or how to vote, or where to spend their money, or whom to associate with, or even what to drink. He believed that if the press gave the people the facts without fear or favor, the people were capable of finding their own way to whatever conclusion these facts dictated.

Today the petroleum industry has reached the point where it must give the people light so they can find their own way.

For too long, politicians and businessmen, and even educators and professional men in all disciplines, have been too coy with the public. They have been less than frank, and in some cases, less than honest. Even parents have not been candid with their children or with each other. Evidence of the deceit that has been practiced on the American people is easily recognized in TV commercials or newspaper advertisements. In too many instances, these media display misrepresentations or outright lies. In addition, the public is mollified or, more accurately, mesmerized by tongue-in-cheek promises of politicians, slanted news, or the one-sided press releases issued by most sources.

For years, even the petroleum industry has been attempting to communicate to the public through a controlled system of public relations or public affairs. We have answered questions that have not been raised, but we have not always subjected ourselves to questions the public might want to ask. We have used competition as an excuse for silence in far too many cases.

For many years, petroleum industry spokesmen have been mouthing a set of clichés. Some of them have been set to different music, but the words have been the same. They deal with high risks, high costs, low average profits, excessive imports, depletion, and price controls.

Of course, all these clichés are true, but they are the industry's problems. The public has its own problems, and is not listening to oilmen. Our cries, laments, and pleadings go unheard because they have been made and are still being made by industry trade organizations or by industry leaders—all considered by the public to be self-serving. We have wasted millions of dollars attempting to inform the public and, in turn, the people have laughed at our antics and referred to those in the industry as selfish, rich, and arrogant.

Even worse, the great majority, if not all, of our messages are delivered at oil and gas meetings. Press releases have been seen solely in the oil country press, completely out of the general public's exposure. The monotony of the monologue has been boring. None of it seems very interesting or educational, and even to those who do listen, it is not very informative.

The public has not heard many facts about the petroleum industry that deal with problems confronting not only the industry but people at the grass roots. These facts deal with threats to our national safety, important international matters, jobs, profits for investors, improved products for customers, effective controls over pollution, relations with Canada, the threat of a Soviet control of or influence over world oil reserves and what this ominous fact means to the future of world freedom. These are only a few of the facts which oilmen could easily shed light on from our store of expertise and which we should present properly to the public.

I am not particularly concerned over the Soviet Union ever directly threatening our country through control of world petroleum outside the North American continent. In my opinion, there is sufficient energy on this continent to supply its needs for as long as necessary. We have found less than half the oil and gas in the lower 48 states, and Canada and Alaska hold the potential of reserves to approximate the Middle East. A treasure of kerogen lies in the shale of the Rockies and untold reserves of potential fuel in the tar sands of Canada. The industry is on the verge of commercial development of both gas and gasoline from coal.

But what about our allies in the free world? What about western Europe and other areas of the world which depend on petroleum from the Persian Gulf, Africa, and South America?

Here is a danger the public should consider. If the Soviets are able to put our allies under economic pressure, that is, make their economies dependent on oil the Soviets control, into what kind of position does this place every American? We will eventually find all the world communized except those who inhabit a part of this continent. Then the question would become "How long can we remain free?"

Without a doubt, the greatest sources of oil reserves on earth at this time are the Middle East and Africa. Today most of the countries of the Middle East are either hostile to the United States and friendly to Russia, or they are under overwhelming pressure from the Kremlin and their own leftist neighbors.

In Africa within the past year, one regime after another in the important oil countries—regimes once friendly to the free world—have been replaced by those favorable to the Russians.

In the last year, in Libya, one of the most prolific oil areas of the world, a government friendly to the United States has been overthrown and replaced by a puppet of the Soviets. Probably the oil industry there will not go unaffected for long.

In Nigeria, which is rapidly showing tremendous offshore oil reserves, the present government owes much of its existence to the Soviet Union. We backed the losers!

In Indonesia, where a considerable potential for new oil reserves is being proven, only the action in Vietnam has prevented Communist control so far.

Communist influence is spreading in South America, also. Castro's agents are a threat to Venezuela and its great oil reserves. In fact, that country is communism's prime objective in this hemisphere.

In Bolivia, a friendly government has been thrown out by allies of the communists, and already Gulf Oil Corporation's significant holding have been expropriated and the Bolivians are discussing deals with the Russians.

The only place on earth outside the United States where the energy supply potential is high, and where there is no present serious threat from the communists, is Canada.

Because of this, it mystifies me that the United States and Canada have not, long ago, reached a firm international petroleum policy. In fact, I strongly advocate a free trade policy of oil and gas between these two countries. However, to have such a policy, it probably will be necessary to reach a common understanding on national security aspects, particularly, since Canada is now a net importer of crude. From the national security standpoint, which is the basis for the import program, a strong tie exists between the two countries.

The demand for Canadian oil is growing rapidly in the United States, and government action officially limiting Canadian imports has caused some misunderstanding. Lower Canadian crude prices of 35 to 60 cents a barrel induced United States buyers to raise import figures until the levels exceeded the original voluntary agreement between the two governments. So a cutback was ordered and caused cries of economic discomfort from United States oil buyers and Canadian producers. More important, it appears to have caused a temporary misunderstanding between these two friendly powers.

However, I believe this will be only a short term deterrent to a common energy policy. The United States will gradually need to import more and more Canadian crude to combat our dwindling reserves and increased requirements. We will have to either (1) find quickly our own substantial amount of new reserves, or (2) depend on Middle East, African, or South American crude, or (3) supplement our needs as much as possible from a nation friendly to us, close to us, and one we can depend on—namely Canada.

The petroleum industry should encourage the best of relationships and free trade on items needed by both countries, especially on petroleum. Under a common policy, I feel incentives to find additional crude for United States and Canadian security would be forthcoming. The serious implications of the international petroleum situation in respect to the welfare of the Americans and even the Canadians can hardly be overemphasized.

Not so far removed from this situation is a movement by some in this country to convince our government to renounce this country's heritage and legal rights to all resources beyond water depths of 200 meters.

Indeed, President Nixon stated on May 23, 1970,

> "Therefore, I am today proposing that all nations adopt as soon as possible a treaty under which they would renounce all national claims over the natural resources of the seabed beyond the point where the high seas reached a depth of 200 meters (218.8 yards) and would agree to regard these resources as the common heritage of mankind."

The proposal means United States ownership would extend only to 200 meters, or three miles, whichever is greater. If adopted, this proposal would affect leases already issued in the offshore, such as in the Santa Barbara Channel, and more particularly, those leases now held by a company which just announced a major discovery in this Channel. By my estimate, the leases which would be affected in all the Santa Barbara Channel waters alone have oil reserves in the billions of barrels.

While not readily apparent, this problem revolves around the extent to which this nation and other nations will claim jurisdiction in the territorial sea and the submerged portions adjacent to the continents. In the last few years, the limit of the territorial sea claimed by coastal nations has expanded outward from the historic three-mile limit. While the United States and 32 other nations still adhere to this limit, 79 countries now claim more than this mileage, with several claiming 200 miles.

The value of our resources affected by the President's suggestion is not theoretical. It is very real. Approximately 27 natural resources are involved, including, but certainly not limited to, all the petroleum deposits in federal lands off Santa Barbara, lobsters off New England, King crabs off Alaska, and phosphate and other minerals off all our shores.

Estimates of the United States Geological Survey indicated that the total potential petroleum-in-place resource of the United States Continental Slope—an area of more than 500,000 square miles immediately beyond the Continental Shelf underlying water depths of 200 to 2,500 meters—may range between 640 and 800 billion barrels of oil and from 1,590 to 2,230 trillion cubic feet of natural gas. This potential resource-in-place nearly equals that estimated for the United States Continental Shelf itself.

If only 10 per cent of this potential could be recovered, that is, 60 to 80 billion barrels of oil plus 160 to 225 trillion cubic feet of gas, the value of the giveaway would be great.

In my opinion, the Geneva Convention gave America the right to all resources on the seafloor and subsoil of the submerged portions of the continent or those resources adjacent to it. Whether this means to 2,500 meters, 4,000 meters, 100 miles, 200 miles, the end of the continental rise, the foot of the slope, or what, I do not know. But surely the terminology of the Convention means more than 200 meters deep or three miles out.

In pronouncements of this import, a government customarily does a tremendous amount of "homework." They consult those concerned and study all the implications and ramifications of the move. The question can be asked, "Was this procedure used in this instance?" If it is not too late, I suggest the people of this country express their opinions to President Nixon and Congress.

Another problem which faces the petroleum industry and the public is nationalization. Most Americans have no idea how close we are to nationalization, or even what nationalization means. First, nationalization means the taking over of private property or industrial organizations, or the control of any class of labor.

A synonym for nationalism is collectivism. Others are bolshevism, socialism, and communism. Nazism and fascism could be included. They are all the same with slightly different shadings. By any name, I want no part of any of them, and I dare say no other real American feels any differently.

Yet a member of the board of directors of a California organization, GOO (for Get Oil Out), an outgrowth of the hysteria over the Santa Barbara Channel incident, was quoted in the Oil Daily and other newspapers recently as calling for the nationalization of the petroleum industry in an address before the student bodies of Occidental and California Lutheran Colleges as they participated in an environmental teach-in.

Today, the nationalization of the oil industry: tomorrow, other business, industrial, and professional complexes, including labor. That is what Americans are being inspired to believe is right and to advocate. That is the goal of the agitators and militants who are prodding young people in this country. Do the average citizens of this country realize this threat? Do they want to change our government? Do they want free enterprise, capitalism, and individual freedom swallowed up by nationalism, or socialism, or communism?

They do not.

Yet if the petroleum industry and other industries, businesses, professions, and organizations in this country, such as labor, do not begin to speak up, educate, inform, and create a dialogue with the people of this country; if we do not end our monologue with ourselves, and our talking to, instead of with, the public; if we do not listen, if we do not entertain an outside viewpoint; if we do not answer some simple questions and give some straight answers, nationalization is inevitable.

We are being attacked today from without and from within. The insidious forces within are by far the more dangerous. When Krushchev said, "We will bury you," he did not mean by armed forces, but by forces within.

In recent weeks, we have been directly threatened by a spokesman for Syria who warned that we could be cut off from Middle East oil unless we accommodated certain positions of the Arabs regarding the Israeli war.

This incident should be enough to point up the vulnerability of dependence on outside sources for oil. Of course, we get very little oil, probably 3 per cent of our imports, from the Middle East. But if Venezuela made such a threat, it could cause immediate concern, and Venezuela, as a member of the Organization of Petroleum Exporting Countries, is an ally.

The Middle East is now providing 67 per cent of our oil requirements for the war in Vietnam. If the Arabs carried their threat far enough, which they might well do in their desperation in the Middle East war, they could cut off oil supplies to our allies and friends. Approximately 66 per cent of western Europe's oil and about 90 percent of Japan's oil is supplied by the Middle East.

Under present conditions, this country could not provide its allies and friends with oil over an extended time. Since the last Suez crisis, when we supplied our friends in the free world with oil when it was denied them by the Arab countries, our own surplus producing capacity has been reduced by something like a million barrels a day, and is down 30 per cent from last year, the first decline since statistics were first compiled on surplus in 1954.

Is the American public aware that more than 75 per cent of the known proven free world reserves of oil are located in the Middle East and Africa in countries either hostile to us or under unrelenting communist pressure?

Do the Americans, who depend on petroleum to fuel their economy far more than any people in any other part of the world, realize that we have only 10 years' supply of crude reserves? And if they know this, do they realize its full implication? I doubt it seriously.

Whoever believes that oil is not today's most important international commodity in either war or peace, either hot war or cold, is unaware of the situation. And the American people do not have this necessary information to provide light by which they might find their own way.

But it is time for the American public to realize facts such as these. For too long, spokesmen for the petroleum industry have attempted to tell Americans that *unless* certain things were done, *the oil industry and the oilmen would suffer.*

That is not the story Americans are interested in. They are interested, however, in their own personal and individual survival as well as that of the country and freedom as we know it today.

It is up to oilmen to furnish that information and to provide whatever education is needed in this area where we are experts. We cannot assume that because these facts are so clear to us, if indeed they are, that they are clear to the public. The American people know as close to nothing about the oil industry as possible. This is not an idle statement, but a well-documented fact.

America is unaware that it depends entirely on energy for economic and social sustenance, that 75 per cent of that energy comes from the petroleum industry in the form of oil and natural gas, and that demand for energy, here and in all the free world, is expanding at an alarming rate.

The light we must give the people today is that Russia hopes to dominate the world through this dependence on petroleum. Their interest in Vietnam is the oil in Indonesia, not in helping the North Vietnamese. Their interest in the Arab-Israeli conflict is their plan eventually to control Middle East and African oil, not their love for Arabs or Africans.

The people of this country might not appreciate this threat to freedom and capitalism as well as they should.

The six-day war in mid-1967 offered an unusual opportunity for the Russians to explore their sphere of influence in the Arab world, and they have taken full advantage of their finding.

This influence gave the Russians opportunities the czars never dreamed of. Through dramatic moves, almost unnoticed by American citizens, the Russians have established economical beachheads in parts of the world they have never penetrated before. For example, they have only recently established diplomatic relations with Singapore and Malaysia in their thrust toward Indonesia so they can remain in that area if the Vietnam war fails for them. In one way or another, they have penetrated almost every single important nation in Europe with unexpected ease. Through their maneuverings in gas, they now threaten the success of the North Sea exploration. To dispel talk of their oil shortage, which encouraged American oilmen for a while, they recently announced a 14.6 billion barrel field discovery at Samotlor in western Siberia. They are involved in oil programs in more than 20 important nations around the world at this moment and are moving into others rapidly.

Thus, the Russians are using every device necessary to get a foothold for their projected petroleum domination. They are boosting their foreign aid, both military and economic. They are sending advisors and technicians into every country that will take them. Their petroleum marketing arrangements have reached almost every capital of Europe. Their basic plan is, as most people can see once it is shown them, to make all oil-consuming nations, including us, dependent on petroleum they control in any part of the world. With that goal accomplished, the cold war will end; the communists will be victorious. The only battle left then will be for the Russians and the Chinese to decide what type of communism will rule the world.

This is not a bright prospect, and its success is far from a foregone conclusion. But it is the obvious Russian plan for conquering the world. Their threats of military action have a hollow ring and serve only to frighten the weak-hearted and the intellectually incompetent. They are designed to give hope and strength to radicals, anarchists, local communists, socialists, left wingers, and liberal extremists in all countries.

There is still time and hope that they will fail. Many of our friends in the Middle East, such as Iran, Kuwait, Saudi Arabia, and others, are resisting as long as possible against their have-not brothers in Egypt, Jordan, and Syria where the United Arab Republic is in direct conflict in the Israeli war.

The hope of thwarting the world conquest by communism through energy control of the western world lies in this country. It lies in the knowledge and education the American people have on the subject.

By understanding the situation and adopting a resolute attitude, the American people can defeat the communist design for world domination. The oil industry cannot do this alone, but the industry can do its part by giving the American people light on the importance of petroleum to their lives, to this nation, and to the entire world.

Then the people, through their leaders in government, can begin to get results. The Russians are still struggling to attain their goal. They are patient, but they are relentless.

It is the oil industry's job to get the story to the public objectively and as soon as possible through every means of communication before it is too late.

Oilmen have concentrated so much valuable time and talent on telling the American people about the risks we take, the need for tax advantages, the virtues of conservation, the pros and cons of import controls (depending on who was telling the story and when), and other problems and controversies that we have neglected to tell the story of the industry. Therefore, the public is uninformed and unconcerned about it.

We have been concentrating on propaganda and promotion when we should have been concentrating on facts, while keeping an ear open for reasonable viewpoints, attitudes, and questions from the public.

Our attempt to give people light about the industry in this country has been arrogant and incompetent and actually has done more harm than any occasional good that might have filtered out of its ineffectiveness.

We in the industry have ourselves to blame for this. We have been preoccupied with our own well-being and the welfare of our industry instead of being involved and concerned about the country as a whole at the same time.

When we talk about giving people light so they might find their own way, we might also start directing some of that light toward our fellow oilmen.

We have permitted a strong movement toward nationalization and socialism to grow up right in our own states, cities, offices, the oil industry, and even our homes, in our blind march toward the goal of protecting depletion or controlling imports of oil.

We have ignored our civic and political obligations to the point where our state houses and national capitol are becoming infested with ignorant, selfish, ambitious, and irresponsible men who do not care whether or not we continue as a free people so long as they can remain on the public payroll under any form of government.

It is ironic and yet tragic that we have failed because we have an industry so useful and a story so honest and inspirational that we should need no special lobbies to gain us friendship if we were merely to tell it and, at the same time, listen to what the people, our customers, the voters, and tax payers at the grass roots are saying to us.

The petroleum industry must accept the challenge to follow the slogan Mr. Scripps gave to his newspapers. Let us do our part to give the people light about their greatest and most essential industry so they might find their own way.

And let us pray that while we are giving light about our industry, the public will in turn shed a little of it in our direction so we might penetrate the darkness that has blocked the way to understanding things we as an industry should know.

3
PERFECTING
THE SEARCH
FOR PETROLEUM

A Geologist's View of Geophysics
Maximum Brain Power—
 New Exploration Breakthrough
Economics—The New Dimension
Optimism–Key to Future Exploration
Heritage of the Petroleum Geologist
Creativity in Geology
Needed—Greater Teamwork
Supply and Demand

Introduction

Ever since the invention of the wheel, man has probed the earth and plumbed the ocean and tested the skies, seeking ways to go faster, farther, deeper and higher.

Thus the search for petroleum has grown wider and more urgent, fueling the dreams and needs of mankind.

In a 13-year period between 1955 and 1968, Michel T. Halbouty sounded a tocsin call to the industry: a call for a maximum effort with more order and less selfishness.

In the eight speeches reprinted here, Halbouty deals honestly with the many roles of the modern geologist; the demands yet to be made on his skills and creative capacity; how the new economics will affect his and the industry's future, his relationship to other members of the petroleum team, and his uneasy coexistence with geophysicists.

The speeches contain several provocative conclusions:

• As exploration becomes more complex and reservoirs more difficult to find, the traditional separation of roles—with the scientist as seeker and the engineer as developer—is no longer efficient or practical.

• In an era in which only 8,000 wildcats are being drilled where 25,000 are needed, the existing philosophy is outmoded and ineffective. (Halbouty made headlines with one more specific charge, that management had pitted the geologist and geophysicist against each other too long.)

• Geologists must make themselves aware of the economics involved in the discovery and recovery of oil and gas. (Nor did he spare management for its offhand treatment of geologists as he pressed his points on a 200,000 mile odyssey throughout the U. S., Canada, Mexico, England and Europe as president of the AAPG.)

• The damaging secrecy on exploratory research indulged in by major companies must end. Optimism, insisted Halbouty, at a time when gloom generally shrouded the petroleum industry, could be the key to cooperation among the exploratory sciences.

• Technical improvements in exploration, drilling and recovery are a joint responsibility of the geologist, geophysicist and petroleum engineer, operating as a team in a favorable managerial climate.

• The bewildering policies of the major oil companies tend to discourage students from careers in petroleum geology, and the increasing demand for teachers in the field of earth sciences has heightened the shortage. (Under Halbouty's direction, the AAPG created advisory committees to work with industries and universities for mutual understanding of the problems involved.)

• Geologists and geophysicists must divide the blame for their failure to cooperate, to assess and correct their shortcomings. Management is at fault, Halbouty argues, for not bringing the two disciplines together.

• If the oil industry could coordinate its exploratory efforts, the immediate result would be the elimination of unnecessary wells, which have wasted over $10 billion in Texas alone. The engineer, as the developer and producer, must combine with the geologist and geophysicist, as the seeker and finder, to properly evaluate all new data obtained from development drilling.

And the search continues.

A Geologist's View Of Geophysics

"The weakness in the coordination of the two sciences lies in certain basic items which could so easily be eliminated. It is silly for them to have ever existed."   September 22, 1955

Between 1955 and 1975, oil will be found in types of traps and under conditions we do not even dream of today, but these new fields can be found only through the cooperative work of geologists and geophysicists. A joint geological-geophysical re-examination of old condemned areas could lead to the discovery of vast reserves not only in new provinces but in existing provinces. To achieve this, we must close the gap separating the two professions that are the exploration brains of the oil industry.

In the past year, a number of papers have been written by geologists and geophysicists with these typical titles:

1. "Geophysics to Stage Comeback"[1]
2. "$2 Billion Worth of Seismic Records—Is the U.S. Oil Industry Making the Most of this Investment?"[2]
3. "Geophysical Activity Drops Again in '54—What is the Remedy?"[3]

4. "Better Seismic Interpretations Needed"[4]

5. "Exploration Staffs *Can* Succeed in Correlating Geological and Geophysical Data"[5]

It is healthy for geologists and geophysicists to recognize shortcomings in their work and try to correct them. In turn, such measures will prove beneficial to the entire oil industry. As one writer put it:

> Geophysicists are convinced they can improve their skill in finding oil. Their formula calls for better interpretation of seismic findings and closer coordination with geologists.[6]

Geologists now want that coordination although in the past, the farther apart geologists and geophysicists stayed, the better each liked it. The lack of coordination of exploration activities between the two professions is really the fault of management. The "big men at the top" should have forced the two professions to get together whether or not the geologists and the geophysicists wanted to do so. They should have been forced to get in the same room together, discuss their respective data, coordinate it, and mutually submit the results. Paul L. Lyons, past president of the Society of Exploration Geophysicists, ably stated the point when he said:

> The men (management) who conceive such programs, in which geology and geophysics are *intermixed*, not 'coordinated,' will be the oil finders of the future.[7]

A recent editorial by The Oil and Gas Journal said about both professions:

> Geologists and geophysicists deplore any suggestion that there is a 'gap' between them. But—call it what you will—there is a degree of rivalry, or prejudice, or self-centeredness which hampers the fullest coordination of their respective skills in the difficult task of finding oil.

A very wide breach once existed; a narrower one now exists although at times it seems as wide as ever. Nevertheless, this "misunderstanding" should be eliminated and replaced by coordination and cooperation.

The wide gap started between the two sciences unintentionally. It happened because certain conditions unfortunately existed.

Prior to the discovery of Spindletop, there were no petroleum geologists practicing as such. All the geologists were professors and were retained by oil interests only when extremely necessary. The great discovery of Spindletop in 1901 was the result of the faith of one man—Pattillo Higgins. The recognized geologists of that time turned the prospect down as unworthy of exploration. This fantastic discovery began to take the geologists out of the classroom and into the field as employees of oil operators.

Higgins said surface indications made him believe that oil existed in the area. These surface indications were listed as a mound or small hill perceptible above the prairie lands of the Gulf Coast, gas seeps that bubbled out of the ground, paraffin dirt that felt like rubber when squeezed in the palm of the hand, and sour waters in shallow water wells.

These indications led to the drilling of the first well at Spindletop and in turn became the signs sought in the search for other structures. Every native became a geologist when someone remembered a gas seep, a mound, sour water, paraffin dirt, or a combination of these indications in some locality. Professional geologists were employed by oil operators to locate these same indications on a scientific basis.

So intensive was this search for surface indications in 1901 that during the year, 11 domes were discovered. From 1901 to 1905, another 29 were discovered, and 17 of these produced oil. From 1905 to 1924, the percentage of discoveries decreased to such an extent that the over-all cost of wildcat drilling became unprofitable. In 1917 alone, 675 wildcat wells were drilled at a total cost of $20 million. Only one dome was discovered, and it proved to be unproductive.

At the end of 1923, the discovery rate became so low in the Gulf Coast, experts predicted that known oil reserves would not take care of the demand for oil for more than a few years. Only 47 domes were found by surface control wildcatting from 1901 to the end of 1923. Many of these were unproductive. Those that produced penetrated only into the caprock. No serious attempt was made to find production on the immediate flanks of these structures.

So thoroughly was the Gulf Coast area combed by geological crews that by the end of 1923, geologists frankly admitted they did not believe any more structures could be found by surface indications. Geologists themselves said some other means had to be employed to find new structures in the Gulf Coast. At this point, in 1924, geophysics made its advent in the Gulf Coast as a medium of exploration. So ended the first era of the geologist. With the meager tools of that time, he had done very well.

The success of geophysics was tremendous. In the nine years from 1924 to 1933, some 75 domal structures were found by geophysical instruments compared with 47 found otherwise in the previous 23 years. Geophysics also proved that productive structures other than piercement-type salt domes existed on the Gulf Coast. Thus, the geophysicist supplanted the geologist, and the first era of the geophysicist began.

At this point the gap was created; neither the geophysicist nor management needed the geologists for exploration work. He was relegated to an office-boy status. He brought the maps in and was immediately excused. It was not necessary for the geophysicist to have any geological data; his structures had from 400 to 1,000 feet of closure. Fields like Hastings, Friendswood, and Anahuac were found, and exploration in any other form was superfluous. Management became so geophysical-conscious that the geologist was forgotten. This was management's great mistake because years of valuable coordination of data were lost. In dollars, the figure must certainly be staggering. Instead of training the geologist to understand the geophysicist and vice versa, a great wall formed between them. The geophysicist was successful and did not care about or consider the geologist. The ignored geologist just fumed and waited.

The years from 1940 to 1945 were uneventful in geophysical discoveries. The war sapped brilliant manpower. After the war, geophysical discoveries continued to decline. The Gulf Coast had been combed, and the structures with big closures were not to be found. Only deep low-relief structures with 25 to 50 feet of closure were mapped, and most of those drilled had disastrous results. Geophysical domination of exploration was rapidly ending.

In the meantime, the geologist had obtained more tools and had more data from drilled wells. He became more subsurface-minded and began interpreting the geology at various depths below the surface. When the geophysicist ran out of good areas to recommend for drilling, the geologist was ready with subsurface anomalies he had worked out. So, management began to recognize once again the importance of the geologist and to ask for his recommendations. His subsurface control was based on sound data. When it was turned over to the geophysicist to check, the attitude of the geologist was, "Let's see how good the geophysicist is now." No thought of coordination entered the geologist's mind.

He remembered the years he suffered as the forgotten man. Because of the different types of anomalies that can be mapped by subsurface geologists, the geophysicist had difficulty in checking him, and the fight began all over again. The geologist was making the same mistake the geophysicist made over 20 years ago, and management did nothing to eliminate this reciprocal, antagonistic attitude.

New oil-producing structures are now becoming harder to find, so those engaged in exploration must work together. The weakness in the coordination of the two sciences lies in certain basic items which could so easily be eliminated. It is silly for them ever to have existed.

Some of these items and some suggestions on achieving coordination follow:

(1) *Management must straighten itself out.* Primarily it must remember that an increase in discoveries and a decrease in exploration costs may be realized only by a close relationship between geologists and geophysicists. Management should make it compulsory for the members of the two professions to work together on all exploration problems.

(2) *Geophysical and geological departments should be combined.* It is absurd that, in some companies, these two departments are located in separate buildings and contacts between individuals in these departments are negligible and sometimes do not exist. One department should be organized and referred to as an "Exploration Department." Both geologists and geophysicists should be placed in the same room so their ideas may be constantly exchanged.

(3) *Fear of unusual interpretation of data should be eliminated.* The geophysicist has a fear of interpreting, then recommending an unorthodox or completely new idea—such as thrust faulting in the Coast—even though his records are full of multiple reflections. The fear lies in trying to sell his client or boss on something completely foreign to usual interpretation. Lack of geological knowledge contributes to this fear. Geological coordination could clarify these interpretations.

(4) *Strict geological coordination should precede the mapping of any geophysical fault.* The geophysicist often maps a fault as a single line. In the majority of cases, this is incorrect and has led to the drilling of unnecessary dry holes. Faults are not merely straight lines representing a few feet on the contour map. They are zones consisting of one or several faults in which a relatively wide area has been affected. The accurate mapping of this zone is vital for locating the exploratory well.

(5) *Combined geological-geophysical mapping should result in the location of lateral closures and stratigraphic traps.* The geologist's attitude of "Let's see the geophysicist find a stratigraphic trap" is wrong. The geologist should give the geophysicist all of the data available and help him locate these important traps. Presently, it is impossible for the geophysicist to locate this type of trap by geophysical data alone. Geophysics combined with geological data may reveal undiscovered facts that may assist in locating areas in which these traps may exist. This problem in exploration certainly needs the utmost coordination between the two professions.

(6) *Determine usefulness of geological surveys.* It is most difficult to make usable seismic interpretations on the immediate flanks of piercement-type salt domes. Although an operator may request surveys on the flanks of these structures, the geophysicist should, by all means, discuss the proposed work with the representative geologist as to the necessity of the surveys. In many cases, seismic surveys on the immediate flanks of these domes would be a waste of time and money, and the results would be confusing and inconclusive. Such surveys should not be recommended by the geophysicist. (NOTE: This reference applies only to geophysical work authorized on the flank of the dome very near the salt plug. The reference does not apply to off-flank areas, that is, areas located some distance away from the dome.)

(7) *The geophysicist needs a better knowledge of regional and local geology of the area to be explored.* In the client-contractor relationship, the geophysicist may be too eager to please and may not argue his convictions sufficiently when they are in conflict with those of the geologist. A knowledge of the regional and local geology would enable the geophysicist to argue his point well.

(8) *The geologist needs to learn more about geophysics and its problems.* Continuous studies with geophysicists would help the geologist coordinate his work better with that of the geophysicist.

(9) *A coordination session should precede entry into the field.* The geophysicist has for years been making geophysical interpretations without due regard to geological facts existing in the subject area. No geophysical crew should enter the field before its party chief and/or its interpreter consults the representative geologists. In coordination sessions, the geophysicist and the geologist should exchange ideas about the area to be surveyed. The geologist should have already prepared cross-sections showing all formations down to the required depth and giving the physical properties and thicknesses of these formations. The geologist should also prepare maps

showing the general regional geology of the area with known faults and other pertinent geological conditions. Well control such as log correlation, electric log characteristics, and representative electric logs of wells in the general area should be discussed and all of these data made available to the geophysicist for his continued use.

(10) *The first few geophysical records should be brought in to the geologist and thoroughly discussed with him.* The geologist should check the records against his geological cross-sections and other data, and both the geologist and the geophysicist should discuss the results obtained from these records. Emphasis should be on accuracy centering around detailed velocity control and more accurate velocity functions with a continued coordination with the geological data.

(11) *Successive meetings of the geologist and geophysicist should be held as the geophysical survey progresses.* Every effort should be made during these meetings to coordinate all data.

(12) *Progress maps, and certainly the final geophysical interpretation, should be made by both the geologist and geophysicist working together.* Each contour and fault should be discussed, weighed, and agreed upon by both men before being mapped. The result would be a coordinated effort of two professional sciences. If the area is condemned, it should be mutually done, and the operator will still have the benefits of a coordinated exploration effort.

If the area is approved for drilling, it should be a mutual conclusion. In the long run this will result in more oil being found. These men will become oil finders instead of critics of each other's work and importance. The operator and the industry will profit. When the gap between these two professions has been closed by cooperation, coordination, and the joint use of imagination, the plain good "horse sense" of pulling together toward a common goal will result in more accurate structural and stratigraphic interpretations and the finding of more oil and gas.

REFERENCES

[1] Gardner, Frank J., Oil and Gas Journal, April 4, 1955, p. 101.
[2] Peacock, H. B., Oil and Gas Journal, March 14, 1955, pp. 180-182.
[3] Hammer, Sigmund, Oil and Gas Journal, April 4, 1955, pp. 138-144.
[4] Morrisey, Norman, Oil and Gas Journal, February 14, 1955, pp. 72-74.
[5] Skeels, D. C., Oil and Gas Journal, August 8, 1955, pp. 156-157.
[6] Morrisey, Norman, op. cit., p. 72.
[7] Lyons, Paul L., quotation taken from Norman Morrisey, "Better Seismic Interpretations Needed," Oil and Gas Journal, February 14, 1955, p. 72. Word "management" inserted by Halbouty.

Maximum Brain Power–New Exploration Breakthrough

"For awhile the 'black box' replaced the brain. During this time, geophysicists performed as technicians..."   June, 1958

All predictions of the nation's growth indicate an increasing need for new petroleum reserves. For the United States to maintain an adequate reserve position until 1975, it is essential that we find a minimum of 45 billion barrels of oil and 275 trillion cubic feet of gas. These figures represent the equivalent of this nation's crude oil production for the past 19 years and natural gas production for 30 years.

With these future requirements facing us, it is ironical that in 1962 and 1963, successively, we found less crude oil reserves than we produced, and in 1964, we barely discovered more reserves than we consumed.

In 1964, we drilled 9,250 exploratory wells and 36,200 development wells; in 1963, the figures were 8,607 and 35,471, respectively; and in 1962, there were 9,003 exploratory wells and 37,419 development wells. It will be impossible for this industry to meet the reserve requirements of the future by drilling such a small number of exploratory wells.

To meet the demand for just the next 10 years, we should be drilling approximately 25,000 exploratory wells and 35,000 development wells annually for a total of 60,000 wells a year beginning immediately.

It is obvious that 25,000 exploratory wells per year must require 25,000 drillable prospects per year, and this means a threefold increase in the industry's exploration program.

Following the Spindletop discovery and into the early 1930's before the advent of the seismograph and the electric log, management relied primarily on the conceptual skills of its geologists to find drillable prospects. Imagination and vision were the prime guides, and these were stimulated by use of at least four of the five senses. Thus, this era might be called the see-touch-taste-and-smell period. The basic exploration technique was surface geology in which geologists came into direct contact with the rock outcrop. Drillers, using these same sense skills developed by much exposure and experience, provided the log of the well; and geologists, studying and analyzing the samples at the well site, filled in the detail of the driller's log.

With the development of the electric log and the seismograph, management acquired new instruments which, at first, seemed destined to replace geological brain power. After a series of spectacular successes, many management groups believed that these new geophysical exploration instruments had, at last, solved the problem of finding new reserves. During the thirties and forties, any anomaly conceived through geological thinking was submitted to the seismograph and was classified as drillable only after the "black box" confirmed it.

For a while the "black box" replaced the brain. During this time, geophysicists, who were primarily mathematicians, physicists, or electrical engineers, performed as technicians, transcribing the data provided by the seismogram into comprehensible form. When more and more seismic "structures" proved to be dry, management became disenchanted with the new cure-all exploration tool, and many geophysicists found themselves presenting only those data which they could positively defend before and after the area was drilled.

As the original instrument began to fail more and more frequently, innovations and improvements were developed. Finally, in the early 1950's, management realized that geophysical data are no better than the creative skill of the explorers who use them. This same thing can be said of structural, stratigraphic, and other subsurface geological data. With this realization, management began a concerted effort to encourage strong cooperation and coordination between the geologists and geophysicists. Once the geologists and the geophysicists were able to exchange ideas and work together, the exploratory effort would be upgraded. During the past 15 years, many important discoveries have been made as the result of joint work by men in these two exploration activities, although a great deal of coordination is still needed to close the gap which yet exists.

At this point, however, the explorer must examine his own actions. Geologists and geophysicists are prone to "play it safe" by accepting precedent too readily, and many use precedent as a means of dodging progressive thinking. With improvement in techniques, explorationists comforted themselves by anticipating that their new discoveries would be from conventional structures at depths previously unattainable or from virgin oil provinces at geographical localities previously inaccessible.

The industry's performance in recent years has shown that the ability to drill to greater depths and to develop more sophisticated instruments will not assure the exploration success needed to meet future reserve demands. At least one warning flag has now been raised. Atwater and Miller (1965) have suggested that the reserves to be found at great depths may not prove to be as large or dependable as we now believe. Many additional data are needed before reaching a positive conclusion, but available evidence indicates that, at least on the Gulf Coast, reservoir rocks lose favorable characteristics below 20,000 feet. If this initial observation proves to be true for provinces other than the Gulf Coast, then we must expect to find future reserves in traps which we have missed or in traps different than those for which we have routinely explored in years past.

To find 25,000 drillable prospects per year in the years immediately ahead, the oil industry is going to have to employ maximum brain power. There are several avenues by which this maximum exploration brain power can be achieved.

First, the management teams of exploration companies must create an atmosphere which generates maximum creative exploration thinking. Concurrently, management must reappraise its inclination to demand seismic confirmation of every geological anomaly presented by its oil finders. In addition, management must resist the temptation to play the role of Monday morning quarterback.

Creative thinking does not bloom readily in a stifling atmosphere clouded by second guesses and recriminations. Management can assure a creative atmosphere by amply rewarding those members of its exploration team who provide imagination and forward thinking. Management also should appraise severely all exploration people early in their careers to weed out those who lack conceptual skills. Many sound geologists lack this streak of creativity but can still render their company good service in field development and data compilation activities.

Second, assuming a favorable atmosphere for creative work, the explorationists must strive to stimulate their own creative processes. We live in an age of specialization. It is no longer reasonable to assume that one geologist can master all the skills necessary to unravel and solve the mysteries of petroleum generation and accumulation. Teams of stratigraphers, log analysts, geochemists, geophysical interpreters, palynologists, paleontologists, structural subsurface experts, and others must pool their individual specialties to derive maximum benefit from all the data available to them. With the advent of data-processing tools and the resulting ability to handle innumerable data rapidly, there is also room on the exploration team for mathematicians with strong geological backgrounds. Teams of experts such as these, working closely together, are bound to stimulate new thinking which would not be possible by any single group.

Explorationists also can stimulate their creative ability by a continuing program of self-education. It may sound naive to suggest reading papers published by other exploration geologists; however, much important new geological thinking with universal application is prepared and published but lost to the industry because the very people who should be reading and studying the data never do. Another channel of self-education is an organized continuous education program of short courses sponsored and approved by the American Association of Petroleum Geologists and its affiliated local societies, or in conjunction with the Society of Exploration Geophysicists and the Society of Petroleum Engineers (AIME). The faculty for these courses could be drawn from both the academic and industrial fields, and the classes preferably should be held at selected regional universities or at seminars sponsored by local geological societies.

Third, to achieve maximum brain power, management should add a third member to its exploration team: the petroleum engineer. In his routine work in and around producing fields, the petroleum engineer develops many data which have unique exploration significance. Everyone who works in exploration will acknowledge the importance of changes in bottom-hole pressure, rates of decline, water contacts, etc., as possible indicators of areas of new reserves. Nevertheless, in day-by-day practice, the integration of significant engineering data seldom is employed by the geologists or geophysicists in their exploration thinking and work.

Geophysicists, geologists, and petroleum engineers have a great opportunity to find the much needed reserves of the future by working together in areas above, below, and around producing reservoirs. The exploration team must be bold, willing to take the risk in the realm of exploration or in the use of a new tool. Unorthodox thinking might well be the key to the discoveries of giant reserves.

The earliest petroleum geologists looked for simple surface anticlines. Later, geologists and geophysicists combined their efforts to look for the less obvious subsurface anticlines. But the era of the perfect geophysical anticline is behind us (unless activity is conducted in a virgin area), and the creative imagination of the exploration team—the maximum use of brain power—must be the new exploration "breakthrough tool."

The geologist, geophysicist, and petroleum engineer as an exploration team have a joint responsibility to develop new tools and new techniques which will save time, money, and reserves. The petroleum industry is long overdue for some technical improvements in exploration, drilling, and recovery.

The responsibility for scientific invention and creative ideas must not be relegated solely to the research and development laboratories. In the immediate future, the industry will have to find new methods of improving discovery rates, new ways to reduce drilling costs, new approaches to stimulating flow from low porosity and permeability reservoirs, better methods of achieving more complete recovery, and better devices for accurate evaluation of potential reservoirs penetrated by the drill (Halbouty and Barber, 1964). No geologist, geophysicist, or petroleum engineer can do this alone, but all three working together as a unit—as a team—surely can do these things and more.

This maximum brain-power team must entertain new concepts concerning stratigraphic traps, shale oil development, thermal exploitation, deep-seated structure, and sedimentation. It must also generate more progressive thinking toward the unexplored basins such as those in Arizona, Nevada, Idaho, and in other states, and the still untested possibilities onshore and offshore along the entire eastern seaboard.

Fourth, we must be bold in recommending the drilling of stratigraphic tests within small limits. The electric log is one of the most vital tools the petroleum geologist has ever been offered, but even today the log still is not fully used to achieve the maximum in exploration. For instance, we are reluctant to drill a well between two deep holes only a mile or so apart, especially if no structure or relief of any kind is apparent. But the up-dip pinchout of a reasonably thick reservoir between the dry holes, ably revealed by the correlation of the electric logs of the two wells, could result in an elongated, highly prolific field. It is conceded that this kind of thinking is bold and of high risk, but it is this type of reasoning which will result in the big discoveries of the future.

Finally, a team of explorers using maximum brain power must also develop maximum resolution power. A dry hole should not stifle the courage to seek reasons to drill another hole on a prospect. Every geologist can name from his own memory many fields in which one or more dry holes have been drilled before production was discovered. Consider High Island salt dome in Galveston County, Texas, which currently produces 10 million barrels per year. There have been approximately 100 dry holes drilled within or adjacent to the productive limits of the field. Admittedly, not all of these dry holes were drilled before the first production was obtained, but this theoretically would have been possible. Therefore, all who search for new petroleum reserves, from the geologist in the field to the chairman of the board, must develop a tenacity and vigor which are not weakened by one dry hole.

The oil industry will meet the reserve demands of the future. The most successful members of the oil industry in the future will be those who not only use wisely the scientific tools which are available, but who also place maximum reliance on their own conceptual skills.

It is now time for our industry to form this brain-power exploration team. Our discovery rates will not improve unless we do, but will surely improve if we act positively with the knowledge that faith, determination, and optimism are the doors to scientific exploration success.

BIBLIOGRAPHY

American Petroleum Institute Annual Report, December 28, 1964.
American Petroleum Institute, "Facts and Figures," 1959-1963.
Atwater, G. I., and E. E. Miller, "Deep Louisiana Holes Put a Squeeze on Payouts," Oil and Gas Journal, Vol. 63, No. 18 (1965), p. 71.
Halbouty, Michel T., and T. D. Barber, "The Responsibility of Geologists and Petroleum Engineers in Meeting Exploration Demands in the Future," Journal of Petroleum Technology, Vol. 16, No. 3 (1964), pp. 239-243.
U.S. Bureau of Mines, 1962-1963.

Economics—The New Dimension

"There should be good taste in exploratory methods—data gluttony is an exploratory sin which can not be afforded in today's economic climate."   October 20, 1965

The geologist in today's oil business must face a hard, realistic, and most critical fact: The average petroleum geologist knows little about the industry he serves. He has limited his interest to geology—period. He has not concerned himself with the complexities of the oil and gas business and the many difficulties it continually faces.

Today four dominant types of problems confront the petroleum industry: geological, technological, political, and economical. Although the geologist has a fundamental knowledge of the first and is familiar with the second, he usually is completely oblivious to the third and fourth. To become more effective as an explorer or developer, he must become more involved and astute in all these areas.

The political atmosphere has decisive effects on the economics of the nation and, inasmuch as all business activities are affected by the policies, laws, regulations, and controls of the government, the petroleum geologist must become alert to economic implications and changes—good or bad—inherent in pending legislation and political actions. He should understand especially their effects on the petroleum industry.

For example, there is no question that the industry as a whole has been handicapped by the Federal Power Commission's continued desire to control natural gas. The industry cannot perform its primary task of finding and developing ever-increasing supplies of gas to meet expanding requirements in the face of the frustrations and uncertainties imposed upon it by the time-consuming, costly, and burdensome regulatory proceedings of the FPC.

Geologists should know that commodity price-fixing by government is wrong in principle, and 10 years of experiments have proved it wrong in practice. It is essential that petroleum geologists understand the handicaps that such unjustified control imposes on the economy of the petroleum business.

The domestic petroleum industry has been involved in an economic climate beset by reduced margins of profit and steady declines in drilling, discoveries, reserves, and employment during the past decade.

The still-current problems of expensive exploration, imports, overcapacity in production and refining, and the continued loss of investment capital through increased government control have brought about a situation in which the economics of finding and selling petroleum have not provided a proper return on investment and effort. As a result, the list of companies and independents willing to sell out rather than stay in business is growing each year.

It is costing more to find reserves, and reserves found in recent years are declining as the exploratory effort decreases. The petroleum industry will be required to find in this country within the next 20 years more petroleum than it has produced since 1859. The nation's ever-increasing consumption of petroleum products will demand this. These needed domestic reserves will be impossible to find if our exploration and development activities continue to decline as they have.

Of all activities engaged in by the petroleum industry, the exploration for new reserves of oil and gas is the most essential to its welfare and future. The petroleum and associated industries surely would wither if new discoveries of oil and gas reserves did not keep pace with the steadily growing consumption of petroleum.

What can the geologist do to improve the outlook for exploration and industry growth? First, he should take a positive interest in new geological concepts; second, he should become familiar with all types of exploration technology, including new well-logging and seismic techniques; third, he should be aware of and fight pending political actions and developments which are detrimental to the welfare of the petroleum industry; and fourth and most important, he must begin thinking about oil exploration as a business for making money. He should be aware of the economics involved in his everyday geologic thinking.

The policy of finding oil without regard to cost is out of date in today's cloudy economic climate. Today's goal is and should be the discovery of adequate amounts of profitable oil. This can be done only through upgrading of geologic thinking by enlarging the scope of this thinking to include an economic evaluation of geological conclusions.

Profits come from good oil or gas fields, not from marginal ones. Good fields are located in known prolific producing trends, or in so-called pedigreed oil country; in the more geologically favorable parts of less prolific fairways; and in currently overlooked geological provinces or trends. They occur within depths where economics indicate that returns will not be eaten up by deep or hazardous drilling costs. These fields generally are found through sound geologic thinking by imaginative, scientifically minded, experienced geologists who base their recommendations on reliable geological and geophysical evidence and retain a practical economic sense in making evaluations.

Only those geologists who are more interested in the economic productive capabilities of a geologic trend or prospect rather than in the possibility that an area is prospective can evaluate the increased quality of prospects which are likely to provide profitable reserves. In short, geologic thinking must be projected toward economics as well as toward geology.

The geologist, on the other hand, who believes that a good job has been done when he maps a closure or when he recommends geophysical work which maps a structural anomaly, without relating the productive capabilities of the prospect to profits and risks involved, is not a complete explorationist.

Wildcatting for petroleum has been, and probably will continue to be, of two types—scientific and haphazard. The latter generally is practiced by promoters without geological background or assistance, who depend on "lady luck" to find their oil and gas. Because chance necessarily enters into a picture as speculative as oil finding, the haphazard wildcatter has provided tremendous discoveries in the past. Since the odds against such finds are great, the scientific approach, combining geology, physics, engineering and, to a degree, chemistry, has commanded most of the exploratory effort in recent years and will continue to do so in the future.

Conditions in the petroleum industry today are economically stifling to the domestic operator, whether major or independent. There is a world-wide surplus of petroleum, and oil operators in the United States are experiencing more difficulty in finding profitable reserves as the cost of exploration goes up and discoveries become increasingly marginal.

Alleviation of this economic distress lies in (1) reduction of the cost of exploration, and (2) geological upgrading of the exploratory search.

In their efforts to reduce costs, many large and small oil companies have released or given forced early retirement to many employees including some geologists.

These companies wanted to get rid of the mediocre and non-productive geologists, an economically proper objective, but many excellent and productive geologists just happened to be caught in the same seniority classification as their less efficient colleagues. This is false economy.

Some companies candidly have admitted that the majority of those terminated should not have been hired in the first place. The tragedy here lies in management's failure to release the undesirables early. The wholesale, indiscriminate termination of geologists has tended to create confusion and bewilderment within companies, in the profession, and among young students.

Along with cutbacks in personnel, oil companies have reduced drilling and other exploratory costs with the net result that they have been drilling more mediocre prospects more efficiently. This procedure will not garner profits. The requirement for profits is efficient drilling of prospects where a profitable field discovery is likely. The discovery of profitable fields requires an emphasis on the increased use of capable experienced geologists and not on reduction in their number.

It is surprising that the interest in cost reduction has not extended to other uneconomical practices such as:

1. The hiring of geologists as they come out of schools and almost immediately making them geologic observers on seismograph parties. Work of this type should be limited exclusively to experienced geologists who have regional subsurface mapping as a background and therefore can more effectively portray a geologic picture from seismic data.

2. Use of the same type of inexperienced geologists to sit on wells, to be responsible for evaluation of logs, and to supervise coring operations and examine cores for shows without the proper background for qualitative analyses. Their opinions are used as a basis for company action, and results have proved to be extremely costly. A well should be evaluated properly by qualified geologists at the well-site because it may be expensive or impossible to gain this information at a later date.

3. Use of a geologist with Gulf Coast experience to sit on a West Texas well, and vice versa. Well-sitting in a particular region should be assigned to geologists whose training and experience qualify them to evaluate petroleum shows in that region.

4. Selection of some geologic supervisors on the basis of personality instead of on geological competence and ability in inspiring geologists under them to sound exploratory thinking. Talent working under such men is not used to best advantage and commonly is shunted aside or not given recognition because of professional jealousies.

5. Insistence on geophysical confirmation of all geological prospects, regardless of their excellence. The inability of seismic analyses to verify some geological prospects has condemned areas which eventually proved to be productive for other operators who based their play strictly on subsurface geology.

6. Exploration without benefit of regional subsurface maps to guide the geologist or geophysicist to the more favorable parts of particular trends, insofar as geological environment and reservoir-rock characteristics are concerned.

7. Geological prejudice on the part of oil company executives and oil operators against or for particular geologic provinces, usually based on adverse early personal experiences.

8. Slighting the importance of oil company well-spotters in drafting departments. Nearly all maps used by geologists have been spotted by such draftsmen, and a careless well-spotter can bring about serious financial blows if a spotting error is not recognized by the geologist who maps, or fails to map, a prospective area on the basis of a misspotted well.

9. Reluctance of many companies to provide their geologists, and especially line geologists, with expense-paid trips to sectional, regional, or national geological conventions. The intangible value derived by the geologist such as furthered education and personal contacts represents potential tangible economic value to the company.

10. The permitting of other petro-professionals to take over important responsibilities which belong to the geologist. The geologist should coordinate his activities with others on the exploration team, but he should be firmly against giving up his responsibilities to them. For example, after the geologist finds, works out, and recommends a prospect, management turns to other petro-professionals for an economic appraisal of the prospect. Too often, each member of the exploration team inflates his cost estimate to give him leeway for error. Thus the prospect is rejected because of unreal economic evaluation and not because of geologic reasons. The geologist should be permitted to discuss with other petro-professionals their ideas of costs, but the geologist should turn in his own economic analysis and figures.

11. Refusal of managers to permit the geologist who originates and works out a prospect to present the prospect to management personally. This is the worst kind of coordination and surely results in economic losses to the company. Also, this fails to take advantage of a highly valuable means of providing essential training and experience to the geologist. After all, the originator is more familiar with the details of the prospect and is the person best qualified to defend the play. Every exploration geologist must be made to feel that he is a part of the company team, the company thinking, and the recommendations which are made. Most of all, the geologist who actually originates a prospect which becomes a discovery should be sought out and congratulated personally by the chief executive officer of the company.

12. Use of geologists for menial and clerical duties. Although companies who do this are keeping the payroll down by not hiring the proper personnel to do this ordinary kind of work, they are losing millions of dollars in unfound oil and gas through unjustified waste of geological time and talent.

13. Continuous payment of annual rentals on acreage blocks acquired on the basis of good data which warranted prompt acquisition and drilling of the prospect. The millions of dollars paid each year for unnecessary rentals easily could be used to drill thousands of needed domestic wildcat wells.

Though some of these practices do not entail additional expenditures for operations, all can be the cause of heavy economic losses sustained through mistakes which prevent or hinder proper exploration or evaluation of prospective areas or drilling ventures.

Because funds for exploration are limited today, prospects should be subject to a most thorough economic evaluation by management. Such an appraisal would take into consideration but would not be limited to basic items such as the following:

1. *Risk factor*—If it can be shown, for example, that one out of 10 wildcats located on the basis of geologic and seismic data finds a new field of suitable productive capability in a particular region, the normal risk factor for finding this type field in that area is given as 1:10. Other prospects are then compared with that type producing field. The prospect which most favorably qualifies in the characteristics of the type field probably will be selected for acquisition or drilling.

2. *Returns on investment*—

a. *Payout period* is obtained by dividing total investment by annual income. This factor may be misleading if a field has a short life because estimates of payout do not include economics after the payout period has ended.

b. *Rate of return (without regard to time)* attempts to determine the ratio of anticipated total profit to original investment. Companies usually do not consider a wildcat prospect seriously unless the rate of return is at least 50 to 1. In some cases, however, wildcat prospects have been approved for drilling where the economic ratio has been less because some other favorable factors overshadowed the economic deficiency.

c. *Rate of return (with regard to time)* relates the annual profit to original investment and expresses the answer as a single percentage profit for the life of the field. The most common method of doing this is to reduce future cash income to present worth by discounting it at an interest rate that will make total present worth equal to the original investment. The interest rate used in this computation is the project's rate of return.

For example, assume a property costing $2 million which will produce an average profit of $775,000 per year or $3,100,000 during the life of the property, which is assumed to be four years. The present worth of $775,000 per year during a four-year period at 20 per cent equals $2 million. Therefore, the rate of return is 20 per cent, meaning that the expected income is sufficient to return the investment during the life of the property and provide a 20-per-cent profit each year on the unrecovered cost. This is considered a minimum return.

3. *Size of possible reserves* will have an immense influence on management's selection of prospective areas, all other factors being equal.

Decisions for or against prospect selection should be based on the amount of profit to be made from a particular prospect in relation to the risk and investments involved.

To determine risk factors more properly and to evaluate economic possibilities within a geologic province, the geologist should outline the more favorable parts of all productive trends with structural, isopachous, and isolith maps, and by studying the past producing history of the area or province.

Better trends should be differentiated from less prolific ones on the basis of per-acre-foot recoveries, types of sediments and structures present, and possibilities for the development of favorable structural and stratigraphic zones which offer promise of additional reservoirs.

In short, the exploration geologists, through investigation, study, and inquiry, should evaluate and compare the several trends or areas in his working province to determine the possibilities for finding profitable reservoirs of oil or gas in each one, and then relate the exploratory effort to the economic policies and capabilities of his client, his company, or himself.

The recommendation of prospects initially is a responsibility of the geologist. He must be informed fully about the prospective area so that his presentation will answer all questions of management on necessary seismic evaluation, cost of leases, cost of drilling and possible completion of the initial well, expected cost of a development program if a discovery is made, and how much profit may be expected from anticipated reserves.

Through such data, management will be able to evaluate the prospect better, compare it with other submittals, and assign its exploratory funds to the more deserving areas.

Explorationists can expect a great deal of "static" with management in discussing their proposals to drill in unknown territory. Although risks are involved in normal wildcat drilling in known and proved oil country, the risks in unknown areas are astronomical in comparison. These greater risks must be accepted without depending on all the answers—economic or otherwise.

Even with such caution, the search for petroleum in the United States has involved a great outpouring of money into geophysical research and into the development of new and improved logging and other exploratory tools during the past decade. This, unfortunately, has been accompanied by a lessening of the geological effort. Although technology is, and must be, an integral part of successful exploration, its use is expensive, and when used to explore without full benefit of sound, practical, geological guidance, it makes petroleum exploration a basically misguided and economically unsound procedure.

It is imperative, however, that geologists employ available technical exploration tools properly and efficiently. Excessive coverage of subsurface prospects by seismograph surveys, for example, has in many cases led to confusion and frustration in prospect evaluation. Data gluttony is an exploratory sin which cannot be afforded in today's economic climate.

A geologist aware of weaknesses or problems in the seismic-reflection results of a particular area or trend should question seismic results when he believes that interpretations have not taken into account all such factors.

Perfectly conscientious and capable seismologists may overlook prospects because of their unfamiliarity with the detailed geology of certain areas. This is unnecessary economic waste. It is essential that geological ideas and reasoning, backed by geological experience, be incorporated into all seismic results if full economic value of the seismic survey is to be realized. Much difficulty may be averted by an exchange of ideas between geologists and geophysicists before, during, and after seismic operations.

In interpreting data, the geologist should take the initiative in recommending that his company participate in small available interests when large ownership is not possible or feasible. Sizable reserves have been lost by companies refusing to own partial or small interests in prospects.

In foreign areas and in expensive tidelands (offshore) ventures, large major companies long ago realized that there is safety in numbers and that partners in a project keep losses down when expensive wells are drilled.

Besides bold thinking, optimism and enthusiasm have been required characteristics of the explorer since the discovery of oil at Titusville. Because domestic petroleum is becoming more difficult to find and pessimism has gripped many geologists in the industry, these virtues have real economic value for today's explorer.

Exploration for petroleum demands an optimism which must encompass everyone from the geological trainee to the highest responsible officer in the exploration organization. Selling a prospect certainly is as important as finding one. The geologist, therefore, must be completely sold on his ideas and must be enthusiastic about them. The geologist should remember that management generally takes a critical view of prospects purposely so that it may be shown why particular areas are of interest.

However, the geologist must be careful of being enthusiastic about and selling management on mediocre prospects which should be left alone.

Management, on the other hand, should be certain that the policies and philosophies of exploration which it directs do not discourage optimism and enthusiasm among its exploratory staff. Instead of ridiculing or reproving geological boldness in the ranks, management should compliment and encourage the free-thinking, enthusiastic, and intelligent geologist to present more and more bold ideas.

Repeatedly an enthusiastic, talented geologist wastes his efforts because his ideas are turned down by the management, supervisor, or client who is prejudiced against certain areas or ideas because of early unsuccessful experiences. Many oil and gas fields will be found on valid prospects which have been tested by one or more dry wildcats and have been abandoned as condemned areas.

The history of the oil business proves that the negative viewpoint is more detrimental to the exploratory effort than any other single factor.

A generally lazy attitude of exploratory thinking seems to have affected explorationists who prefer the easy-to-find, low-cost foreign reserves to domestic enigmas. It is true that in this country much of the easy-to-find oil and gas already has been found. There are many large occurrences of petroleum, however, which have not been discovered because they are contained in traps which are not obvious to the explorer. Finding them will require original, positive, and enthusiastic geological thinking.

To meet the challenges inherent in future successful exploration, geologists must revert to the best tool in our possession: sheer brain power. There is no substitute for sound, constructive, geologic thinking and hard work. We would be better off, more accurate and productive, if we did more field work instead of attempting to explore within the confinement of four walls and behind a big mahogany desk.

The time is here when ideas incubated in the minds of interested, well-trained, and devoted geologists must replace the easy systems. We must progress constantly in our geologic thinking so we can stay far ahead of today's needs.

The geologist must come out of hibernation and take a look at the industry as a whole. His knowledge must expand beyond his own science. He has to broaden this thinking into the area of economics more than ever before. The geologist must realize that the industry is changing fast in exploration, production, refining, marketing, and in just plain thinking. The sure methods used in the past may bring sorry results now.

The geologist must emerge as the undisputed leader of the exploration team and as the coordinator of all exploration activities. The sooner management accepts the geologist as the leader, the sooner the exploratory effort of the future will succeed. A new exploration era is upon us, and the geologist is needed to put into operation the necessary exploration concepts which will lead to the discovery of large fields and reserves by finding the more difficult and less obvious petroleum deposits in the more subtle traps.

To be the leader of the exploratory team, the geologist must look outward—not just straight ahead, but in all directions. He must be aware of what is happening in today's new technology, the ever-changing economic conditions, new political concepts, intense fuel competition, world petroleum outlook, and world markets—but above all, he must learn what significance these things have for his industry, his company, and his own future as an explorationist.

BIBLIOGRAPHY

Dillon, E. L., and L. R. Newfarmer, "Exploratory Drilling in 1964," American Association of Petroleum Geologists Bulletin, Vol. 49, No. 6 (1965), Figure 7, p. 652.

Frick, T. C., "Fossil Fuel Resources in the United States," Society of Petroleum Engineers, AIME, preprint, 1964, Charts 2, 3, p. 4.

Halbouty, M. T., "Maximum Brain Power: New Exploration Breakthrough," American Association of Petroleum Geologists Bulletin, Vol. 49, No. 10 (1965), pp. 1597-1600.

Hollister, J. C., "Tomorrow's Explorationist," World Petroleum, March, 1963, p. 35.

"Proved Reserves of Crude Oil, Natural Gas Liquids, and Natural Gas," joint annual release of American Gas Association-American Petroleum Institute, Vol. 18 (December, 1963), Table 5, pp. 14-15; Table 3, p. 25.

Struth, H. J., "Why Operators Are Looking for New Energy Source," World Oil, June, 1964, Table 3, p. 168.

"Trends in U. S. Petroleum Exploration and Development, 1952-1963," Independent Petroleum Association of America, Independent Petroleum Monthly, December, 1964, p. 12.

Optimism—Key To Future Exploration

"Only an optimist can succeed because he is
ready for—even expecting—the surprises that
comprise the oil industry."   October, 1965

Often predictions that this country, some state, or some geological province has passed its peak of oil and gas discoveries recall the words of the "experts" who told Pattillo Higgins and Captain Anthony Lucas no oil would be found in "the unconsolidated sands" of the Gulf Coast, or the great Standard Oil genius who told a prospector in Kansas that he would "drink all of the oil found west of the Mississippi." Even after the petroleum exploration sciences had begun to take definite form, no learned geologists or geophysicists were willing to go along with "Dad" Joiner's idea that oil could be found where he was drilling in East Texas.

The petroleum exploratory sciences have earned a humility they often fail to recognize. That is not to say that they have not made the greatest of all contributions to the finding of oil and gas. They have. But far too often untrained gamblers, adventurers, and promoters show them up when they become too smug. The day of such embarrassments might not be over, especially in the Gulf Coast.

Just after World War II, the recoverable reserves in the United States were 20 billion barrels. In spite of the gloom-spreaders of that day, we now have 35 billion barrels of reserves besides the 25 billion barrels of oil produced in this country in the meantime. In fact since 1946, we have discovered more oil than we had actually produced up to that year.

There have been no major discoveries in this country since 1953. Yet we have added consistently to total reserves while production from those reserves was increasing with each passing year.

What we have been doing is finding more and more small fields. This fact alone has discouraged exploration more than we realize. In the wake of one great discovery usually come others.

Of course there will be many great, new discoveries in the United States before another 10 years have passed. The oil is somewhere to be found. Market forecasts indicate tremendous growth in consumption and even the forecasters anticipate that most domestic consumption must come from domestic production.

General Ernest O. Thompson, senior member of the Texas Railroad Commission, has pointed out that the Russians have 500 submarines ready to cut this nation off from oil anywhere beyond the shores of this continent. That makes it increasingly important from a standpoint of national defense to continue to find more oil. The people of this country recognize that fact, and they will not long listen to those who crucify so vital an industry for the sake of either demagoguery or socialism. Even demagogues and socialists eventually respect a threat to our basic freedoms when it is clearly evident.

So, operators will keep bringing in the small prospects, letting them barely or almost pay for themselves while the search for the big fields and their profits continues.

What the oil industry must do, though, is find enough oil and produce it cheaply enough to meet the competition of ever-increasing low-cost imports. Some would depend on legislation or help from the government for this and thereby lose the independence and freedom essential for domestic suppliers to compete with foreign oil sources, no matter how widespread or prolific they might be.

The only way to ensure domestic production in a free industry is to eliminate the rivalry between the exploratory sciences and replace it with cooperation. There also must be more intelligent spacing of wells, even if this means eventual total unitization, which is far preferable to elimination.

Explorers are going to have to be more accurate in selecting prospects to drill. Some individuals or firms are doing far better than the nine-to-one average in wildcatting. Of course, as many are doing far worse. To improve the ratio will require better techniques and better tools. The tools are now under development. They came to our rescue in the past (largely from the efforts of the Schlumberger brothers), and many new tools will come now as other sciences and technologies progress also. Petroleum exploratory scientists must learn to use those tools, as well as learn to use more intelligently those now in existence.

Drilling and production are much improved because of new equipment that will reduce costs. A breakthrough from the old concepts of oil tools was made in the last three or four years and is just beginning to take hold. The cost of drilling wells should now go down instead of up, despite greater depths.

Oil companies and investors have begun to seek quality instead of quantity in exploration. This new attitude demands better petroleum exploration scientists. The unqualified will be left behind while the good men of science move with the times. The industry needs not more prospects but better prospects for oil exploration. This goal will require better thinking and cooperation between geology and geophysics. The cooperation is already developing, but it has not entirely eradicated the senseless, wastefully expensive rivalry between the egoists in either of the fields.

The rivalry between major companies that perpetuates secrecy in their so-called exploration research is just as damaging. That is like holding back a log on a well. It might get out late, but somehow it gets out. The only effect the majors create by withholding information is to retard progress instead of promoting it.

It is most revealing, yet extremely disturbing, that most of the research studies and work published on salt domes in the last decade have been done mostly, if not wholly, by independents. Some majors must be conducting research and studies on salt domes, but the geological profession as a whole seldom, if ever, receives the benefits and results of this work. The independents have not held back. There is no desire on their part to hoard the new-found data. They know that new facts and new ideas promote new thinking if everyone has the benefit of the data.

At least some of this secrecy practiced by the majors should be eliminated. A new openness would promote better cooperation not only between the major companies themselves, but also between the independents and majors which in turn would lead to greater efficiency and lower costs of exploration—and great savings in preventing duplication of manpower, brains, and time on similar projects by different companies.

The petroleum exploration scientist of the future must be a well-informed man in fields beyond his own. He will have to be part executive, at least. The better scientist will have also to be a good manager. He will have to know something about petroleum economics, politics, and even public relations, as well as taxes, regulations, and the effects of gasoline price wars.

Some companies have begun to eliminate geological and geophysical departments as such and combine them under a single head as exploration departments. The head of such department can be either a geologist or a geophysicist, but it is possible he might be neither if he is a good executive who understands the "why" of what he is doing instead of simply the "how." Unification of the petroleum exploration sciences is necessary because their goals are identical and their division is utterly ridiculous and disasterously expensive from a management standpoint.

Great oil reserves are not found overnight. It takes years to collect and correlate the information that leads to really good prospects. That is, unless those prospects are found accidentally, as many of them have been found. But the day of the accidental discovery is almost over. It costs too much to wildcat in the dark today. Investors are more cautious with the million dollars required for exploration today than they were with the few thousand or even few hundred dollars in years before.

The Gulf Coast province holds great potential. From the standpoint of geology, its prospects are brighter than they have ever been. Imports or the replacement of markets by gas or nuclear fuels are only temporary worries.

Forecasters have said consistently that within a few years demand for petroleum will double. Today as we recover from a rude push by a mild depression, it is difficult to realize the good opportunities the future holds. But prospects do exist and optimists will turn these prospects into producing fields.

Not a single pessimist has ever succeeded in the oil business, and only few realists have survived for long.

Only an optimist can succeed because he is ready for—even expecting—the surprises that comprise the oil industry. Any quest for the unknown has its risks and gambles and setbacks. Optimism is the key to success in the search for oil as in the search for any unknown, since only an optimist can see through the dry holes and meager producers to the inevitable big producers that have earned for the oil industry its status among world enterprises.

Heritage Of The Petroleum Geologist

*". . . The true explorationist must get out of
the office, into the field, and transverse the
plains and valleys, the woods and mountains
and seashores . . ."*   November 11, 1966

As geologists, our professional heritage has no rival in the spectrum of science. The story of this earth, the evolution and destruction of continents, the procession of life which, since the beginning of time, has passed over its surface—these and a thousand closely related themes which geology touches have attracted countless men to its realm and produced the most interesting record of human endeavor and achievement in history. In fact, the very essence of our geologic heritage is the history of its development. In no other discipline of natural science is history more important and necessary than in geology.

From the beginning, geology has grown and advanced on the balance-scale of probability rather than in the rigid, less flexible framework of mathematics; thus geology always has been an inexact, speculative science. Commonly suffering from speculation beyond the limits of observation and experience, geological hypotheses and theories have been promulgated and dissipated, but not without some benefit to each succeeding generation of earth scientists. It is precisely this inexactness of our science which makes it such a great challenge. It takes real courage to meet this challenge.

Thus, the philosophers of nature during the Middle Ages undoubtedly were influenced by the "Aristotelian elements" of fire, air, earth, and water. Werner and the Neptunists, and Hutton and the Plutonists, gained many of their ideas from the published works of Agricola on mineralogy. Each of these men had a heritage on which he progressed in his own pursuits. These men, their forebears, their colleagues, and their successors all contributed in some measure to our heritage.

Lesser known, yet very influential men, such as John Walker, a professor and a naturalist, established the existing foundation for seeking and probing into the earth. Walker's influence must have been most profound because among his students are the names of James Hutton, John Playfair, James Hall, and Robert Jameson—all of whom later became great geologists and scientists. In 1779, at the University of Edinburgh during a series of lectures on geology, John Walker told his students:

> The objects of nature themselves must be sedulously examined in their native state, the fields and the mountains must be traversed, the woods and the waters must be explored, the ocean must be fathomed, and the shore scrutinized by everyone that would become proficient in natural knowledge.

As geologists, by inclination and thorough training, we should be imbued with a love for exploration of the earth in order to solve its many mysteries. To be recipients of the geological heritage, we can do no better than follow the advice of Walker.

The heritage of the petroleum geologist, that avocational specialty which most of us have adopted as our professional domain, has a broad base, developed and matured by scientists and non-scientists alike. It is built on the labors and achievements of our predecessors, who, by meticulous observation of nature and careful deduction therefrom, laid the scientific foundation of the profession. It is also built, in no small measure, by the successes, failures, and experiences of many non-professionals—such as the non-scientists who probed beneath the surface of the earth in search of hydrocarbons.

Among our early petroleum-minded predecessors who contributed to our heritage is Sir William Edmond Logan, the Montreal geologist who was director of the Geological Survey of Canada for more than 25 years. In 1842, or 17 years before the birth of the oil industry, Sir William Logan studied the petroleum springs at Gaspé in his native Province of Quebec and stated that they were located and associated with anticlinal folding. Probably Logan's comments on these seeps were the first expression of the anticlinal theory with relation to oil accumulation.

Another early pioneer was Henry D. Rogers, once head of the Pennsylvania Geological Survey, who lectured at the University of Glasgow in 1860, shortly after the Drake well came in, on the distribution and probable origin of petroleum in western Pennsylvania.

About this time, discussions of the anticlinal theory as it relates to petroleum became one of the most controversial geological subjects. The participants included the versatile but sometimes erratic T. Sterry Hunt, Ebenezer Andrews, J. P. Lesley, and the brothers, William and Henry D. Rogers.

This select group might be called the instigators of interest in petroleum geology, although they did equally well in confusing the subject. As a result, it took another 20 years for Dr. Israel C. White to found the petroleum geology profession.

Lesley, for example, after his early pronouncement of the anticlinal theory in 1860, changed his mind and vigorously denounced the theory in a paper published in 1863. As recently as 1880, he referred to the theory as that ". . . now deservedly forgotten superstition." He was indirectly replying to the Austrian geologist, Hans Höfer, who was taking a new and serious affirmative interest in the theory.

Three years later, independently, John Galey, the wildcatter, and William A. Erseman, a Pennsylvania oil operator, called White's attention to their field and drilling observations that there definitely was some relation between existing gas fields and anticlines. White immediately became interested. He diligently studied the concept. He went into the field, studied the rocks, and finally concluded that the theory was sound. He believed in it so strongly that he took leave of his position as professor of geology at West Virginia University to form a company which drilled a well, using the anticlinal theory as its basis.

The result was the discovery and establishment of the first significant production in West Virginia. White then returned to the university a much wiser, wealthier, and more respected professor of geology.

Later White announced his rediscovery of the anticlinal theory, but in doing so he acknowledged freely the priority of others. This he made clear in his 1885 paper on "Geology of Natural Gas." That paper was followed by the publication in April, 1892, of another on the anticlinal theory in the Bulletin of The Geological Society of America. Undoubtedly these two papers by White gave petroleum geology its first status and the anticlinal theory, permanency.

Petroleum geology had numerous difficulties remaining a respected profession. Many errors and misconceptions by geologists, and condemnations by geologists of areas which turned out to be productive, caused the oil industry to be not only reluctant but also most hesitant to recognize the profession.

Although the founders of our branch of geology were beset by great problems, they were true investigators and in a scientific manner tried to form concepts on a subject which was new to them. They stuck their necks out, and some were "chopped off." However, through the efforts of these stubborn pioneers, the fundamental pieces of petroleum geology gradually were put into proper place. The fact that these early petroleum geologists were, at times, wrong did not discourage their search for the truth.

Through their discoveries, their mistakes, their confusions, and their solutions, we have had given to us the total results of their efforts; *this* is our heritage. It consists of geologic truths and carries no obligation—except that we carry on from where our predecessors left off. Thus, this heritage must be a continuum, based on more study, exploration, curiosity, failure, success, and total effort so that we, in turn, may hand down to our geological successors a heritage greater than that which we received. We must not break the continuum. This is our responsibility to geologists of the future and to the science of geology, and to petroleum geology in particular.

The heritage of geological fundamentals that was handed down to us was accompanied by another kind of inheritance—the application of common sense, courage, stubbornness, and intestinal fortitude in the search for oil—from the non-professional, the wildcatter.

Such men include Edwin L. Drake, the railroad conductor, and his associates who explored, experimented with, and gave birth to the petroleum industry in 1859. Another is John Galey, an adventurer in the oil fields, who was bold enough to suggest and promote in 1883 a practical application of the anticlinal theory when the geologists chose to criticize and write papers about it.

Still another is a woodsman named Pattillo Higgins who learned to know and love what he called the "signs of nature," and thereby led Captain Anthony Lucas, a marine engineer, to the 1901 discovery of the gusher at Spindletop that brought forth the liquid fuel age.

To these I would add the name of Marrs McLean, a man educated as a lawyer, who made a living selling advertising and then promoting oil leases until he conceived the idea in 1923 that oil could be found on the flanks of salt domes. His concept was rejected by the most renowned petroleum geologists of his day. Nevertheless, McLean's theory became completely accepted by our profession in 1926 when my first employer, Miles Frank Yount, bought the idea and leases from McLean and was rewarded with a new great discovery at Spindletop—the opening of the vast reserves on the flanks of this historic salt dome.

Another adventurer had an idea based on an unsound theory by a self-styled geologist, an idea which brought forth the greatest oil discovery in the history of the North American continent, in Rusk County, Texas, in 1930. His name was Columbus Marion Joiner. He was a 70-year-old promoter whom everyone called "Dad." He accepted the word of Dr. A. D. Lloyd—a man who was trained as a veterinarian but who delved into geology as a hobby—that oil was to be found in East Texas. Almost every geologist and geophysicist of that period regarded the area as worthless and condemned it as an economic graveyard that would be studded with dry holes. In fact, by the time Joiner and Lloyd arrived on the scene, nothing but dry holes dotted the sandhills of East Texas.

Nevertheless, Lloyd wrote Joiner a letter telling him almost exactly the depth at which he would strike oil. He also told him why. We know now that scientifically his reasoning was wrong, but we also know that what Lloyd and Joiner combined to accomplish led our profession to a greater recognition of the vast potential of the stratigraphic trap.

The books are full of examples of men finding oil by the "seat of their pants" in areas where geologists feared to tread. The reason for this fear is that geologists had forgotten—or never learned—the words of John Walker. They failed to examine on the ground "the objects of nature"; they failed to traverse "the fields and the mountains"; they did not explore "the woods and the waters"; above all, they failed to examine the *rocks*.

These daring wildcatters gave petroleum geology new concepts, new ideas, and different viewpoints; they gave greater strength to the profession which they generally regarded as inadequate and inefficient. Their accomplishments further prove that scientists are helped sometimes by the bold, imaginative, creative thinking and exploration of those who are not formally educated or even trained in the scientific method.

Of course, it is a compliment to our profession that these suddenly discovered ideas were seized by our predecessors, placed in the proper frame of nature's jigsaw puzzle, and put to use to find many times more hydrocarbons.

Scientists whom many of us have known or know now—E. T. Dumble, J. A. Taff, Charles N. Gould, Charles Eckes, W. A. J. M. van der Gracht, W. E. Wrather, E. DeGolyer, Alexander Deussen, Paul Weaver, Ben Belt, A. I. Levorsen, Wallace Pratt, Frederic Lahee, Frank Morgan, Lewis G. Weeks, Frank Clark, Sam Grinsfelder, Ira Cram, and a host of others—have added to the heritage handed them and have brought us to the point where we now are.

To this list one might add the names of better and lesser known men of geology who have contributed their ideas and concepts, large and small, important and less consequential, to the reservoir of knowledge we now have available in the field of earth science as it applies to petroleum. We might also add the names of numerous non-scientists, in addition to Drake, Galey, Higgins, Lucas, McLean, Yount, and Joiner, whose natural instincts or good fortune have led them to geological achievements which have benefitted all of us and all of mankind.

Each of us also might recall some men who have stifled brilliant ideas with the overbearing arrogance born of ignorance because it is from men such as these we learn that all is not as it seems in this inexact science and that without open minds, we commonly veer from the truth.

Thus this heritage of the petroleum geologist is based on the works of many men, those who have been right and those who, from time to time, have been dramatically wrong.

This heritage serves as the framework and guidepost to our knowledge of petroleum geology. We must build on it and hand down to the next generation a stronger and broader heritage of knowledge. We must boldly and creatively seek new knowledge, through ingenuity, and, although beset with failures and wrong turns, we must ferret out this new knowledge and add it to our heritage.

What about our shortcomings as petroleum geologists? The truth is that, as a whole, we have failed many times to employ our science properly. We have depended too much on other disciplines to guide us and have not practiced our science as it should be practiced—in fact, *we have lost, in some measure, direct contact with the earth.* By losing this contact, we have lost our curiosity for its mysteries and, in turn, we are becoming less creative and less courageous.

We have subjected ourselves to routine thinking, without probing and seeking to understand better the meaning of our science. We have become afraid to experiment mentally with an unusual concept or idea. Ironically, those who employ or use our knowledge do not expect our bold and creative ideas always to be right. A major company official said to me not long ago, "Show me a geologist or geophysicist who is afraid to make a recommendation for fear of his making an error in judgment, and I will show you a man who is not only stealing my company's money and time but one who is hardly worth being called a scientist."

What this executive was saying is that such fear stifles boldness in the explorationist. In short, this executive was complaining that some geologists and geophysicists are not willing to take a chance—and are not willing to express an unusual exploration idea or concept for fear of losing their jobs. As a result, creativity and boldness in the exploratory effort are discouraged by this fear of failure, and nothing is contributed to exploratory thinking; instead, mediocrity, "going along with the boys," and implied assent by silence are the credos of many who are engaged in petroleum exploration.

What John Walker said in 1779 is as applicable today as ever. The true explorationist *must* get out of the office; go into the field, the plains, and valleys; traverse the woods, the mountains, and the seashores. He *must* look hard at the rocks and at any other "signs of nature" he can find.

Pattillo Higgins observed the "signs of nature" and led all men to a new age of progress—yet he was not a geologist. He went to the top of a little rise in a flat prairie and observed that there was a sandy loam where clay was supposed to exist, a peculiar substance in the soil which had a "waxy" feel and which later was named "paraffin dirt" by geologists. He also tasted brackish water in wells of fresh water. These "signs of nature" enabled him to proclaim openly that he could drill wells on that spot which would produce tens of thousands of barrels of oil daily. He was condemned by experts, including geologists, and even scorned by his neighbors. But his faith in what he believed led to one of the world's most important mineral discoveries of all time.

Ben Belt, the scientist, crossed and criss-crossed the arid land of West Texas, facing hired gunmen guarding "posted" signs or ranchers with shotguns, to seek out rocks that would tell him what he wanted to know. When he had finished his study of the rocks and plotted his data on his maps, he developed an idea that convinced his company to purchase hundreds of thousands of acres of land in the Permian basin. On this land production was found which helped make the name of Gulf one of the greatest in our industry's history.

Charles Gould, in addition to his many other achievements, went into the field in the Texas Panhandle and came back with a geologic report to his employers recommending the drilling of a well. This well led to the discovery of the vast Panhandle gas reserves.

The prolific Yates oil field—one of the richest in the nation —came roaring in in 1926 west of the Pecos River in Texas. Here was an area where wildcatters—and geologists—had said that "there is no oil." However, Frank Rinker Clark thought otherwise. Even in the early 1920's, petroleum geologists were still the object of scorn, and a well witcher who located drilling sites with a sprig cut from a peach tree was considered to be more scientific and much smarter than a college upstart like Clark who hammered on rocks trying to find the right spot to drill for oil.

Clark's surface studies convinced him that the area was a favorable one for the accumulation of petroleum. His recommendation to the Ohio Oil Company—now Marathon Oil Company— resulted in the discovery of this giant field. Contrary to the opinion of the best minds of that day, Clark stuck his neck out, supported his own convictions, and proved that oil could be found west of the Pecos River.

In each case, Higgins—the woodsman—and Belt, Gould, and Clark—the geologists—used their God-given right to think boldly —to think contrary to everyday, run-of-the-mill mediocre reasoning. They observed the earth; they understood what they observed; and they brought forth new discoveries, not only in energy but also in our science. By so doing, their names went down in history and up in the respect of their fellow men.

Today, the world consumes oil at a rate of approximately 30 million barrels a day. Economists now say the 60-million-barrel day is now almost upon us. During the next 10 years, our industry will be required to find 55 billion barrels of oil and 300 trillion cubic feet of gas in the United States simply to maintain an adequate reserve position with the increased demand.

This will require us both to utilize all our heritage and to add much more to it; if we do not, we shall have considerable difficulty in meeting this tremendous challenge of the near future. Unless we think as creative scientists—without fear of honest mistakes—and by so doing create new concepts, many of us will live to see petroleum geology become as unacceptable as it was in its founding years.

The one factor which the explorer must have to succeed is the strength of his convictions.

Some of us can recall the time when a man first became a true, well-rounded geologist and later specialized to become a petroleum geologist. When full courses in petroleum geology were established, many students bypassed the path of a well-rounded geologist; instead they took the short route to a quick degree—in petroleum geology.

Today matters are even worse. Petroleum geology specialization is reaching a ridiculous extreme in some university departments with the result that many petroleum geologists are completely out of touch with the broad spectrum of geology, *including* the whole spectrum of petroleum geology.

The time has come for us to return to the practice of being, first of all, true, well-rounded geologists. Today it is imperative that we know all aspects of our science. We must return to the role of the flexible, fully informed geologist who can answer any call, anywhere, at any time, for whatever reason. In my opinion, this is precisely what Walker meant when he lectured his students nearly two centuries ago. *We must get back to the earth* if we are to succeed in our objective of finding petroleum for the future.

The purpose of becoming well-rounded geologists is not to prepare ourselves for such disasters as those which happened in the late 1950's and early 1960's when oil companies, large and small, started firing or laying off geologists or transferring them to some other work, or retiring them years ahead of time. The real purpose is to broaden our outlook and provide us with the opportunity to develop ideas outside our own limited spheres of activity. The value of a good petroleum geologist will rise in direct proportion to his ability to see, to comprehend, and to be a part of the whole landscape of geology.

I believe that a good geologist should break out of his geological shell and observe what is going on in the world of industry, economics, politics, and civic affairs. He should not permit himself to remain isolated—an island unto himself. He will have to meet and know the people with whom he lives and works. By doing so, he will be able to broaden his thinking and his understanding of all that exists in the world around him. He will then be able to absorb valuable ideas, to revitalize his own processes of thought, to gain courage to express himself, and to be able to withstand any crisis.

He should know his community, work with it to help build a hospital or a museum, serve on a school board or a symphony orchestra committee, or lead a fund drive, as well as learn something about the other segments of his own industry.

While improving his position economically and socially, however, let the petroleum geologist not lose sight of the geological heritage which was his for the taking and which prepared him in the fundamentals of his profession. Let him realize that he does, after all, owe something for having it. Let him learn to be a good steward, not to hide his knowledge, but to expose it and let it grow so that the heritage he leaves to his successors may be even finer than that which he received. This is his duty.

BIBLIOGRAPHY

American Petroleum Institute, "History of Petroleum Engineering," (Dallas: API Division of Production, 1961), 1241 p.

"Mannington Oil Field and the History of Its Development," Geological Society of America Bulletin, Vol. 3, No. 4 (1892), pp. 187-216.

Walker, John, "Lectures on Geology," Harold W. Scott, ed., (University of Chicago Press, 1966), 280 p.

White, I. C., "Geology of Natural Gas," Science, Vol. 5 (June 26, 1885), pp. 521-522.

Creativity In Geology

"The geologist will develop new ideas. The new ideas will develop new prospects. This kind of leadership will bring about more wildcat drilling than ever before—provided the incentives follow."   February 13, 1967

Our domestic petroleum exploratory effort has been declining steadily since 1958. Consequently, our reserves have been declining, and for the past four years, we have found less reserves than we consumed in this country.

This sad state of affairs has not been brought on by lack of undiscovered oil in the ground. It is the result of a drastic decline in the industry's effort to locate the existing undiscovered oil in the United States.

The petroleum industry has become great because of its past successful exploratory efforts. These efforts, always beset with great risks, were carried on because the incentives to find oil and gas overshadowed the risks.

In recent years, government regulations and price inadequacies have served to reduce incentives while risks inherent in exploration have continuously increased. In addition, obvious structures simply do not exist anymore. Drilling depths and costs are greater. The domestic exploratory effort in 1967 was approximately 35 per cent below the 1956 rate. The drilling decline, which recently reached a 23-year low, sinks each month.

Of all activities engaged in by the petroleum industry, the exploration for new reserves of oil and gas is the most essential to its welfare and future. The petroleum and associated industries would disappear if new discoveries of oil and gas reserves did not keep pace with the expanding consumption of petroleum. Yet, reserve discoveries in the United States are not keeping that pace.

Were it not for discoveries in the tidelands and offshore areas, we would be dependent right now on foreign sources for our petroleum needs. Even with tideland and offshore exploration, this country is barely holding its own in the discovery of new oil and gas reserves. This nation could be facing a very serious petroleum crisis within as little as 10 years.

What amazes me is the apathy with which some industry leaders and the public regard this situation.

The more than 32 billion barrels of crude oil reserves in this nation are "piddling" compared to those in foreign lands. For example, in Kuwait, just slightly larger than the state of Rhode Island, one field has more oil reserves than those known to exist in the entire United States.

Whether the people of this nation realize it or not, in the next 10 years our industry will be required to find in this country 55 billion barrels of oil and 300 trillion cubic feet of gas just to maintain an adequate reserve position against increases in demand. Over the past 10 years, our discoveries have averaged about three billion barrels of oil and 12 trillion cubic feet of gas annually, a discovery rate which is much below minimum requirements for the future. And were it not for recent offshore discoveries, the nation's reserves would be at a more critical level. So it is imperative that we double our oil discoveries and triple our gas discoveries.

Under existing high costs and risks and low prices for oil and gas, meeting the necessary exploration goals for the next 10 years is a difficult objective. If we are to meet the requirements for only the next 10 years, we will have to drill in this country alone 25,000 wildcats, that is 25,000 meritorious drilling prospects, instead of the meager 8,000 now being drilled.

We cannot possibly find these prospects and the required new reserves by employing present exploration philosophy and methods. New exploration ideas are needed. Ideas stimulate bolder exploration. The more unusual the concept, the greater the possibilities for larger discoveries. The industry is on the threshold of a new era of exploration. The geologist must be the accepted leader in establishing the policies for our future exploration activities.

The geologist will develop the new ideas. The new ideas will develop new prospects. This kind of leadership will bring about more wildcat drilling than ever before—provided the incentives follow.

New ideas and new incentives are the two ingredients for successful exploration in the future. The incentives involve less, and more intelligent, government control and more realistic prices for petroleum products. The new exploration ideas and concepts involve the nation's geologists.

Presently, the odds against successful wildcatting for petroleum are staggering. The 8 to 1, 10 to 1, and 12 to 1 success ratios have been accepted by the public and even by the un-informed in the industry as facts. These odds are now but a day-dreamer's hope.

The real odds of finding a profitable field of any consequence are one out of 56 wildcats.

An operator cannot depend on "lady luck" to find his oil anymore. Every means must be employed to reduce the odds and risks inherent in petroleum exploration. This calls for con-centrated study of all available information on a more coordinated and knowledgeable basis.

Management has pitted the geologist and the geophysicist against each other too long. Neither the geologist nor the geo-physicist should permit this to continue. They should try to con-vince management either to coordinate their efforts or to suffer the consequences of finding less and less reserves. The geologist and geophysicist can and must work together; management should not only encourage but should force this alliance.

When geologists first began to search for oil and gas, they had little difficulty in locating places to drill. Anticlines, major fault systems, and even buried salt domes were easy to work out and map because of the many outcrops and surface indications which existed.

But, gradually what could be seen on the surface became less and less obvious, and the geologist had a hard time finding anything to recommend for drilling.

Then, when a real breakthrough was needed, geophysics ap-peared. Geophysics could work below the surface, beyond the limit of the geologist, and the industry eagerly welcomed this new ex-ploration method.

The geologist has been playing a secondary role for a long time, in fact, because geophysics has been doing the thinking for him.

Now, the cycle has turned a complete revolution. The geo-physicists cannot find the structural traps any more. At least, geophysical structural anomalies are getting harder and harder to find. The geophysicist—like the geologist before him—has thor-oughly combed the domestic petroleum provinces, and very little remains to be found by the methods now in use.

The big domestic reserves of the future lie in the less obvious traps such as stratigraphic, which geophysics so far cannot iden-tify. Finding these elusive traps will require highly imaginative thinking combined with every applicable scientific discipline under the direct supervision of the geologist.

The geophysicists' black electronic boxes, computers, and new chart mechanisms are tremendous aids in developing some of the scientific facts needed for finding these subtle traps. But these instruments should be a supplement to geological thinking and certainly not supplant our thinking, as was permitted for the past three decades.

This is not a condemnation of geologists or geophysicists, but of management for not coordinating their separate skills early and waiting until famine is upon the industry to realize the need.

The successful oil finder of the future will be the geologist who thinks and one who realizes that he must use his imagination and the very best ideas and tools from others to get optimum value from the available knowledge. This means coordinating the talents of geophysicists, paleontologists, sedimentologists, stratigraphers, mineralogists, and other geo-scientists.

With this coordination, we will be finding oil and gas as true scientists—as pure, thoroughly trained, well-rounded geologists and not as unilateral specialists limited in scope, in knowledge, and in thinking power.

To be pure scientists, we must rely on the fundamentals requisite for sound thinking which can be summed up in one word—ingenuity. The synonyms of ingenuity would cover several pages. A few are inventive talent, keen perception, skill, resourcefulness, readiness, acuteness, intelligence, inspiration, cleverness, proficiency, competence, expertness, dexterity, efficiency, mastery, excellence, and genius.

These various meanings are combined into still one other word —creativity.

The one difference between a masterpiece and a good painting, in spite of the fact that two artists have the same background and technique, is ingenious creativity. Both artists have created, but the masterpiece has something extra, a little more effort and a sense of perception. The master artist has a feeling for the subject that the other does not have. In other words, one is more ingenious than the other.

Basically, geology is an inexact science. That is why a good exploration geologist has to be an artist, working with knowns and unknowns, mixing together ideas and suppositions and facts. And this is why geology is so fascinating; the geologist works with nature's mysteries, trying to relate the past to the present.

The geologist's possibilities for creativity in ideas are limitless. Bound by no exact numbers or equations, he is in a position, like the artist, to resolve ideas into practical masterpieces through unorthodox thinking and the unusual approach to a problem. When tied to common sense and reasoning, this king of creativity is the key to nature's secret hiding places for petroleum, to the discoveries of the nation's giant oil and gas reserves.

The geologist will be required to form new concepts relating to the art of finding oil, whether it be for new reserves in old, explored provinces or in basins or areas which are unexplored or inadequately explored. His geological deductions will have to be daring and imaginative, yet attuned to fundamentals of geology and economics.

In recent years, too many geophysicists have devoted the major portion of their time to improving techniques of display, while too many geologists have devoted the major portion of their time to correlating logs and mechanically contouring smaller and smaller "footballs."

Neither has made the effort to learn of their respective limitations.

After all, the geophysicist is a specialized earth scientist who makes geological interpretations from geophysical data.

As an explorationist, he has a broader base in the application of his science than a geologist who has had no experience in geophysics.

Nevertheless, if a geophysicist is not fundamentally a geologist by training, education, or in the application of his science, he is either a technician or an engineer.

The geophysicist and the geologist each represent half of the meaning of "petroleum explorationist." The exploration effort would be materially upgraded if both groups realized what their limitations are and each attempted to fill the gaps with geological and geophysical ideas and concepts that would help both professions.

Bold, coordinated thinking associated with courage, conviction, and determination will sell new ideas to a management which really wants to be shown.

The large, obvious surface and subsurface structures are known and probably have been tested. Also, many sedimentary relationships favorable to the entrapment of petroleum in stratigraphic traps occur in basins throughout the country. Some of these traps contain large amounts of petroleum that already have been found.

Geologists know that some stratigraphic traps do not contain hydrocarbons. But they cannot get away from the feeling that great quantities of undiscovered petroleum occur in strat traps throughout the country, just waiting to be found. Almost every geologist has a pet area which is a strat prospect but has done nothing about it because his company or his client wants only a structure to drill.

The geologist will have to convince management that large fields are to be found in the subtly hidden traps which defy the "black electronic boxes."

The finding of accumulation in such traps requires that a geologist be a bold, creative artist if it is to be found on purpose. Anyone could find oil accidentally by drilling in the right place for no particular reason, but just try to sell that haphazard method to management!

When an area of unusual interest is found through imaginative thinking, a geologist's job is only half done. The job will be completed when he convinces management or his client to initiate drilling.

Man forever is prone to follow precedent, however antiquated; so exploration in a province always begins with probes of structural anomalies and continues enthusiastically as long as the effort to evaluate geologic structures is rewarding. The influence of the fundamental anticlinal theory of accumulation still prevails, even in areas where the search for stratigraphic accumulations might be more successful than the drilling of giant structures.

An example of this influence is the promising Cook Inlet Basin of south-central Alaska. Here, there have been 5 major oil discoveries and 11 gas discoveries on 16 separate anticlines, but 15 barren anticlines were drilled in the basin during the same exploratory period. The barren structures all have demonstrable closure but were formed after hydrocarbon migration had taken place.

Based on the pattern of exploration in this area, it is reasonable to predict that all known anticlines probably will be tested before a single stratigraphic prospect is deliberately drilled. Despite this, sufficient geologic information indicates that large stratigraphic accumulations are highly probable in the Cook Inlet Basin.

Fortunately, the guidelines which govern exploration thinking and procedures more often than not have unanticipated results. Were this not true, many of the world's great stratigraphic fields would not have been discovered.

Admittedly, it is more difficult to sell management on the merits of drilling a 100-per-cent stratigraphic prospect than to sell them on a mediocre structural prospect; yet, paradoxically, we, as scientists, recognize that hydrocarbons commonly are indigenous to the sediments in which accumulation occurs and that many of the world's oil and gas fields are, in part at least, stratigraphically controlled.

Unlike discoveries on known anticlines, diapirs, or fault-controlled structures, most of the stratigraphic trap fields were discovered either by accident or by geologic reasoning that turned out to be incorrect.

The legendary oil pioneer, Columbus M. "Dad" Joiner, at 70 years old, promoted the drilling of a test well on what he called the Overton Anticline, a nondescript topographic high which had no subsurface expression whatsoever and which was created in the mind of Joiner, who can only be termed a promoter. Regardless of Joiner's geologic reasoning, he discovered the East Texas field, the largest oil field in the Western Hemisphere.

Most of the major (50 million barrels and greater) fields discovered within the onshore confines of the continental United States during the past decade are stratigraphic or structural stratigraphic accumulations where stratigraphic variation is the dominant factor causing entrapment.

The search for purely stratigraphic traps usually does not begin until late in the exploration history of a basin, after a great amount of geological and geophysical information has been collected and assimilated.

However, creative, bold thinking by geologists, combined with an aggressive search for sedimentary traps, will do much to get wells budgeted for stratigraphic exploration much earlier in the development history of a basin than in the past.

Management, whether independent or major, must be receptive to and encourage new exploration ideas. Management should realize that only creativity and boldness, a high degree of imaginative deduction, and an unyielding courage of conviction on the part of the explorationist can find the big, unobtrusive fields in the future; therefore, management should support the exploration team in the application of new approaches to the exploratory effort.

Management should be certain that the programs and theories of exploration which it directs do not discourage creativity in ideas or dampen the willingness of an explorer to promote a radical idea for fear of being fired or ridiculed.

Management must instill confidence in the geophysicist and the geologist that they can find these strat accumulations by purposely seeking them as true scientists.

A pioneer of modern petroleum geology, Wallace Pratt, said that "oil fields are found in minds of men."

So, to find our needed future domestic reserves, the explorer will have to convince himself first and then the wildcatter that a new, different exploration approach is the key to the discovery of the vast accumulations of oil and gas within our reach.

Oil and gas in the future will be found by well-rounded exploration teams composed of geologists, geophysicists, paleontologists, petroleum engineers, chemists, scouts, and landmen. They will use every known tool whether it be surface or subsurface mapping, computers, electronic boxes, field work, the laboratory, or whatever else is necessary and available.

Such teams will be led by the most enlightened, intelligent, and resourceful members. The thinking of the leader must be sound, but daring. He must be creative in the fullest meaning of the word. He cannot simply be a painter. He must be an accomplished artist. His work cannot be an exercise in mediocrity. It must be a masterpiece.

Needed—A Greater Teamwork

". . . These men who worked in the field with countless improvisions and inventions developed the know-how recognized throughout the world as distinctly American."   October 3, 1967

There is no question that greater teamwork among the disciplines of geology, geophysics, and petroleum engineering is needed today more than ever before. During the so-called golden years of the industry, little attention was paid to combining the resources of these three powerful technical segments.

In order to understand what is needed today and what will be required in the future from these three disciplines, it is important to reflect on the status of world petroleum production on January 1, 1901. The world's annual production was about 138 million barrels. Russia was the leading oil-producing nation with 68 million barrels. Of the 58 million barrels produced in the United States, 92 per cent, or 53 million barrels, was from the so-called oil region of Ohio, West Virginia, Pennsylvania, Indiana, and New York. Four million barrels, or 6 per cent, were from California, and the remaining one million barrels, or 2 per cent, were produced from the Corsicana field in Texas.

The average production for the so-called large producers in the United States was 75 barrels per day. The entire world production was consumed in lubrication and illumination. Civilization was still in the lubrication age. There was not enough petroleum produced to justify its use as a liquid fuel. But Spindletop changed all that.

On January 10, 1901, in the dawn of a new century, the Spindletop discovery fired the imagination of the entire world. The potential from the discovery well, if estimated on a per-year basis, was more than the combined production of the entire world. Spindletop brought on the liquid fuel age and was the beginning not only of the world's industrial revolution, but also, certainly, of the oil industry.

Prior to the Spindletop discovery and for a decade after, the status of the petroleum geologist was that of a college professor who was retained occasionally by oil companies to do consulting work. On the other hand, the early engineer was merely a roughneck or a roustabout or a driller who had no formal engineering education. But these men who did the work in the field with countless improvisions and inventions brought about the know-how that is recognized throughout the world as distinctly American.

From 1917 to 1930, when the rate of discovery of new reserves was slow, full field geological crews hunted for surface indications and made whatever recommendations were appropriate for the drilling of wildcat wells—which were few.

At this time, geophysics entered petroleum exploration. The impact was terrific. Here was an exploration method that revolutionized the very word "exploration." The other methods of looking for structures to drill were pushed to a background position. The geologist lost prestige, and the geophysicist gained it. Management backed the geophysicist because of his tremendous exploration success. The hiatus between the geologist and the geophysicist was so profound that management foolishly went so far as to put the departments into separate buildings and, in some cases, in separate cities. For more than three decades, the geophysicist and the geologist never got together. We now know that this was a great waste of brain power and that it greatly hampered exploration efforts.

Since 1957, there has been a continuous slowdown in the number of discoveries made by geophysicists. Management has only recently realized that the geologist and the geophysicist must work together, and in most major companies, a fervent attempt has been made to bring this about.

However, management still is making a mistake in that there has been very little coordinating, if any, of the efforts of explorationists and petroleum engineers.

In order for the United States to maintain an adequate reserve position during only the next 10 years, we must find a minimum of 55 billion barrels of oil and 300 trillion cubic feet of gas, based on the expected increase in annual demand.

If these demands are to be met, we should be drilling a minimum of 20,000 exploratory wells and 40,000 development wells annually. In fact, the ratio would be better if we drilled 35,000 development and 25,000 exploratory wells each year.

How can the required new reserves be found? We must concentrate upon new geological, geophysical, and engineering thinking. We cannot and *must not* stay in a rut. As scientists and technicians, we are inclined to accept precedence too readily, and many of us use it as a means of dodging progressive thinking. This has been true throughout the history of the oil industry, but for the future we must be progressive in our geological, geophysical, and engineering thinking.

In their search for new fields, geologists are investigating (1) new trends that become available for exploration as their potential is recognized, or as the industry is able to drill to greater depths and extend the downdip limits of formations with proven productive capabilities; (2) deep-seated structures whose existence is not reflected in shallow horizons; (3) remnant accumulations of oil and gas associated with earlier movements of known structures; (4) stratigraphic and paleogeomorphic traps; and (5) extensions to old fields. They also are re-evaluating studies of old trends.

Geologists should concentrate their exploration efforts by looking at certain new provinces:

1. Revitalizing old areas, such as Ohio, Pennsylvania, New York, and East Texas;

2. Exploring new areas, such as offshore Oregon and Washington and the offshore areas of the eastern seaboard;

3. Considering the unexplored areas of Kentucky and North and South Carolina, and the unexplored basins of Arizona, Nevada, and Idaho;

4. Entertaining new concepts concerning stratigraphic traps, shale-oil development, thermal exploitation, and deep-seated structures; and

5. Using photogeology and geophysics.

Above all, the geologist must be *bold*—willing to take the risk in exploration or in the use of a tool. The electric log is possibly the greatest invention in the oil industry, and it should provide us the means of delineating our areas of interest within what we now consider small limits. We are reluctant to drill a wildcat well between two dry holes that are only a mile or so apart, especially if no structure or relief of any kind is apparent. But the pinchout of a reservoir between the dry holes, a change in sedimentation and a permeability barrier, or lateral dips from the strike as revealed by a geophysical appraisal could result in an elongated, prolific major field between two dry holes. Certainly drilling here would be bold. But we must think boldly and not be afraid of taking risks.

Geophysicists are applying their greatest efforts to improving the signal-to-noise ratio through application of repetitive recording or "stacking" techniques, in which a sequence or series of recordings is added together. This effort has been going on for about five years and apparently has caught on in the last three years. These techniques are employed to eliminate random noise (such as from wind, traffic, etc.) and to give more resolution to true reflection signals.

Mass processing of data by means of the digital computer has been applied vigorously by the geophysicist.

Unless we geologists and petroleum engineers recognize the potentials of this digital technology to enhance our exploration efforts, we are in danger of relinquishing a large area of our responsibility by default to the other discipline, geophysics.

Paul Farren states that

> the objective of the geophysicist is beautifully simple: his every effort in applying the most complex geophysical technology of the present and the future is to see the *geology* a little clearer.

Despite what he calls himself, and the tools he uses, he is an active exploration geologist. The best geologists of the future will be the best geophysicists. The best geophysicists of the future will be the best geologists.[1]

It is appropriate to paraphrase Farren's statement by saying that the best explorationists of the future will be the ones most knowledgeable in the three disciplines of geology, geophysics, and petroleum engineering.

Petroleum engineers are applying efficiency and economy in their continuing efforts to increase reservoir yield by (1) developing, improving, and applying new techniques of drilling, completing, and producing; (2) perfecting new and improved methods of stimulation; and (3) developing better techniques of secondary recovery and making more universal application of these techniques to producing areas.

A coordinated effort between the engineer and the explorationist is a must. There is an area of joint responsibility among geologists, geophysicists, and petroleum engineers that up to this point in the industry's history has been neglected. Fifteen years ago, members of the industry recognized a need for better coordination between geologists and geophysicists. Although it took approximately 12 years for this coordination to become effective, most exploration efforts today integrate the unique contributions of both the geologist and the geophysicist. However, there still are several major companies that have not yet brought the geologist and geophysicist together. They are paying dearly for it because they have the lowest discovery ratio in the industry.

To meet the challenge of the future, every effort must be made to utilize the combined efforts of geologists, geophysicists, and petroleum engineers.

Geologists and petroleum engineers have a great opportunity to find new reserves by working together in areas above, below, and around producing reservoirs.

Traditionally, the geologist and the geophysicist seek and find, and the petroleum engineer develops and produces. Once a discovery is made, the geologist and geophysicist tend to lose interest and to yield responsibility for the area to the petroleum engineer, who has a development geologist working with him. Once the engineer assumes responsibility, he is inclined to devote his interest only to development of the initial reservoir or reservoirs found in the discovery well. Although development planning and drilling are rightfully under the jurisdiction of the petroleum engineer, it does not follow that the geologist has no responsibility to continue to explore the area. Nor does it mean that the engineer has no obligation to look for and identify data that may have exploratory significance.

In sharing this joint responsibility, both geologists and petroleum engineers should be certain that the transition from wildcat prospect to producing field is accomplished with a full disclosure of all information, including revised geophysical interpretations. Too often petroleum engineers are forced to take over a producing area in its early stages of development with little more than a vague description of the general nature of the local geology. The geologists have an initial responsibility to provide the engineers with complete information on all the geological complexities that are known or expected.

And geologists, geophysicists, and petroleum engineers should evaluate the exploratory potential of all new data obtained from development drilling.

Following are some areas that should be investigated jointly:

1. All electric logs should be studied for unexpected structural relationships, faults, isopach thinning or thickening, and lithological changes indicating possible new reservoirs.

2. Differences or changes in bottom-hole pressure, gas-oil ratio, gravity, fluid contacts, and fluid analyses should be observed and explained.

3. Changes in the decline rates of bottom-hole and flowing pressures should be recorded and explained.

4. The significance of reservoir limit determinations to help locate fault traces and to establish possible reservoir pinchouts should be evaluated.

5. The areal extent of production indicated from subsurface control should be compared with the areal extent indicated from material balance determinations.

At one time or another, every petroleum engineer or geologist has acknowledged the value to exploration of incorporating this type of information in geological interpretations, but in actual practice little progress has been made in the use and implementation of such data. If future demands are to be met, the exploration team must make full use of all engineering data.

To make this joint effort a success, geologists must realize that engineering data are as valid an exploratory tool as the electric log or the geophysical device. Geologists should strive to obtain and incorporate all engineering information in geological interpretations. At the same time, petroleum engineers must realize that their data have potential exploratory value; must develop an aggressive, inquisitive attitude; and must promptly advise geologists of all unusual and significant data they uncover. The exercise of this responsibility on the part of geologists and engineers is a professional duty and not one that can be or should be officially delegated by management. However, management should force such coordination if necessary.

Geologists, geophysicists, and petroleum engineers should work together in planning long-range exploration programs. This is particularly true in the Gulf Coast region where productive trends coincide with geological trends. Joint studies of fields typical of the various producing trends should identify those whose economic and engineering performance shows the highest rate of return per dollar invested. Then, during a time when limited exploration money is available, it can be spent exploring those geological trends whose fields have demonstrated the highest profitability.

All drilling should be jointly planned and evaluated. Too many engineers think that the best well is the one that has been drilled and plugged at the least expense. Too many geologists think that any sort of completion is better than a dry hole. As a result of poor planning, too many companies suffer the embarrassment of having one of their plugged wells produce for someone else, or one of their condemned prospects produce in an offset well 30 feet below their total depth. In planning jointly for the evaluation of wells, geologists and engineers should (1) utilize development wells to explore whenever possible, (2) anticipate information that will be desired or needed later so that it can be obtained in initial wells, (3) think of secondary objectives that can be achieved by early planning, and (4) conduct objective post-mortems of all wells drilled to evaluate the accomplishment of planned objectives and identify new data with potential exploration value.

Geophysical exploration of all prospects should be characterized by cooperation between geologists and geophysicists. Geological ideas and reasoning, backed by geological experience, must be incorporated into all seismic results if full economic value of the seismic survey is to be realized by the exploratory effort. Conscientious and capable seismologists may overlook prospects because of their unfamiliarity with the detailed geology of certain areas. Much of the difficulty involved in incorporating geological knowledge and seismic results may be averted by an exchange of ideas between geologists and geophysicists before and during seismic operations. The final interpretation also should reflect this cooperation.

We all recognize that an obvious, large gap between the three disciplines is caused by vocabulary. Many times one group does not know what the other is talking about—especially if the talking gets highly technical. This gap can be eliminated, or at least minimized, through joint continuing education programs. At the same time, distrust for one another would disappear as would the problems. Self-education is a paramount requisite for better understanding and results among disciplines. Management should encourage and assist in defraying part, if not all, of the expenses and fees attributable to joint continuing educational programs.

Geologists, geophysicists, and engineers should work together in planning development programs to eliminate the drilling of unnecessary wells. This can be accomplished in several ways:

1. Prior to the drilling of the initial well, exploratory units should be formed by the various companies represented on a prospect. With the establishment of an area of mutual interests, a proper spacing pattern can be developed based on geological and engineering data rather than on conflicting and competitive operations.

2. As soon as possible after discovery, field-wide units should be formed not only to assure proper spacing and to protect property rights, but also to provide the framework for early initiation of secondary recovery programs.

The figure of 60,000 wells a year over the next 10 years to meet the nation's demand for oil and gas becomes significant when compared with the all-time high of 58,200 wells drilled in 1956 and the low figure of 36,628 wells drilled in 1966. Most of the money required to drill these necessary additional wells must be generated within the oil industry. A major source of revenue to drill these wells can be made available through the efforts of geologists and petroleum engineers in eliminating the drilling of unnecessary development wells.

Over $10 billion has been wasted in drilling unnecessary development wells in Texas. If this same money had been used in bold exploration, many more billions of barrels of oil and trillions of cubic feet of gas would have been found as new reserves that would have enhanced the economy of the state and the industry as well. We can all be thankful for the pooling bill that was passed in Texas in 1966. This important new statute already has saved several million dollars that might have been spent in drilling unnecessary development wells, and it will save many more millions throughout the years.

If future demands must be met with limited resources, then geologists, geophysicists, and petroleum engineers have both a joint and an individual responsibility to develop new tools, new techniques, and other innovations that will save time, money, and reserves. The petroleum industry is long overdue for some technical breakthrough in the areas of exploration, drilling, and recovery. As professional men, geologists, geophysicists, and petroleum engineers need to encourage each other to create new tools and techniques for tomorrow. The responsibility for scientific invention must not be left solely to the research and development laboratories. In the immediate future the industry will have to find new methods of improving discovery rates, new ways of reducing drilling costs, new approaches to stimulating flow from low-porosity and low-permeability reservoirs, better methods for improving recovery of reserves, and better devices for accurately evaluating potential reservoirs penetrated by the drill.

Things are being done today that would have been thought impossible 10 or 15 years ago. Who would have thought 15 years ago we would now be using any of the following: (1) casing with sufficient strength to control bottom-hole pressures up to 15,000 psi; (2) logging tools that would log wells with temperatures up to 500° F; (3) perforating guns that would also operate at a temperature hot enough to melt lead alloys; (4) downhole packers that would operate safely with differential pressures above 10,000 psi; (5) drilling rigs that would be able to drill and complete wells on the ocean floor in 500 to 600 feet of open water; (6) plastic coatings and special alloy tubing that would withstand the corrosion of gas containing a high percentage of hydrogen sulfide and carbon dioxide at temperatures in excess of 300° F; (7) packer seals that could operate in steam wells with temperatures of 500 to 600° F; (8) downhole television; and (9) logs that could measure water saturations through casing—a boon to evaluation of possible productive zones in old wells? In addition, these logs can be used effectively for evaluation of recovery efficiency in water-drive reservoirs.

Are these exploration tools? Yes. They provide the means to establish, test, and produce from formations that might under other conditions be considered too dangerous to justify the expense of finding and developing. These tools were developed because forward-thinking people saw to it that they were made available to the petroleum engineer.

Geologists and petroleum engineers have a professional responsibility to work together in supporting scientifically valid conservation laws and practices. This responsibility becomes more imperative as the complexities of the economy necessitate the establishment of laws and regulations by the various levels of government. It is the professional duty of technically trained men to speak up on every issue whose final disposition should be based on the application of scientific principles. Geologists and petroleum engineers should step forward to offer testimony on issues involving geological and engineering principles. Through their individual professional organizations, they should form joint committees to study pending legislation and proposed regulations and distribute the results of their findings to the proper decision-making bodies.

In the last decade, there has been a severe and critical drop in the enrollment of petroleum engineers, geologists, and geophysicists in colleges and universities. The number of engineers graduating and available to the petroleum industry each year in all classifications is less now than the annual turnover in the industry due to retirement, death, and other causes. This same general pattern is true for graduating geologists and geophysicists. Therefore, in order to fill the responsibilities that will be imposed by the demands of the future, geologists, geophysicists, and engineers should be *encouraging* outstanding young men to consider careers in these fields. The opportunities offered by these professions have never been greater.

Finally, to assure the discovery of needed future reserves, geologists, geophysicists, and petroleum engineers must meet their responsibilities as (1) citizens interested in preserving the country's defense capabilities, (2) members of a major industry essential to the national economy, and (3) professional men specifically responsible for meeting the nation's exploration and production requirements. This responsibility must be exercised jointly and individually by working to preserve and maintain a political and economic atmosphere in which the oil industry can wage an aggressive, competitive, and rewarding search for new reserves. For too long, professional men have considered themselves immune from the responsibility of actively engaging in political affairs. Circumstances in this country no longer permit such an attitude. Along with all other concerned citizens, geologists, geophysicists, and petroleum engineers must take an active interest in politics, must stay aware of pending legislation, and must make their own opinions known to their congressmen and to others.

All predictions of the nation's future growth indicate a compounding need for petroleum reserves. In the past, the petroleum industry has overcome every crisis with which it has ever been faced. The future will require the combined efforts of new geological, geophysical, and engineering thinking to meet this challenge. Just as geologists and geophysicists must stop thinking of what has been done in the past and start thinking of what must be done now and in the future, engineers must be capable, in addition, of supplying the necessary tools to help in exploration, in production, and in deeper drilling. A strong and binding coordination, fostered by management, of the geologists, geophysicists, and engineers not only would result in the discovery of new reserves, but also would enable the petroleum industry to meet the heavy requirements of the future.

REFERENCE

[1] Farren, Paul, "Geological-Geophysicists and Geophysical-Geologists," Houston Geological Society Bulletin, April, 1967.

Supply And Demand

"But where will these earth scientists come from? At this point, unfortunately, no one knows."   March, 1968

The petroleum industry is facing a drought—a skilled manpower drought—which could have frightening consequences for our nation in its continuing need for petroleum products, which provide three-fourths of this country's energy requirements.

National leaders and industry officials are becoming increasingly concerned with the widening gap between supply and demand figures as they apply to earth scientists and as they apply to the parallel gap between available domestic hydrocarbon reserves and soaring demand for petroleum products.

A severe shortage in manpower skilled and experienced in the earth sciences was recently reported by the Department of the Interior. J. Cordell Moore, assistant secretary of the interior for mineral resources, told the House Interior Committee that both government and private industry are "having an extremely difficult time in hiring technologists with the right combination of skill and experience. And we see no reason for optimism about the near future."

This is an ominous indicator for a petroleum industry charged with the responsibility of finding and producing more petroleum products in the next 20 years than have been found or produced totally since 1863.

Without sufficient reserves of petroleum within the continental United States, our economy and our defense system are in jeopardy. Our domestic reserves of crude oil are estimated at just over 31 billion barrels—which, to the uninformed, seems a sizable figure. But during recent years the pace of exploratory wells drilled for new reserves has decreased. Our actual reserves are not increasing, and demand is continuing to go up by over 3 per cent every year.

Even at our present rate of consumption, we have only a 10-year domestic supply of crude oil. If the 31 billion barrel figure seems large, just reflect that our domestic petroleum industry is using up an estimated eight million barrels per day, with an added dependency for about 17 per cent more on imports from foreign countries with which the United States has friendly relations— today! And it is estimated that our nation will require 17.5 million barrels of oil per day by 1980.

Exploration and exploitation teams of earth scientists representing the collective knowledge and experience of all the scientific disciplines must be available to locate new hard-to-find reserves in stratigraphic and paleogeomorphic traps and other subtle sources. Becoming equally important as we strive to improve our recovery rate are the scientists who are developing methods to improve recovery in already discovered fields.

But where will these earth scientists come from? At this point, unfortunately, no one knows. The problem has gained prominence and national attention only in the last year or two, although authorities sounded warnings long before.

An understanding of the problem may be gained by putting together reports and studies from various sources. Caution must be applied, however, in any general interpretation of such material because the guidelines for each study are varied and, in some cases, even contradictory. Some studies encompass all earth scientists, some geophysicists and geologists, some only geologists. Some are historical studies, and others are projections.

Perhaps the most illuminating report in recent years was "Supply and Demand for Geologists and Geophysicists, 1965-67" by J. S. Royds, H. L. Thomsen, and J. W. Strickland in the Bulletin of the American Association of Petroleum Geologists in December, 1965. Review of that report's abstract is quite revealing:

> Demand for geologists and geophysicists, which declined from 1957 to 1962, has increased modestly since that date and is expected to continue to increase through the next three years (1965-67). The number of geology and geophysics majors and graduates also is increasing, but the number of these graduates available for employment will not be sufficient to satisfy the anticipated demand. There will be a particularly acute shortage of geophysicists during the three-year period. The effect of the shortage in both professions is reflected in higher starting salaries. Although there are newly developing areas of job opportunities both for geologists and geophysicists, major domestic oil companies will provide almost 45 per cent of the job opportunities; universities and colleges and federal and state agencies will provide another 35 per cent. In greatest demand are new graduates with master's degrees who have had field courses and have stressed advanced geological and basic sciences in their academic work.

Although the number of geologists graduated by our universities has curved slightly upward, the percentage of geology graduates compared to graduates in all scientific fields has been steadily dropping during recent years. This is in direct contrast to every other scientific occupation. The supply of trained geologists may eventually reach such a low stage that other less qualified people will enter the field with the result of lowering the present high standards of the profession.

Employment opportunities for newly graduated geologists are most favorable in the foreseeable future, with the most preference in jobs and salaries going to those with advanced degrees. But while job opportunities beckon, the supply of available petroleum geologists dwindles, even though geology enrollment is up slightly. Why?

Some say that areas such as earth-science education and space related programs are currently attracting an increasing percentage of available geology majors. The advent of geology programs and increased need for teachers in many small schools across the country have also placed a further demand on the limited supply of available geologists. The University of Oklahoma, for instance, will not graduate enough geologists in the foreseeable future to replace retiring Oklahoma University graduates in the profession.

Perhaps the greatest inconsistency within the profession, and the one which has the most detrimental effect on students considering careers in petroleum geology, is the fact that while students in many areas have literally a choice of jobs, there are numerous older and experienced geologists who are without employment due to multiple layoffs by oil companies.

Some geology professors allege that employment practices of oil companies have caused a serious decline in undergraduate geologists, which will affect the supply for years to come. These college professors say they cannot recommend the oil industry to their students until it changes its policy of hiring young geologists, before they have a chance to take their advanced degree, when exploration is booming, and then firing older men when exploration declines. Some say that, until there are industry-wide stable working conditions, they will not recommend petroleum geology as a career.

Such feeling is not an exception in academic circles. These academicians claim the solution rests with the oil companies and their personnel policies. This premise is true to an extent. However, this is not the proper attitude for reaching an over-all solution, as it only creates a greater breach between the industry and the universities. The actions of the past should be forgotten because of the tremendous need for petroleum geologists in the future.

The American Association of Petroleum Geologists, through its newly created industrial advisory, academic advisory, and federal, state, and local agencies advisory committees, is diligently working with industry and universities for a mutual and better understanding of the problems involved.

The future? Many challenging opportunities now exist in the petroleum industry and will exist in the future for well-educated geologists.

Unfortunately, studies on supply and demand of geologists and geophysicists have been made only on an irregular basis. Although some excellent reports have resulted, the trends reported can be considered reliable only at the time of issue. We live in an age of such rapid industrial and technological change that what is true today may change completely overnight. Absolutely reliable trends in this area of manpower needs will be available only when such studies are undertaken on a consistent and regularly scheduled basis to provide industry and university geology departments with the information necessary to project estimates of supply and demand.

4
CONSERVATION
AND THE PUBLIC

Introduction

It has been written that Mike Halbouty possesses a fine sense of indignation. Nowhere is it more effectively employed than in this section on his public utterances dealing with conservation and the public.

The issues in the oil industry, indeed throughout the nation, are perplex, and honest men disagree. Halbouty's points cut across party lines and ignore special interests. He serves notice that short-term sacrifices must be made to assure an expanding, meaningful future for the petroleum industry in America.

In a sense, these speeches cast Halbouty in the role of a missionary, and history tells us that the lot of a missionary is hard and thankless. By the nature of his call he seeks out those with a prejudiced viewpoint, or those too uninformed to have a viewpoint.

Mike Halbouty's vision extended so far beyond the thinking of the men of his time, as to border on clairvoyance. He was the first to warn of a coming shortage in oil and he said it, for the record, 15 years ago.

In 1959 Halbouty set forth on a six-month speaking campaign to preach a new religion, called total conservation, and that effort eventually resulted in the passing of a state compulsory pooling law.

At that time, Billy G. Thompson, then oil editor of the Houston Post, hailed Halbouty as "the trailblazer of a new philosophy about the state's most important industry. In the memory of other oilmen and Texas business leaders, never has one man launched himself on such a strenuous, controversial and one-against-the-field task."

The texts which appear here view the subject of conservation with balance and honesty. In business there is no place for the salesman who, in demonstrating a vaccum cleaner, gives both sides of the story. But, clearly, there is still room in the oil sciences for one who believes that the public welfare and the goals of the industry can and should be compatible.

A dozen years before total conservation became an American catchword, Halbouty was urging that its principles be applied to oil and gas production. The thrust of his speeches can be seen in these conclusions:

• Random court decisions in the last three decades have encouraged excessive drilling in Texas, favoring the so-called "little man" in a supposed conflict with powerful interests. The rights of the true "little man," the taxpayer and consumer, were slowly undermined as small-tract operators turned quick profits at the expense of their neighbors.

• Although its early laws were a model for conservation, Texas' present measures, however enlightened in 1930, do not cope with the realities of today. Halbouty argues that they tend to create the very conditions they were meant to eliminate.

• Foreign sources, by carefully protecting their reservoirs from waste, can produce oil at a fraction of our domestic costs, thereby gaining a competitive edge in the market.

• While early laws were designed to control physical waste in producing fields, a growing awareness exists today that economic waste must be similarly attacked. Rising demands for domestic energy require an increasing number of exploratory wells each year. Under existing economic and regulatory conditions, the incentives for this activity are diminishing.

• You begin with the fact that twice as much oil is lost as is recovered, and you look for answers. Halbouty supports unitization, on the basis that such a step would improve the relation of the producer to his property, assure more intelligent drilling practices, and best serve the interests of conservation. Ironically, Halbouty was the first independent to not only favor this program but to practice it, and because of his stand on unitization was severely criticized inside and outside the state. His motives were maligned, and he even endured threats of bodily harm when he persisted in speaking.

Now, 25 years later, it is coming to pass.

Conservation—Total Or Partial?

"It is indeed shortsighted to permit the waste of even one barrel of oil or a cubic foot of gas —irreplaceable minerals, which once wasted are gone forever."   December 1, 1959

Conservation involves the protection or guarding of our oil and gas resources so that the maximum public good may be derived from them. To accomplish this, every barrel of oil and every cubic foot of gas our knowledge and techniques discover must be produced. Total conservation must be employed through the use of the best known primary and secondary recovery methods such as cycling and recycling of gas reservoirs, water injection and water flooding, gas injection into certain types of oil reservoirs, miscible phase injection where feasible, fire flood, or any new techniques that may be developed. Most of these methods have been developed since conservation received its greatest impetus in the 1930's.

Known recovery methods usually involve putting fluids into some wells and producing out of others. The result is sweeping hydrocarbons from some tracts onto or under other tracts. For the most part, field-wide unitization is necessary to the use of these techniques. In Texas, laws do not compel field-wide unitization or pooling. Unitization must be on a voluntary basis; it cannot be ordered. However, some regulations encourage voluntary unitization, and some discourage it. In the interest of total conservation, oilmen should urge the adoption of orders which foster conservation and make voluntary unitization easier.

It is indeed shortsighted to permit the waste of even one barrel of oil or a cubic foot of gas—irreplaceable minerals which once wasted are gone forever. Any kind of law, rule, regulation, or practice, or any kind of action or inaction that fosters physical waste of our natural resources should be rectified immediately.

Once engineers believed—and asserted—that the more wells drilled in a given field, the more hydrocarbons would be recovered. But today information on reservoirs is available that was impossible to obtain 10 or 15 years ago. New knowledge indicates that as many and, in some cases more, hydrocarbons can be drained with a few wells properly spaced than with many wells placed at random.

But many authorities still base drilling decisions on old theories even though they have been superseded by newer technology. Such decisions work against the best public interest since, under most conditions, many wells are unnecessary to drain the maximum amount of hydrocarbons and may actually result in a loss of recovery.

Before the East Texas field was discovered in 1930, the oil industry was an all-or-nothing business. Wells were drilled and fields were gutted in wild splurges of overproduction. The oil industry was so chaotic that no bank or financial institution could afford to risk a dollar in financing petroleum production ventures.

The great East Texas field was so vast and the waste so great that some remedial action was needed to prevent a recurrence. During the boom days of East Texas, the sound principles of petroleum conservation, which had long been preached by a few farsighted oil pioneers, were first effectively used in Texas and elsewhere. New conservation laws were passed, and conservation practices were accelerated.

Within a very few years, twice as much oil will be needed to meet the requirements of this country as it takes today, despite accomplishments in nuclear energy, fuel cells, solar energy, and other energy sources. Therefore, petroleum conservation is far more vital today than in the 1930's when most of the present laws on the subject were adopted. Conservation is more important to the public interest and public welfare than it is to the petroleum industry or to any individual geologist or engineer or manager in the industry.

Petroleum's primary usefulness lies in the energy that is constantly ready to be released for the good of mankind.

Herbert Hoover, Jr., told a symposium on "Energy and Man" at Columbia University:

> Over a period of almost two centuries in our national existence, one of our strongest assets in working toward peaceful and constructive solutions to many of the world's problems is that we have been independent in one of our most vital resources—energy. It is of paramount importance to the security of our nation that we remain so in the future.

Our domestic petroleum industry is a vital energy source and therefore of utmost importance to the security of our nation. The public should know that today petroleum conservation laws, rules, regulations, and applications in Texas, the most experienced state on the subject, are behind conservation needs. Our citizens should be made to realize that our country needs total conservation, not just partial conservation.

Some people believe total conservation is contrary to their particular proprietary interests. They feel that certain aspects of partial conservation as practiced today are beneficial to them, and therefore they bitterly oppose any action or order which would change present practices and effect total conservation. One group of opponents are those oil and gas operators who obtain and drill segregated small tracts and town lots located in a previously discovered oil or gas-condensate field. These people are not wildcatters. They do not discover oil or gas fields. They come in after discovery, and through wells closely drilled under the exception to Rule 37 and produced under inequitable allocation formulas, profit by draining their neighbors' oil and gas.

The industry and the public must beware of political conservation which can develop before it is recognized as such. Political conservation is conservation as practiced when political expedience rather than sound engineering and geological considerations guides the decisions of a regulatory or legislative body. This kind of conservation is attempted to be justified by catch phrases such as "protection of the little man."

To Americans, protection of the "little man" in any situation is appealing. But who is the "little man?" Is he the small but poor-boy oil operator, or is he the small but wealthy operator? Is he the small but poor landowner, or is he the small but wealthy landowner? He is none of these. The "little man" is the average citizen, the consumer, the taxpayer.

But the popular view is that the "little man" is the operator who owns a lease on a small tract of land. Actually, the people who own leases on small tracts are not little financially; they are usually among the richest people in the state. But whether the "little man" be rich or poor, a big-lease owner or small-lease owner, bears no relation whatsoever to conservation or the prevention of waste. Misinterpretation of this distinction leads to the undesirable political conservation that thwarts production in a state.

However, political conservation is already threatening us in the form of people who, in the name of conservation, actually advocate that the federal government take complete control of the entire integrated oil industry. These people use the evils and results of partial conservation to support their views.

Partial conservation is a made-to-order vehicle for the proponents of federal control and makes the industry vulnerable to such attacks. For instance, the most recent attack on petroleum conservation at the state level, and particularly the attack on the Texas Railroad Commission, is contained in a book published with a direct grant from the American Petroleum Institute. Written by two economics professors, Melvin G. de Chazeau and Alfred E. Kahn, the book is entitled "Integration and Competition in the Petroleum Industry," (Yale University Press, 1960). If the recommendations in this book were followed, the oil industry would soon be federally controlled.

The authors contend:

> It is clear that state control under prorating has failed to achieve attainable standards of efficiency in the development of oil reservoirs. In our view, these goals stand a better chance of attainment if a uniform federal statute governing oil development is substituted for the present multiplicity of state regulations.

These authors advocate "mandatory unitization for all pools throughout this country under federal law." This attitude is fuel for the fire of federal control—even eventual public utility status for the oil industry. Federal control is the consequence if conservation at the state level is not revised to meet the demands of the times. And if federal control should occur, what would happen to the operators who specialize in drilling segregated tracts? They would be out! So would most independent oilmen. That is what partial conservation can lead to, so we must help the Railroad Commission achieve total conservation in Texas.

The views of people like Chazeau and Kahn are supported by some leading business publications—Fortune, the Wall Street Journal, Barron's, and others. Attacking our system of state-regulated conservation has become a popular national pastime!

These attacks should point out that unless conservation laws, the application and interpretation of these laws, and the rules and regulations adopted under these laws are modernized to meet the needs and demands of the industry in the 1960's as opposed to the 1930's, the industry is in real danger of having bureaucratic, federal control imposed from Washington.

Mandatory unitization under federal control as advocated by the economic professors should be a warning to all. The evils which result from federal assumption of any state regulatory problem would be multiplied if applied to the purely local function of regulating the production of oil and gas.

The best protection for the industry lies in strengthening state conservation laws and regulations in Texas and elsewhere. If mandatory field-wide unitization ever becomes necessary, and the evidence is that it will, then it must be under state mandate rather than federal if the industry is to avoid federalization. Give oilmen proper well spacing and more realistic allocation formulas, and they can avoid federal control.

A law suit is now pending in Austin which involves the special field rules in effect at Port Acres. The case is a timely example of how inadequate conservation rules, regulations, and laws are as compared with what should exist.

The Port Acres field was discovered in August, 1957. It is a prolific gas reservoir. Production is from a depth of around 10,500 feet, and initial bottom-hole pressure was approximately 9,000 pounds per square inch. The gas is rich in condensate.

Hearings were held before the Railroad Commission in April and May, 1958, and much testimony was given on the proper spacing pattern and allocation formula for the field. At these hearings, I advocated 320-acre spacing and a 100-per-cent allocation formula. There were no segregated small tracts then productive or which appeared even likely to be productive. On June 30, 1958, the Commission adopted special field rules, providing for 160-acre spacing and an allocation formula based two-thirds on acreage and one-third per well. I vigorously protested this order by application for rehearing, but the Commission denied my application.

After more wells were drilled in the field, waste due to retrograde condensation became evident. To correct this, an application was made to the Commission requesting that pressures be maintained in the field and the allocation formula be revised so as to permit equitable pressure maintenance and recycling.

The applicants based their request on article 6008 of the Texas statutes relating to the conservation, production, and use of natural gas. It defines waste in several ways, but in particular, as "underground waste or loss however caused." In the Port Acres case, the applicants clearly proved that underground waste would be caused by certain liquids remaining in the reservoir due to loss of pressure. On this basis, the applicants requested an order requiring that pressure be maintained at a level sufficient to permit these liquids to be produced while in a gaseous phase in the reservoir rather than have them drop out and liquefy in the reservoir due to pressure reduction under a depletion operation.

At an extensive hearing, the testimony of applicants established that, under depletion operations, more than seven million barrels of condensate would be lost due to retrograde condensation, and if this reservoir were cycled and pressure maintained, these seven million barrels of liquids could be conserved and eventually produced.

Voluminous testimony was offered. The evidence showed that the Commission had fixed 160 acres plus a tolerance of 10 per cent as the density pattern for the field; that the development of the field had progressed on the basis of units of that size; and that, as development proceeded, the field was extended across two small-lot subdivisions, Port Acres and Montrose. More than 500 separate leases had been executed on lots in these subdivisions, and while most of these leases permitted pooling for the purpose of forming full units under the spacing pattern, numerous tracts remained which could be separately drilled. The applications for a pressure maintenance order and revised allocation formula were vigorously opposed by the owners of these small lots, and the applications were denied. Thus the ⅓ - ⅔ formula for the allocation of gas production from the field was left in effect, and the requested pressure maintenance order was not entered.

At this time, there were 23 regular unit wells in the field to which approximately 3,700 acres have been assigned (an average of about 161 acres per well), and 35 applications for Rule 37 permits. Of these, 32 have been granted; none have been denied. Thirty law suits have been filed to set aside permits granted. The 35 applications collectively cover approximately 25 surface acres, about 0.7 per cent of all the assigned field acreage. If all 35 wells should be drilled, the ⅓ - ⅔ allocation formula would enable these wells to drain away approximately 20 to 25 per cent of the total field reserve from only 25 acres of land!

The ⅓-well, ⅔-acreage allocation formula in effect at Port Acres bears no relation whatsoever to the gas and other hydrocarbons underlying the numerous tracts in the Port Acres field. The applicants felt this formula was not only inequitable but that it was causing waste by encouraging the drilling of wells on town lots by the overgenerous well factor. This formula is wholly arbitrary. It is not based on either scientific or technological considerations.

In lieu of the ⅓ - ⅔ allocation formula, the applicants advocated a more equitable allocation formula based on the total number of acre feet underlying each tract in the field irrespective of the size of the tract. This formula would prevent waste since it would permit pressure maintenance.

The acre-foot formula is more in accordance with the mandatory provision of the conservation statutes of Texas, which requires that each month the gas allowables for each field and each well be prorated to give each well its fair share of the gas to be produced from the reservoir.

In the Port Acres and Montrose subdivisions are about 500 drillable tracts varying in size from a twentieth of an acre to a few acres. Some of the town lots already drilled were not even large enough to accommodate the full equipment of the rig that drilled the well.

In the part of the field where these small tracts exist is approximately 110 feet of gas pay. A one-acre tract of land has recoverable from it alone by primary means of production approximately 275 million cubic feet of gas and 9,000 barrels of condensate. This quantity of products would net the one-acre producer exclusive of royalty approximately $53,000 at current prices. The average completed well at Port Acres costs approximately $300,000 with storage and line facilities. Why would any prudent operator spend $300,000 when he knows before the well is ever drilled that the maximum amount of gas and distillate under his own one-acre tract would only net him approximately $53,000? The answer is obvious. He does this at Port Acres because the allocation formula permits him tremendous net uncompensated drainage from adjoining tracts. For instance, based on the ⅓ - ⅔ formula, the operator of a one-acre tract will recover approximately 20 times more than the amount under the tract.

What about those who drill on town lots of less than one acre? Their recoverable reserves under these small tracts would be even less than $53,000. For instance, the promoter who drills on a quarter-acre tract has only $13,250 of products under his tract, yet he spends $300,000 to drill the well. Four wells on four quarter-acre tracts, containing a total of one acre, are permitted to produce from the reservoir approximately one and one-third times more than a well located on a full-size 160-acre unit. Each of these four wells would, therefore, be entitled to produce approximately 80 times the gas originally in place under each of these tracts.

Even though the law may permit each owner of a town lot to drill a well on his lot, the income to the operator from the well is determined by the allocation formula.

Rather than preventing waste, the proration system at Port Acres actually promotes physical waste. It encourages and invites people who are not interested in conservation measures to drill unnecessary wells. It should be changed! The same system exists in other gas-condensate fields.

The town-lot operators are unconcerned with how much waste occurs, so long as they "get theirs" through the ⅓ - ⅔ allocation formula. They are not concerned that gas and condensate which they produce is substantially withdrawn from beneath their neighbors' land. These people want no part of a pressure maintenance program. They know that such a program might deprive them of the unfair advantage they now enjoy under the $\frac{1}{3}$ - $\frac{2}{3}$ formula.

Any arbitrary allocation formula for well allowables disregards the principle of ratable and equitable production and completely obliterates correlative rights. The most damaging and destructive result of arbitrary, inequitable formulas is that they encourage or even force unnecessary drilling of wells just to get an allowable. These unnecessary wells contribute absolutely nothing to the oil industry in discovery or ultimate recovery. In fact, in most cases, pressure from the reservoir is prematurely reduced, and physical waste occurs.

As editorialized in the January 18, 1960, issue of the Oil and Gas Journal, this modus operandi of oil and gas rules and regulations

> certainly fosters economic waste and conflicts with the industry's need for over-all economy and efficiency. Such regulatory practices simply increase current production capacity, but not future reserves at a time when excess capacity is the industry's biggest burden.

The consequences of the present Port Acres-type development under the arbitrary allocation formula are detrimental to the people of this state and to the industry.

The increased recovery of condensate alone resulting from a recycling operation would exceed seven million barrels. This represents a liquid recovery of approximately 58 per cent more than expected from straight depletion operations. The record in the Port Acres case shows that the total value of increased condensate recovery would be approximately $22 million. As matters now stand, there will be no pressure maintenance program or recycling program at Port Acres. As if the deliberate waste of irreplaceable hydrocarbons were not enough, a plant will not be built, jobs will not be created, property values will not increase, and over-all progress of a community will suffer. For all of this, the taxpayer must pay.

As long as the people of Texas permit this kind of waste, those who seek personal gain above all things that are just and right will continue to ravage other gas reservoirs where the condensate content and allocation formula make it financially profitable.

The problems at Port Acres today are typical of those in many gas-condensate fields where recovery is high enough to make drilling on small tracts profitable under the $\frac{1}{3}$ - $\frac{2}{3}$ allocation formula.

The legal background of these problems is interesting and important. Before Texas adopted conservation laws, an operator could drill as many wells as close together as he desired. If a neighbor was draining him, this operator could simply drill enough wells to stop that drainage. He had the remedy of "unlimited self-help." However, in those days, fields were rapidly drained of their flush production, reservoir pressures were prematurely dissipated, and many fields were abandoned in a very short time. Examples are Burkburnett and Ranger. The great East Texas field was threatened with the same destruction before proration was adopted and pressure maintenance commenced.

Texas' conservation rules and regulations contain a provision known as Rule 37. The state-wide spacing rule says first, that no well for oil or gas shall be drilled nearer than 933 feet to another well completed or drilling to the same horizon on the same tract or farm, and second, that no well shall be drilled nearer than 330 feet to any property line, lease line, or subdivision line. In a particular field, the pattern as set by special field rules may be larger, and thus these distances may be greater.

To be constitutional, Rule 37 contains an exception. This exception provides that in order to prevent waste or confiscation of property, the Railroad Commission may permit drilling within shorter distances than those prescribed in the rule.

Rule 37 is absolutely silent on how much oil or gas may be produced from any well drilled, either under the spacing pattern adopted for a field or as an exception to Rule 37. Much confusion arises over the contention by owners of segregated small tracts that in some way, Rule 37, when taken with the Rule of Capture, requires that the operator who drills on a segregated tract be allocated a quantity of oil or gas sufficient to pay for the well and return a profit. As fantastic as such contention sounds in the light of the simple exception to Rule 37, it is repeatedly made. It is argued that if such allocation is not made, then the exception is meaningless and confiscation results despite the exception. I am not opposing Rule 37 or the exception thereto; without them, there would be no proration and subsequently very little regulated conservation. But I do oppose their abuse and misapplication.

The confusion that exists over how much oil or gas the owner of a well should be entitled to produce from a segregated tract is further compounded by misinterpretations of the Rule of Capture. The Rule of Capture is court-made law. It was not passed by the legislature and is not contained in a rule or regulation, but the Rule of Capture is a profound and useful conservation measure. Again, only its misuse, abuse, and misinterpretation are evil, against the public interest, and completely illegal.

The courts define this rule or law very clearly:

> The Rule of Capture is simply this—that the owner of a tract of land acquires title to the oil (or gas) which he produces from wells drilled thereon, although part of such oil or gas may have migrated from adjoining land.

In other words, the owner whose well the oil is produced through or from does not have to account to his adjoining owners for such oil, although it may have migrated to the well from the adjoining tracts. However, this very simple rule has come to mean many things to many people.

The most serious current misunderstanding in the application of this rule is the assertion by town-lot and segregated small-tract operators that the rule means more than non-accountability to adjoining owners. These people contend that it confers an absolute right of a well owner to drain oil and gas from his neighbor. These people contend that the allocation formula must afford the single well on a segregated tract enough production from that well to pay for the well plus a profit, even though that amount is not originally in place under the tract and will clearly have to be drained from adjoining tracts.

The Hawkins case is pointed to as authority for this fallacy. This case was filed by Humble Oil and Refining Company in an effort to set aside the proration order calling for a 50-per-cent-per-well and 50-per-cent-acreage allocation formula for that field. The appelate court decided the case April 10, 1946. The only issue in that case was whether the 50-50 allocation order was valid. There were no pleadings in that case nor any proof on whether the law required the adoption of an allocation formula which would guarantee the owner of a segregated tract with one well on it sufficient production to return his cost of drilling it plus a profit. However, by what lawyers call "dictum," the judge in this opinion did say that

> an involuntary segregated tract cannot be denied the right to drill at least one well on this tract . . . from which it would seem that his allowable cannot be cut down to the point where his well would no longer produce, nor below the point where it could not be drilled and operated at a reasonable profit.

Clearly, the court did not decide that the operator of the well on the segregated area was guaranteed by law a profit from the single well drilled on his tract. The judge merely made a con-jectural comment in explanation of his opinion. No court to this date has decided or held that the well on the segregated tract must be assured the return of its cost plus a profit. Existing statutes specify and the courts have uniformly held that the gas allowable from a reservoir must be allocated among all wells so as to give each well its "fair share" of the gas to be produced from the reservoir. Now what does "fair share" mean?

The courts have repeatedly said that "fair share" means the approximate amount of oil or gas underlying a particular tract. Therefore, according to the interpretation of the courts, an alloca-tion formula is confiscatory and unlawful if it does not allocate to all wells in a reservoir approximately the gas in place under the tracts upon which such wells are located. Yet this interpretation is misconstrued and is not considered by those who have the power to use it.

Part of the problem would be eliminated if orderly well spacing were adopted. It is a mistake to permit the first five or six wells to be drilled in a new field on the state-wide pattern before a spacing pattern is even considered for that field. The present state-wide spacing pattern of 20 acres is completely un-realistic for gas or oil.

Under the present practice in gas fields, an area of unneces-sary well density usually results around the discovery well. This density may cause waste. In any event, it causes offset and operational problems in the area of the discovery well which could be prevented. If temporary spacing were adopted for the field immediately after completion of the discovery well and later drilling should indicate that the temporary spacing was not the proper spacing, the matter could be re-examined at that time.

Montana has recently ordered state-wide 40-acre spacing because it has proved successful in North Dakota. The spokesman for the state observed that exploration money had been diverted from Texas to North Dakota and reasoned the same would occur in Montana due to the wider spacing. This trend should be a warning to Texas.

In a field where small tracts or town lots are drilled and production is based on the now customary allocation formulas, the wider the spacing pattern of the field, the greater the confisca-tion of the property of the operator who drills on regular-sized units. In other words, the arbitrary and disproportionate credit given to a well by current allocation formulas becomes more dis-proportionate as the regular spacing pattern becomes wider. Those who advocate wider spacing must bear in mind that unless the allocation formulas used in Texas today are changed to meet the requirements of wider spacing in a town lot situation like Port Acres, Texas will find itself in a worse position with wider spacing than it is in now.

Wider spacing takes on a new importance when oil or gas is discovered within the corporate limits of a city. The responsibilities of such a discovery should immediately become a primary concern of the city officials and all other citizens. Many times the resulting activities by city officials have assumed the attitude of contests between operators in the newly discovered field. This represents a misapplication of authority and should not influence the city's actions with respect to its newly acquired responsibilities.

In Texas, a well can conceivably be drilled on each separate tract in existence prior to the discovery of oil or gas in the vicinity. This becomes an overwhelming problem when oil or gas is discovered within the corporate limits of any town or city which is divided into countless lots and blocks. Imagine an oil derrick in each front yard of a subdivision or residential area of a city. Imagine the noise generated by tremendous engines driving the machinery which drills the wells. Imagine the view from any front yard with the pits, derricks, machinery, trucks, and pipe throughout the neighborhood. Imagine the offensive odors permeating the whole area. Imagine the dangers to children playing in the area. But, even more, imagine the dangers to the entire population in the event of a blowout and fire, such as have occurred many times in oil and gas fields throughout the country. Imagine a well blowing out and spraying gas and oil over a radius of one mile from the well onto other wells, onto houses and automobiles, and the chaos and inferno which would result if someone should strike a match. These are the possibilities when oil and gas are discovered in a city unless the city properly assumes its responsibilities to reduce the hazards. Every city has a right to enact whatever laws may be necessary for the protection and preservation of the health, safety, and welfare of its citizens.

Many cities have successfully solved these problems with ordinances which prohibit the drilling of wells within given distances of houses or other structures and which prohibit the drilling of more than one well on a given number of acres. Such an ordinance does not deprive the lot owner of his right to possess those minerals under his land and to realize the value thereof because it provides that each owner within the area on which a well is permitted to be drilled is entitled to his pro rata share of any minerals from such well.

The additional revenue accruing to the city through taxes is based on minerals in the ground and not on the number of wells located within the city. Thus, by sound planning, any city so fortunate to have oil and gas discovered within its limits can safeguard its citizens and still enjoy the advantages of increased revenue. The failure of the city officials to protect the citizens could result in disaster. Ordinances should be passed immediately to prevent such tragedies.

The answer to all the critics of the oil industry is to eliminate the weaknesses of our present conservation laws, rules, regulations, and practices. These regulations have served Texas well in the past, but some changes are now needed. To ignore this fact and remain silent is to act irresponsibly.

Some definitions are necessary for an accurate understanding of my first recommendation for needed changes. The word "unitization," as commonly used in Texas, refers to an entire field. On the other hand, the word "pooling," as commonly used in Texas, refers to forming units of less than field-wide area. Pooling simply means the combining of smaller surface tracts into a larger tract equal to or approximating the acreage pattern or proration unit area set by the regulatory body.

My first recommendation is that, as the initial step in modernization of our laws, a law should be passed to make pooling on the established spacing pattern compulsory. Such a law would be helpful if not essential to the regulatory body in discharging its duty to prevent waste and protect correlative rights. It would eliminate the overdrilling which now prevails in townsites and other areas with segregated small tracts. With compulsory pooling as an aid, voluntary field-wide unitization ultimately could follow.

Secondly, the use of arbitrarily selected allocation formulas should be discontinued. An allocation formula should be adopted for each field that will give each well and tract its fair share of the oil or gas underlying the tract, but no more. Such formulas should be in accord with known technological and engineering data for each particular field.

Third, immediately after completion of the discovery well in a new field and before offsets are commenced, temporary spacing rules should be adopted for the particular producing formations encountered until the field is sufficiently developed to determine the best spacing for the field, and in general, wider spacing should be adopted for all fields.

If a fair allocation formula and appropriate spacing are adopted for each field after the first well is drilled, the oil industry's most pressing conservation problems will be solved. In my opinion, the Railroad Commission of Texas has ample authority under existing laws to do this.

Fourth, any town or city in which, or near which, oil or gas is discovered should immediately adopt an ordinance to protect the life and property of its citizens from the hazards which accompany the exploration for and production of oil and gas.

Fifth, this industry and the citizens of the petroleum states must bolster conservation laws—modernize them to meet existing problems—before we are faced with federal laws that would lead directly to federal control of our industry.

The Industry's Stake In Proper Well Spacing

"The main purpose of petroleum conservation is the prevention of physical waste, not the hoarding of oil or gas or the fixing of prices."   October 21, 1960

Conservation of oil and gas resources has reappeared in the public consciousness recently as talk of oil shortages and world surpluses vie for headlines. While most oil states have some kind of conservation practice, there is always room for improvement, modification, and change to keep up with modern production techniques and to take advantage of progress in technology and science.

Controls on waste and use of petroleum are probably more effective at present in the Rocky Mountain province than in any other oil regions.

The chief reason for better laws there is that the region's oil development started after the concept of petroleum conservation was pioneered in older producing states. And, of course, a great part of the Rockies' production area is on government lands, which necessitate good conservation laws. While the federal government has so far left petroleum conservation to the states, it retains the right to dictate conservation practices on its own land. Since vast areas of federal land are under oil and gas development in many states, it is logical that those states adopt laws to deter the government from interfering in conservation matters.

In the past, the definition of conservation included only the developing, producing, and handling of petroleum without waste. Gradually though, the regulatory bodies in many states are realizing that economic waste is as important to conservation as physical waste.

All producing states need to review their conservation programs. Laws and regulations that met yesterday's conditions may not be adequate to meet those of today. Conservation regulations should not be considered permanent statutes but should constantly be examined in light of existing conditions and changed when necessary to accommodate the public interest in the forecoming astronomical demand for energy fuel.

Unsound regulatory practices simply increase current productive capacity at a time when excess capacity is the industry's burden. These practices result in the destruction of reservoirs and the waste of reserves.

Critics of the oil industry have claimed that, under state controls, excessive and conflicting rules and regulations work against conservation. They believe that because of the multiplicity of regulations, the industry should be placed under federal control. They point out failures in achieving total conservation by citing those few local operators who consider their selfish interests above those of the industry or the country in disregarding good conservation practices. The critics even claim that these same operators have had the backing and approval of some state regulatory bodies.

We, who make up the industry, are at fault for permitting a few to jeopardize so many. We obviously are lax in policing ourselves or in speaking out against poor state regulations. Only a few have begun to work for corrective action. The Rocky Mountain region has perhaps accomplished the most toward effective, up-to-date conservation.

Each Rocky Mountain state (including Colorado, Montana, Nebraska, South Dakota, Utah, and Wyoming) has the right to regulate production to prevent waste. Each state requires the compulsory integration of drilling units, and no state requires compulsory poolwide unitization. Only Colorado and Nebraska enforce ratable purchase statutes and protect correlative rights by law. None of the states requires proration to market demand.

Every state in this region of conservation awareness has laws prohibiting excessive or improper use or dissipation of reservoir energy. They all prohibit production of gas in quantities that will unreasonably diminish the quantity of oil or gas that might be ultimately produced. These prohibitions come under the general category of prevention of underground waste.

With the exception of market demand laws, which seemingly are not needed now in these states, and compulsory poolwide unitization laws, these laws are very satisfactory in achieving total conservation. They are unquestionably in the public interest.

By itself, the economics of another conservation measure, well spacing, seems a very simple problem of arithmetic. However, when weighed against its total effect upon the economy of the oil industry, it becomes a vital consideration for the survival of the independent producing segment of the industry.

Basically, there are three methods of increasing profit from oil production. One is to raise the selling price. Another is to produce larger quantities of oil to lower the per-unit cost. And the third is to develop and produce oil more economically.

A world-wide excess of oil, a deterioration of product price, and high inventories have substantially deflated hope for a crude price increase any time soon.

It is hopeless, in Texas at least, to expect an increase in the rate of production on a per-well basis under present conditions. The Texas industry is now experiencing drastic proration, and there is little chance for reversal of the downward trend. The pressure of this unfortunate condition certainly has extended to other important producing states. Eventually the oversupply of crude oil throughout the world will adjust itself, but in the meantime, a strong, healthy domestic industry is important to insure future supply in this country and to avoid dependence on foreign sources of oil.

The one obvious part of producing economics that needs attention now is drilling operations.

The domestic industry is constantly called upon to provide funds to explore for, find, and develop needed reserves. Since the nation's oil industry is already spending several hundred million dollars more than the cash retained from its operations, funds for these new reserves will have to come from either outside sources or improved earnings. It is more and more difficult to attract funds from the capital markets for exploratory purposes. So rare is capital that many independents are folding up, quitting, merging, or selling out. This unhealthy situation has been aggravated by the economic waste of unnecessary wells.

One optimistic note in this distressing picture of the domestic petroleum industry is the certain increase in domestic demand. Assuming a 3.5-per-cent yearly increase in demand for natural gas (a conservative guess) and assuming that we maintain the present reserve-production ratio (20-21 years), we will need to find 275 trillion cubic feet of gas in the next 10 years. This compares with 180 trillion cubic feet of gas reserves which were found in the past 10 years.

Assuming a 2.75-per-cent increase in annual demand (also conservative) and continuation of the present relationship of imports to demand and the present reserve-production ratio (12-13 years), we need to find 45 billion barrels of new reserves in the next 10 years. This is compared to 36 billion barrels of reserves found in the past 10 years. These figures represent total petroleum liquids, or crude oil and natural gas liquids.

Where will the capital come from to finance these new domestic reserves?

One major source of investment capital available to the oil industry is the money now being wasted drilling unnecessary wells. Proper well spacing will result in increased per-well allowables and eliminate useless drilling.

Proper spacing is not a new subject, but little, if any, general attention was given to avoiding economic waste from the thirties to the fifties because of the fruitful times and high earnings in most of those years. Faced with the need for sound economics in the producing segment of the oil industry, management has revived its interest in proper well spacing.

Historically, improvements in conservation practices have been accompanied by noticeable expansion of exploratory activities and knowledge of producing formations. Continued application of scientific principles to oil and gas production has resulted in better recovery. However, the most important factor in effective conservation is still proper well spacing.

Maximum recovery and the elimination of physical waste demands a careful choice of well locations and well spacing to fit the reservoir performance characteristics of producing formations.

So, the reservoir itself presents a challenging problem to the engineer, geologist, and operator in planning a proper well-spacing program to achieve maximum efficient recovery with minimum wells and minimum investment per well, or per barrel of oil, or per cubic foot of gas.

Advances made in the last 30 years in reservoir engineering have demonstrated that the proper location of wells and the optimum efficient rate of production result in greater recoveries. Geology and petroleum engineering, and the principles underlying their application, are accepted by most operators and financial institutions.

Therefore, wells should be spaced to drain a reservoir efficiently with as few wells as possible—or only necessary wells should be drilled. Correct well spacing should automatically include an increase in per-well allowable which is the natural consequence of drilling wells on the proper drainage pattern. It stands to reason that the producer must maintain or raise his projected annual rate of depletion, or he will have no interest in "wider" spacing.

"Wider" spacing becomes meaningless if the wider spacing is not the proper spacing. The reservoir may have such physical characteristics as to indicate efficient withdrawal of its resource on a spacing pattern of one well to 640 acres, whereas another reservoir with more restricted physical characteristics may require a well to every five acres. What we should seek is the elimination of unnecessary wells based upon the physical characteristics of the reservoir itself.

A law to prevent the drilling of unnecessary wells supersedes every other need in the practice of conservation. Every producing state in the union should have such a law since dense drilling results in waste both above and below ground.

Waste below ground is certainly preventable under modern technical practices based on knowledge of reservoirs and their characteristics such as the thickness of producing sands, pressures, water levels, porosity, permeability, and other factors. The combination of these factors dictate the spacing of wells for the most effective drainage of a reservoir. In Texas, the misinterpretation of the Rule of Capture, the absence of a law to protect correlative rights, and an antiquated spacing law have caused severe restriction on the better prorated wells, as evident from the limitation to eight producing days per month. Obviously, Texas needs its current market demand law which controls the extent of proration. Without such controls, a flood of surplus oil from Texas would quickly destroy the industry in this country.

The market demand law is a necessary vehicle to enforce the prevention of waste above and under the ground. Were it not for that law, the 196,000 wells in the 6,000 Texas fields would produce oil far in excess of market demand, and such oil would be stored, subject to the various types of above-ground waste such as accidents, weather, and evaporation.

Of course, Texas' large number of wells stems from the outdated 20-acre spacing law, the era prior to any spacing regulations in Texas, and a catch-all called the exception to Rule 37, the spacing law. Under that rule, any man is entitled to one well on his property regardless of the size or shape of the piece of land, and while no law or court decision requires it, the Railroad Commission holds that each such owner is entitled to produce enough oil from that well to assure its being profitable, regardless of whose property he drains to get the amount to make it profitable. This last part nullifies the honest intent of the law and is, in effect, a license to appropriate a neighbor's property.

Unnecessary wells are a curse on the people of this nation who trust the petroleum industry to protect our natural resources of oil and gas. These wells do not find new oil or gas or increase the ultimate recovery from a reservoir. They are just simply wasteful. The accepted definition of an unnecessary well was adopted by the Independent Petroleum Association of America on December 1, 1936. It labels as unnecessary "any well not needed to adequately drain a determined area because a well has already been drilled which will adequately drain such area."

The great oil-producing states of the Southwest and Mid-Continent areas may be excused for some of their ridiculous conservation regulations since such practices were inherited from an era before either the industry or the state gave more than token thought to oil and gas conservation. While Texas, along with Oklahoma, is the birthplace of effective conservation, the state has not really progressed in its conservation laws. It is still regulating 1960's conditions under 1930's laws. Laws have been passed to regulate gas production, prevent flaring of gas and partially protect reservoirs, but laws that would put Texas abreast of Colorado and Nebraska are lacking.

Texas had no market demand law when it passed most of its conservation laws in the early thirties. But soon it was found that overdrilling necessitated such a law, or other laws would be useless. Yet another Texas law expressly prohibited any consideration of market demand. In fact, Texas and Oklahoma disagreed over this point during the formation of the Interstate Oil Compact Commission. Governor E. W. Marland of Oklahoma wanted a commission with authority to dictate rules, fix prices, and set production quotas in the oil states. This included market demand regulations. Texas Governor James V. Allred opposed any such national cartel arrangement and stated openly that he opposed any form of monopoly, regimentation, or even any vague hint at price-fixing. He also opposed market demand laws, even though one existed in Texas at the time, unless such a law was necessary to prevent physical waste.

There should be no market demand law where one is not needed for the actual prevention of physical waste. Wide spacing and compulsory pooling (or compulsory integration of drilling units) plus a law against unnecessary wells seem to eliminate the necessity for market demand legislation in most areas. Only in states where excessive wells are drilled on extremely close spacing patterns and where compulsory pooling is absent is such legislation necessary as a waste prevention measure. States without these measures might consider passing such a law to have in case production demanded restriction. Passage would be easier now than when the law was absolutely vital.

Some sources have mistakenly identified ratable purchase of oil as market demand laws. Only Colorado and Nebraska have ratable purchase laws. These, of course, are correlative rights laws. They protect the weak from the strong, the little operator from the big company, by forcing purchasers to treat all producers alike in a common field. Otherwise, a producer who controlled a pipeline outlet could take more oil from his own wells than from other wells in the same field. This would mean he could legally produce oil from a common reservoir that belonged lawfully to others.

Ratable purchase means that purchases are made proportionately from all wells in a given reservoir. There is no application in this law to the available market, as in the market demand laws, only to each single common source of oil. Correlative rights laws, like ratable purchase, apply to the protection of each operator and royalty owner in seeing that he gets his proportionate share of the market for any oil produced from a reservoir. Equity between different reservoirs is protected by market demand laws. Equities in a single reservoir are protected by the laws of correlative rights, or ratable purchase. This is the only sure way withdrawals from a given reservoir can be fairly regulated.

Poolwide compulsory unitization has been suggested as another conservation measure. It is good when practiced justly and correctly, but it can lead to gross inequities if handled irresponsibly. On the other hand, where voluntary unitization efforts have been effective, there is no serious need for forced field-wide unitization. Only abuse can make such a controversial law necessary, and these abuses can be eliminated by the state agencies imposing proper rules and regulations on the guilty operators.

Of course, a strong argument for compulsory field-wide unitization is that it is certainly in the best public interest. As the ideal method of reservoir control, it insures the conservation and eventual production of the greatest amount of hydrocarbons in a given field or reservoir.

It can be readily seen how compulsory field-wide unitization could serve, for instance, the state of Texas. Under voluntary unitization, 137 units have been formed in the history of a state which has several times the number of fields, wells, and production as a state like Oklahoma, which has had a total of 197 units formed since 1946. Of those 197 units, 138 were compulsory units, ordered by the state. Generally, they are functioning properly and satisfactorily to all parties.

Oversupply is not a problem in the Rocky Mountain region, though, and market demand laws are not needed now. An educational program might be directed, however, toward the public in preparation for the day when such a law will be necessary. In some instances, ratable purchase laws could have been used in the four states where they do not exist. Pointing out the injustices that can occur in the absence of such laws or voluntary pooling would indeed be a useful, educational service.

The main purpose of petroleum conservation is the prevention of physical waste, not the hoarding of oil or gas or the fixing of prices. Another purpose is the protection of property rights. The ultimate purpose of any conservation, of course, is the protection of the public interest, specifically the consumer and the national security.

The United States is the only nation where property rights for natural resources are held largely by the individual citizen. In almost every other country, the government owns the minerals and usually takes steps necessary to protect those minerals from waste.

In the last 30 years, much has been learned about conservation of oil and gas. In most states, good conservation laws have been passed. In California, voluntary practices have been fairly effective. The older producing states such as Pennsylvania, New York, West Virginia, and Ohio have few, if any, conservation laws since they now produce little oil or gas. In Texas, Oklahoma, Louisiana, Kansas, Arkansas, and other southwestern and mid-continent oil states where production was vigorous before 1930, some good laws exist, but they were designed for the thirties.

Today the need for updated conservation statutes in those states is greater than the incentive. Most regulatory authorities feel that such modernization would interfere with wells, fields, operators, and companies that have grown up under the old system. But new rules, regulations, and laws could be applied only to fields that came into being after the establishment of the new statutes. Louisiana, in the 1960 legislative session, passed a stronger compulsory unitization law, applicable to all new fields discovered after the effective date of the law. This law has already prevented the drilling of many unnecessary wells.

Improper spacing of wells eventually creates a condition dangerous to the operator, to the industry, and to the public interest. Exploration is curtailed, and future reserves are jeopardized. Such a condition tends to demoralize the industry. Every effort should be made to eliminate the drilling of unnecessary wells. Every producing state should adopt a law to make pooling on the established spacing pattern compulsory. Such laws would be helpful —even essential—to regulatory agencies in preventing waste and protecting correlative rights. Compulsory pooling would eliminate overdrilling completely and aid in achieving voluntary field-wide unitization.

Today, the very best hope for the progress of conservation in oil and gas rests in the Interstate Oil Compact Commission. The Commission has been called the "most powerful powerless organization in the world." It was created in 1935 with the sole purpose of conserving and protecting oil and gas, preventing waste of these irreplaceable natural resources, and obtaining the greatest ultimate recovery of these minerals through state authority. It is the only organization devoted exclusively to oil and gas conservation and makes continuous studies to ascertain methods, practices, circumstances, and conditions that will conserve oil and gas. The Compact has no authority over the states; it does not dictate law to any of them. The Compact exists to aid and give assistance and information, but the application of conservation belongs entirely to the states.

Conservation is good only if practiced faithfully by the states as well as the industry. It cannot be partial; it must be total. Partial conservation only creates waste and inequities.

Ineffective laws and enforcement permit one man to plunder another. They permit waste of our most vital natural resources. They demand and encourage the foolish dissipation of capital to the extent that it eventually disappears. They endanger our national defense. They are a burden on the consumer and the taxpayer. They violate the very principles of science and technology. And they are an abuse of freedom.

So we must guard our oil and gas resources to derive the maximum benefit for the public. Conservation is more important to the public interest and public welfare than it is to the industry itself. It supersedes the proprietary interest of any landowner, oil operator, or oil company, and the public interest supersedes any personal interest in wealth and power.

But conservation is a cooperative objective. C. R. Henderson, chairman of the Utah Oil and Gas Commission, has said:

> People of the state of Utah would stand up and rebel against any group that came into the state and suggested that, for conservation reasons, we must close down our wells or even restrict them to the level of the production of those states which are still drilling unnecessary wells for allowable or those which are drilling over half of their wells on less than 20-acre spacing.

Total conservation is a national problem, but conservation authority must remain in the hands of state administrators who must be willing to adjust to new conditions. Of course, the extent of adjustment lies with the industry itself and the state administrators. Their weaknesses can bring on federal control which would, in turn, take us to the perimeter of nationalization and even socialism.

But as long as we can face our problems and correct our own shortcomings, we will remain a free industry in a free country.

Present Trends in Well Spacing

"More than anything else, we pointed out who the real 'little man' is in the matter of conservation. He is the consumer, the taxpayer, and the little farmer or rancher whose land was left unleased, unexplored, and undeveloped . . ."

October 5, 1962

Conservation of natural resources has traditionally been a problem of governments as it is in the United States today. National as well as state governments have tried to protect those resources within their jurisdiction. However, effective conservation, it has been found, is achieved only when total conservation is practiced.

Total conservation means developing, producing, and handling a natural resource without preventable waste so that the maximum benefit for the public good may be derived.

In the attempt to protect the natural resources of oil and gas, Texas has practiced partial conservation which has only created waste—both physical and economic.

The first efforts at conservation in Texas concerned field safety. An association of producers was formed at Spindletop to deal with blowouts and fires. The head of the association was J. S. Cullinan, and his committee was authorized to wear and use guns for enforcement.

When several of the old salt dome fields started producing salt water, the farmers, ranchers, and citizens in the surrounding communities became increasingly alarmed over the problem of pollution. Conservation measures were adopted by operators to protect themselves from losses and damage suits.

The first law dealing with conservation in Texas was in 1899 when the legislature declared that any gas well was to be shut within 10 days after its completion until the gas produced therefrom could be used for light, fuel, or power purposes.[1] In 1905, this act was amended to apply to oil, gas, and water wells and regulated the drilling, operation, and abandonment of such. The first waste prevention measure in Texas was passed on April 2, 1913, when the legislature amended a previous law to make it applicable to the prevention of waste of natural gas.

In 1917, when pipelines were declared to be common carriers and put under the jurisdiction of the Texas Railroad Commission, the Commission for the first time assumed authority to administer conservation laws pertaining to oil and gas.[2] By constitutional amendment that same year, the people declared that preservation and conservation of natural resources were public rights and duties and directed the legislature to enact such laws as were necessary to protect those rights. Thus conservation was established as not simply a boon to land and royalty owners or producers, but a public right and duty.

On March 31, 1919, the legislature enacted the first statute requiring conservation, prohibiting waste, and assigning jurisdiction in such matters to the Railroad Commission.[3] Later that year, the Commission adopted the first state-wide rules, including Rule 37 which was designed primarily to reduce fire hazards and to prevent percolating into the oil stratum from improperly spaced wells.

The first voluntary proration group in Texas, formed in 1927 by operators in the Yates field, limited production below capacity and distributed allowable production among operators by agreement with the Railroad Commission. In 1928, the Commission issued its first proration order for Hendricks field in Winkler County.

The first Rule 37 case developed in 1928. When the rule was attacked as violating the 14th Amendment to the federal Constitution, the United States Supreme Court declared that the Texas act of 1919, authorizing the Commission to administer oil and gas laws, was a proper exercise of the state's police power. The state's right to space wells was also attacked.[4]

Just before the discovery of the great East Texas field in 1930, the Commission issued its first state-wide proration order, and the legislature passed the Common Purchaser Act. The year before, the legislature had prohibited any waste prevention act applying to economic waste after the Railroad Commission had issued a proration order for the Panhandle field based on market demand.

But the state and the industry were still in the dark ages of petroleum conservation. Technological progress was coming slowly. The late H. L. Doherty's pleadings for good conservation practices were being ignored at all levels in the industry, and the President of the United States was considering federal control. In fact, the American Petroleum Institute went on record officially as advocating such action. Federal control was actually established a few years later under the National Recovery Act.

The doctrine of correlative rights was stated by the United States Supreme Court as early as 1900.[5] Walter L. Summers, in "The Law of Oil and Gas" (1938), explained this doctrine by saying:

> Correlative rights is merely a convenient method of indicating that each owner of land in a common source of supply of oil and gas has legal privileges as against other owners of land therein to take oil and gas therefrom by lawful operations conducted on his own land; that each such owner has duties to the other owners not to exercise his privileges of taking so as to injure the common source of supply; and that each owner has rights that other owners not exercise their privilege of taking so as to injure the common source of supply.

This doctrine protected the public against wanton waste of its natural resources by the edicts of the earlier courts, particularly the Pennsylvania Supreme Court in the Rule of Capture decision.[6] This decision said, in effect, that the answer to stealing was, "Only go and do likewise." Such laws and edicts, propounded by lazy judicial minds and promoted by selfish interests of the unscrupulous, led to the greatest waste of precious natural resources in the history of mankind.

Texas participated in this waste that started at Spindletop, went through the great salt dome booms, then to Burkburnett, Ranger, and a dozen other areas, and included the criminal loss of natural gas in the Panhandle field and East Texas. A rule-of-thumb in the early days of oil production was that half the recoverable oil came the first year of operation and the rest over the remaining years of life of a field or a well.

The early days of East Texas saw the last wild wasteland of oil production in the "last boom." There will never be another oil boom in this country because we have learned that booms cause waste.

Finally, at East Texas, order began to emerge from chaos. While wells were drilled on top of each other, the state through the Railroad Commission, the legislature, the governor, and the strong influence of many oil companies made the first move toward intelligible conservation. They saw the oil industry facing panic due to overproduction in both East Texas and Oklahoma City, the excessive imports into this country, and the greatest economic depression in history.

Largely through the efforts of public officials such as Governor Ross Sterling and Railroad Commissioner Ernest O. Thompson, the brakes were slammed on in East Texas. While little was done about spacing, significant steps were taken in the area of proration. A market demand law was passed, and the behavior of reservoir mechanics was recognized. A remarkable twin program of salt water disposal and pressure maintenance was begun. But these battles were fought in the courts and the legislative halls before the measures could be applied to the fields of science and technology.

The federal courts insisted on hearing and ruling on matters about which they had no knowledge, matters which confused the judges. In almost every case, the will of the waster was served. Finally the Supreme Court of the United States recognized the "substantial evidence rule" and said, in effect, that whatever rights the state statutes provide should be pursued in the state courts. The court also ruled it an improper function of the federal courts to resolve fact issues contrary to Railroad Commission findings.

With new legislation and new cooperation within the industry itself, Texas' conservation efforts were considered almost ideal.

In the meantime, the Interstate Oil Compact Commission (IOCC) had been formed and had started a serious study of conservation. Its legal committee, under General Thompson's chairmanship, proposed a model state conservation law. But Texas was merely marking time except for a few steps forced by the federal government, such as the system of salt water disposal in East Texas.

Probably the most telling blow to Texas' hopes for conservation progress came in the Hawkins case. A Court of Civil Appeals on April 10, 1946, upheld the arbitrary rule-of-thumb allocation factors established by the Railroad Commission and, in a judge's dictum, ruled that anyone drilling on a tract of land under an exception to the state-wide spacing rule had the right to drill the well and to make a reasonable profit therefrom.

In distributing allowables in fields with small tracts, the Commission employed the per-well factor.

A well factor of one-half was used, with few exceptions, for oil fields and one-third for gas fields where small tracts were involved. The use of these well factors resulted in substantial drainage of large tracts by small tracts.

For example, assume an average 7,500-foot gas field with 3,200 productive acres in a common reservoir is placed on production. There is one half-acre tract in the field. The field is developed by drilling 10 wells on 320-acre units and one well on the half-acre tract. Assume the reservoir had 30 feet of net pay, 27 per cent porosity, 25 per cent connate water, 80 per cent recovery factor, and a yield of 15 barrels of condensate per million cubic feet of gas. If the rules provide for production allocation on a ⅓ well-⅔ acreage formula, each 320-acre well will recover 14.2 billion feet of gas while the half-acre well will recover 4.4 billion feet. The half-acre well will recover 193 times the volume of recoverable gas in place under it. With gas worth 17 cents per thousand cubic feet and condensate worth $3 per barrel, the half-acre well will receive $4,900 for its own recoverable gas and liquids and $941,100 for the gas and liquids which it drains from the several 320-acre units of other owners.

The same situation could exist in an oil field. Assume that one well is drilled on a half-acre tract and the other 10 wells are drilled on 40-acre spacing in the field. The reservoir again has 30 feet of net pay, 27 per cent porosity, 25 per cent connate water, 0.8 shrinkage factor, and a 50-per-cent recovery factor, with allocation on ½ well-½ acreage. Each 40-acre well will recover 720,000 barrels of oil while the half-acre well will recover 347,000 barrels of oil. The half-acre well will recover 37 times the amount of recoverable oil which underlies the tract. With oil worth $3 per barrel, the half-acre well will receive $28,200 for the 9,400 barrels of oil which underlies it and $1,012,800 for the 337,600 barrels drained from the owners of other properties in the field. Assume the Commission used a ¼ well-¾ acreage formula, the half-acre well would produce 179,000 barrels, or 19 times the oil which underlies the tract. In this case, the half-acre tract would receive $28,200 for its recoverable oil in place and $508,800 for the oil which it drained from others.

Normally small tracts of town lot or larger size do not have enough oil and gas under them to pay for the drilling of a well. If a well is drilled and the operator is to recover sufficient production to pay for the well, he must get it from his neighbors. Of course, the rights of his neighbors are then violated.

In addition to protecting the correlative rights of the owners in an oil pool, the Railroad Commission has the duty to prevent waste. Unless the Commission handles the allocation problem within a pool so that the rights of all owners are protected, it in effect realigns the ownership of the pool.

This realignment gains importance not only in the primary stages of production, but also in the secondary stages. If the Commission's formulas give small tracts a disproportionate share of the pool's production, the small-tract owners insist on participating in secondary recovery projects also at income rates greater than their fair share. Other owners in the pool often refuse to make this concession, and, as a result, secondary recovery projects are thwarted, and oil is left in the ground. This is a loss to the state, the taxpayer, and the owners in the pool. It is also a loss to national security, to the consumers of oil and gas products, and to land and royalty owners. Effects spread ultimately to the local community; its merchants and farmers and professional men; the county, school districts, and other taxing authorities.

In 1961, the Commission held 365 hearings on requests for waterflooding, pressure maintenance, and miscible fluid projects. The operators testified that additional oil recovery from operation of these projects would exceed 323 million barrels. Texas has only begun to employ secondary recovery in the more than 7,000 producing fields. Thus it is important that the rights of all owners be protected so that a small percentage of the owners cannot block production by trying to get more than their share.

Undoubtedly some political considerations became obstacles to good conservation in Texas, both in the Railroad Commission and in the courts. Because their views are well supported by technological data, the big companies always appear on the side of justice in matters of conservation, but people naturally favor the little man against the big corporation in any kind of fight, regardless of the justice involved. The Hawkins case was a big corporation against a little man. The little man won so handily that the big corporation did not even appeal to the state Supreme Court. Yet, 16 years later, as soon as the matter came before the state Supreme Court, the interpretation was reversed.

After the Port Acres field came in, in 1957, small-tract drillers hit the field like locusts undeterred by the Railroad Commission. Several hearings were held, but the decision was the same. The Railroad Commission said it could not do anything; the Hawkins case prevailed.

Through speeches and press releases to newspapers, trade journals, radio, and television, a few oilmen criticized the Railroad Commission for some of its shortcomings. More than anything else, we pointed out who the real "little man" is in the matter of conservation. He is the consumer, the taxpayer, and the little farmer or rancher whose land was left unleased, unexplored, and undeveloped because Texas allocation policies were chasing risk capital to Utah, Colorado, Louisiana, and a half-dozen other states where the legislatures were enacting the ideal conservation laws the IOCC had drawn up.

During the crusade, the response was good, except from a few slant-hole drillers in East Texas and small-tract drillers. Eventually the Commission, the courts, and the legislature came to realize that the "little man" was not some rank promoter who talked a little landowner in a newly discovered field into "legally" stealing minerals from beneath his neighbor's land.

Favorable response came from not only the legitimate oil and gas operators in Texas, but also from members of the judiciary, legislature, and even most of the members of the Railroad Commission itself. I was not alone in this effort, although it was described as a one-man campaign. I spent my own money, took the time, and expended the effort to do this job, but others were doing other things on their own. Among these were lawyers, writers, oil and gas men, and some informal groups such as the Conservation Forum headed by Jake Hamon, E. B. Miller, Jr., and Harold Decker. We believed that for the people to understand the facts which would forbid political demagoguery, this message should be spread through the mass media and the podium. Fighting "City Hall" was not easy, but for once it was successful.

In the 1920's, the Independent Petroleum Association of America had passed a resolution urging the elimination of unnecessary wells. This resolution defined an unnecessary well as any well drilled to drain oil which an existing well would drain.

Even in those days, before East Texas, geologists and engineers knew that unnecessary wells were dangerous to reservoirs. They knew that such wells left behind much oil that would probably never be recovered. Unnecessary wells forced excessive investment which, in turn, caused risk capital to turn to other areas. They forced lower and lower allowables and brought on the eight-day month in Texas. This curtailment of production resulted in important losses to state, county, school district, and other taxing units.

Unnecessary wells meant an oversupply of oil so that leasing and drilling slowed suddenly, resulting in the loss of oil-field jobs, serious economic setbacks among drilling contractors and service and supply companies, and the bankruptcy of many small independent oil operators.

This condition prompted the first real threat of federal regulation of the oil industry since the late 1930's when Secretary of the Interior Ickes, by a slip of the tongue, told Dallas oilmen that federal control meant a utility status for all in the producing industry.

The groups most affected by excessive wells are the consumers of petroleum products who pay for the waste and the domestic producer who must learn to operate with lower costs if he expects to compete with foreign imports. Unless domestic oil can compete with foreign oil in price, it will always be in danger of losing out to foreign oil. Drilling only wells that are necessary to drain oil or gas in a given field is one of the best ways to meet this competition.

Since the earliest days of East Texas, oil and gas conservation has largely been ignored in Texas, although important break-throughs in reservoir control, production methods, and other fields have been made.

However, the Railroad Commission has not been asleep during these years. The Commission, through the sheer power of its tremendous influence, has stopped the flaring of gas in most fields, forced the saving of gas liquids, and moved toward the elimination of physical waste insofar as the state laws and state courts would permit.

But during all these years, Texas has had only partial conservation. For years geologists and engineers had been recommending modernization of our conservation laws, rules, and regulations. But improvement was too slow.

Most of us saw a need, for instance, for something more than voluntary pooling. The system was not working. Discovery spacing rules were ridiculous in permitting operators to set a spacing pattern before the Commission could hear evidence and set a pattern itself. The state-wide spacing rule of 20 acres was insufficient; at least a 40-acre state-wide rule was needed. The arbitrary allocation formula dictated by the Commission was unreasonable, unjust, and downright confiscatory. These and other important points were the subjects of continued recommendations to our industry, our regulatory body, the legislature, and our courts.

Finally, it became apparent that the only recourse was the courts. So important suits, now known as the Normanna[7] and the Port Acres[8] suits, were filed and were successful.

The so-called town-lot operators in those cases were trying to defend a ⅓-⅔ allocation formula in those gas fields, even though the formula prevented an orderly development of the fields in accordance with the spacing pattern established by the Railroad Commission. In its decisions, the Supreme Court of Texas very clearly established, or re-established, the following laws:

(1) Texas recognizes the ownership of oil in place and gives to the lessee a determinable fee therein. In turn, oil and gas in place are by the established rules of property a part of the realty and subject to ownership severance, conveyance, lease, and taxation as such. This rule in its simplest terms means that every landowner owns outright the hydrocarbons underlying his land, and any taking of that property by another without just compensation amounts to confiscation.

(2) The Rule of Capture, as applied in Texas, means that, due to their fugitive nature, the hydrocarbons when captured belong to the owner of the well from which they were produced, regardless of where they may have been in place originally, without liability to his neighbor for drainage. Since the gas in a continuous reservoir will flow to a point of low pressure, the landowner is not restricted to the particular gas that may underlie his property originally, but is the owner of all that which he may legally recover.

(3) The dictum contained in the opinion of the Court of Civil Appeals in the old Hawkins field case was overruled. The dictum stated that once a Rule 37 permit well had been drilled, its allowable could not be cut to a point below which it could not be drilled and operated at a reasonable profit. The court found nothing in the law to justify that proposition.

(4) The rule originally laid down by the Supreme Court in the Marrs case was reaffirmed to the effect that every owner or his lessee is entitled to a fair chance to recover the oil or gas in or under his land, or their equivalent in kind, and denial of such fair chance amounts to confiscation of his property.

(5) If, in a common reservoir, one tract owner is allowed to produce many times more gas than underlies his tract, he is denying to some other landowner in the reservoir a fair chance to produce the gas underlying his land.

(6) The gas conservation statutes of Texas require the Railroad Commission to allocate production ratably so every producer in the field has an opportunity to produce his fair share of gas from the reservoir.

Based primarily upon these rules, the Supreme Court in the Normanna and Port Acres decisions held that the $\frac{1}{3}$-$\frac{2}{3}$ allocation formula, as applied to those fields, was invalid because it permitted wells located on small tracts to produce far more gas than underlay those tracts, most of which would be drained from their neighbors. The court emphasized that the Rule 37 permits on which these small-tract wells were located were granted to avoid confiscation of the minerals underlying their properties and not to enable them to drain the minerals underlying adjoining lands to pay the costs of their operations plus profits.

As a result of these, the Railroad Commission established a new allocation formula which operates substantially as follows:

(1) The field allowable is divided among all the wells in the field producing from the same reservoir, based on the proportion of the total acreage assigned to each such well for proration purposes.

(2) Any operator in the field, before drilling a well upon a tract of less than 100 acres, may, after application, notice and hearing, be given a special allowable in excess of the allowable that would be assigned on an acreage basis if the owner of such well can prove to the Commission:

(a) that the drilling and completion of a well under the regular allowable is not economically feasible; and

(b) that the owners of the right to drill upon adjacent acreage have refused to pool with said tract containing less than 100 acres upon fair and reasonable terms. The phrase "fair and reasonable terms" was defined by the Commission as such terms as would allow the owners of a unit to drill, complete, and operate the well on the unit and would provide that all income received from seven-eighths of the production from the unit well and all expense of drilling, completing, and operating said well be shared among the owners of the working interest in the unit upon an acreage basis.

Briefly, the Railroad Commission has solved the small-tract problem at Normanna by saying that if the owners of large tracts refuse to pool with the small tract on a fair basis, then the small-tract owner may have a special allowable. The amount of extra allowable he receives will depend on facts presented at the hearing.

In this arrangement, the Commission has not denied the small-tract owner the right to drill nor has it forced him to pool his property. If he voluntarily pools, his rights are protected. If he turns down a fair offer to pool, the Commission will give him a permit to drill and an allowable commensurate with his rights of ownership. If his neighbors try to deprive him of his property, the Commission will give him a permit to drill with an allowable to return his well cost and give him a reasonable profit even though most of the oil and gas is drained from his recalcitrant neighbors.

If the Commission continues this policy of allocating production in new gas fields, the trend will be toward spacing wells in new fields on an orderly basis in accordance with the spacing pattern established by the Commission. However, whether such a trend does continue will depend upon the cooperation of the operators in each newly discovered field.

Modern drilling and producing technology and the basic economics of oil and gas drilling and development activities dictate a system which will produce the maximum quantity of hydrocarbons, of highest quality, at lowest cost. In other words, the maximum quantity of hydrocarbons from a given field can be produced by drilling the smallest possible number of wells.

Accordingly, it seems that all operators in a given field, whether their leases cover many acres or small tracts, would accept reasonable pooling offers, in order to obtain maximum recovery at a minimum cost.

Texas now needs to enlarge the Normanna decision into a state-wide pooling law whereby small acreage may be combined with larger adjacent tracts in a reasonable and fair basis in any field. Such a statute must consider both the large and small-tract owner. It should protect the small-tract owner and give him the right to participate in the pooling of tracts and in the well to be drilled thereon; it should preserve oil property rights for the large- or small-tract owner; and, above all, it should permit all owners to recover economically and effectively only the oil and gas reserves under their respective property.

Such a statute would mark the beginning of fair equity relationships between landowners and operators and the regulation of production by technological reasoning instead of by arbitrary, inequitable formulas and selfish desires.

With the Normanna and Port Acres decisions, the Railroad Commission has acted as it was prevented from doing in the past by existing court decisions and threats of political reprisals.

Two of the most significant results of the new trend toward better conservation practices in Texas were the Trinidad and Fairway spacing orders. In these fields, wide spacing was ordered in the first year of discovery to encourage rapid development of the fields out to their boundaries, if necessary. Nothing in these orders implied that the Commission, upon the collection of further data, could not change these orders to smaller spacing if the conditions so warranted. This is intelligent administration of conservation rules. Spacing cannot be made broader in any field, but the pattern can be reduced. So if improper small spacing is ordered, the harm is permanent. This way, no harm is done, and even the objections are temporary.

The Commission has recently submitted and may soon order a 40-acre state-wide spacing rule. The proposal followed a state-wide hearing and received the support of every legitimate oil and gas producer in attendance and only the weakest opposition from those who would continue to exploit the people and the state by perpetuating the old system.

No doubt, this sort of legal plundering led to other evil oil practices in Texas. It is probable that East Texas slant-hole drillers justified their actions with the apparent legality of small-tract drainage of adjacent tracts.

It is ironic that the slant-hole scandals in East Texas have attracted the attention of the press and the people of this state, the nation, and even foreign countries. For more than 22 years, responsible citizens, oil companies, independents, engineers, geologists, and a few newspaper writers have been vainly trying to get the press and people in Texas to listen to their pleas for good and total conservation of oil and gas based on sound technological data.

Not until the tremendous press coverage of the "Big Steal" in East Texas permitted the entire world to know of this despicable situation, did Texas respond and demand that it be prevented from happening again. There must be a better way to make the public realize changes are needed in our laws.

Texas is now facing a new era of conservation. The matter of allocations has been taken care of by the courts. The Rule of Capture has been given a use and a dignity instead of its former role of villain of the oil fields. Undoubtedly, the Railroad Commission is determined that proper spacing shall be instituted, and there has been very little opposition to a proposal for compulsory unit pooling. Science, technology, and the strong and effective aid of good attorneys have won the day in conservation.

And this is as it should be. The national security and the public interest are involved. We cannot become dependent on foreign oil, but we will unless the most important domestic producing state in the union overcomes its antiquated attitude toward total conservation as an example for other states to follow.

Many of the things we were fighting for a year ago have been adopted due to the foresight of the Texas Supreme Court. In the next regular session of the state legislature, laws will surely be passed to assure Texas of its continuation as the leading oil and gas-producing state.

At a recent executive meeting of the Committee for Equitable Development of Texas Oil and Gas Resources, drilling contractors, producer and landowner associations, and independent and integrated oil operators unanimously approved a proposal for fair pooling legislation.

If this trend continues, the cause of justice and equity in the matter of petroleum conservation will be largely realized before the end of another year.

REFERENCES
[1] Acts 26th Legislature, Regular Session, 1899, Chapter 49, p. 68.
[2] Acts 35th Legislature, Regular Session, 1917, Chapter 30, p. 48.
[3] Acts 36th Legislature, Regular Session, 1919, Chapter 155, p. 285.
[4] Oxford Oil Co. v Atlantic Oil and Producing Co., 277 U.S. 585, 48 S. Ct. 433, (1928).
[5] Ohio Oil Company v Indiana, 177 U. S. 190 (1900).
[6] Barnard v Monongahela Natural Gas Co., 216 PA. 362, 65 Atl. 801, (1907).
[7] Atlantic Refining Co. v Railroad Commission, 346 S.W. 2d 801, 14 O.&G.R. 362(Tex. 1961).
[8] Michel T. Halbouty v Railroad Commission, 357 S.W. 2d 364, O.&G.R. 788 (Tex. 1962), *cert. den.* 371 U.S. 888(1962).

Unitization For The Public Interest

"It is unthinkable that we should become dependent on outside sources for oil and gas. If that happened, we would surrender world leadership as our country found itself at the mercy of foreign powers."   December 13, 1966

Since the 1930's, the petroleum industry has succeeded in eliminating many wasteful practices in the production of oil and gas. Yet economic waste still exists.

The situation has reached the point where more than the petroleum industry is at stake. Also affected are our national defense, the national economy, our world leadership, and the public interest.

While individual property rights are a tenet of our form of government, these rights, as they pertain to mineral resources, should not be exercised at the expense of the common good of the people.

Therefore, I strongly advocate that all of our producing states adopt statutory unitization of oil and gas fields as the most effective and most beneficial conservation measure as far as individuals and the collective public are concerned.

Unitization is nothing new. John F. Carll, the father of petroleum engineering, advocated unit operations 80 years ago:

> The careless handling of one well, by which water is let down to the rock oil, may spoil several others belonging to different parties. A clashing of interests at once arises and is likely to result in disaster to the whole district.

As early as 1916, the United States Bureau of Mines urged unitization "for the protection of their (the people's) common sources of supply and for their mutual benefit."

In 1923, the late Henry L. Doherty, founder of the Cities Service Companies, advocated a federal unit-operation law. His idea was sound and might have been accepted had he not advocated federal control.

In 1929, the American Petroleum Institute first recognized and approved a policy of unitization. In that year, Pure Oil Company discovered Van field in East Texas, which became the first major oil field to be completely unitized.

By the mid 1940's, Oklahoma started the first legislative steps toward compulsory unitization. This state also initiated most other methods of oil conservation.

The 1941 report of the engineering committee of the Interstate Oil Compact Commission (IOCC) endorsed unit operation as the "best way to operate a pool from a conservation standpoint." Their Oil and Gas Conservation Statute provided for compulsory unit operation when:

(1) such unit operation is reasonably necessary to increase substantially the ultimate recovery of oil and gas, and

(2) the value of the estimated additional oil or gas exceeds the estimated additional cost of conducting such operations.

Ten years later, metallurgical and petroleum engineers stated in the book "Petroleum Conservation" (American Institute of Mining, 1951):

> If efficient recovery is to be obtained, oil and gas must be forced to migrate. The direction and degree of migration required for efficiency in any particular reservoir are dictated by the specific physical structure and by the recovery process. They can, in no way, be controlled by surface property bound-

aries . . . Thus, in many pools, efficient conservation practices may require that oil and gas be deliberately forced to migrate from one property to another and that the opportunity of certain properties to produce oil or gas through wells located thereon be greatly restricted or even denied entirely.

This system is used wherever oil and gas are produced efficiently whether in Kuwait, the King Ranch, or the Gulf of Mexico. In 1924, Henry L. Doherty wrote:

If the unit plan is adopted, we can recover at least double as much oil as we do now and can conserve at least . . . two-thirds of our gas.

Today in dissolved gas drive reservoirs, we can recover 30 per cent or less of the oil, but with selection completion and location practices, we could increase this to 80 per cent. In gas cap reservoirs where recovery is 10 to 30 per cent, it could be stepped up to as high as 80 per cent through controlled production behavior with natural or induced gas cap drive. In even the best type of reservoirs—those with water drives—poorly managed production practices can cause conning and channeling which result in immense reserve losses.

Before the 1930's, our nation was not dependent on oil and gas for energy. We had little knowledge of future demand. Crude oil was not the most important weapon in our arsenal of national defense. And our early system of highway and air communications could exist on a boom-and-bust oil industry.

Today, not only our economy and national security, but our entire way of life depends on energy. Oil and gas provide three-fourths of this country's total energy.

It is unthinkable that we should become dependent on outside sources for oil and gas. If that happened, we would surrender world leadership as our country found itself at the mercy of foreign powers.

We cannot overlook the possibility of shale oil, tar sands, and gasoline from coal becoming available for energy, but now these sources are merely insurance. And we cannot continue as a first-rate power as long as we depend on second-rate fuels. By the time these sources become practical, we will need them in addition to oil, gas, nuclear energy, and any other fuel we can develop.

More intelligent drilling of wells would increase both per-well recovery and per-well reserves and serve the industry and the public interest far better than now.

Books have been written, laws have been passed, speeches have been made, and resolutions have been adopted on how to do this. However, oil surplus and a preoccupation with other conservation practices have delayed our instigating the best solution —total unitization.

Unless industry and government experts are wrong, the present oil and gas surplus is at best temporary. In a very few years, without a crash exploration program, domestic supplies of oil and gas will be inadequate.

A revival of the wildcatter could prevent such a shortage, but only if wildcatting is made profitable can this happen. If the government would stop offering offshore leases for sale or require by law that all oil and gas prospects and fields be unitized, profitability would not be unrealistic.

Unitization would eliminate duplication in labor, materials, and service costs and would increase ultimate recovery. Independents want added incentives. No single program holds more promise as an incentive to explore than total unitization.

The offshore oil and gas belongs to the government. Yet, if offshore exploration and development of government leases were stopped today, domestic explorers would be motivated to return to the onshore hunting grounds. This return is necessary if we are to find the oil and gas we need for the future.

The larger companies have too many corporate limitations and too many natural inhibitions to plunge into the field of total exploration. The drilling program depends therefore on daring independent explorers supported by free risk capital.

The gas-producing industry has displaced much of the crude oil market, and the production of natural gas liquids makes as much competition as the oil industry needs for a while. So why compete with ourselves to develop the government offshore leases when there is so much to explore onshore?

I applaud any movement toward curbing offshore leasing, especially in the Gulf of Mexico. We can tap this reserve soon enough, but first, let us resume the search for liquid hydrocarbon reserves onshore. Thus, we will be protecting ourselves with a continuing supply of new reserves.

We can no more depend on foreign sources for oil and gas than we can depend on Red China for atom bombs. We have to find our own oil and gas, as we have always done. So far, we have found only a fraction of the reserves potentially recoverable in this country; so we still dwell in a land of oil abundance. However, we must drill for it. In fact, we should triple our present on-shore exploration activity.

In a recent book, "A Study of Conservation of Oil and Gas," the IOCC explains a major argument in favor of statutory uniti-zation:

> Voluntary unitization is desirable. This, however, contem-plates an agreement by all owners of tracts or interests necessary to the project. If dependency is placed alone upon volun-tary unitization, any one owner of a tract or interest, regard-less of reason, can in many instances block a plan of operation that is necessary to the greatest ultimate recovery of oil and gas. This power should not exist in any one owner in a com-mon source of supply. There is also the problem of the owner who cannot be located, the incompetent, the title litigation, and many other barriers to agreement.

Even besides the conservation standpoint, statutory unitiza-tion today involves the survival of the domestic explorer.

In the past decade, demand for domestic oil has increased almost 1.5 million barrels per day to 9 million barrels daily at the end of 1965, including natural gas liquids. Natural gas consump-tion has almost doubled from 9 to 17 trillion cubic feet annually, and we have consumed most of the 35 billion barrels of oil and gas liquids that were known recoverable reserves in this country in 1955.

Yet, while our consumption and production have risen stead-ily, the number of exploration wells has dropped from 12,271 in 1955 to 8,265 in 1965.

On a reserve basis, this country has about 10 per cent of the world's oil and about 90 per cent of the world's oil wells. We average slightly over 13 barrels per day per well in production while foreign wells average 20 times that much. Reserves per well in this country are 50,000 barrels while foreign reserves per well are almost 100 times that much.

In other words, we drill too many development wells and far too few exploratory wells. We give too little attention to reservoir engineering and reservoir mechanics, although we were the first people in the world to solve the mysteries of petroleum reservoirs. We overemphasized more politically approachable con-servation problems and left unitization to those willing to under-take such projects voluntarily. We have turned away from the problem of the incompetent, the lost heirs, and oil and gas areas involved in litigation.

The remedy is simply a matter of education. Before the public will be concerned that oil and gas is being wasted in almost every field in this country not totally unitized, they must understand the importance of oil and gas to our economy, our defense, and our progress. Too many people have confused the issues or neglected the subject entirely.

Most of the oil states already have the foundation for statutory unitization. What is needed now is public acceptance to overcome the cries of the selfish, the ignorant, and the helpless. The states have too often yielded to the pressure of small interest groups and individuals while ignoring the best interest of the public in this matter.

My suggestion is an organized national program to tell the public about the petroleum industry, total conservation, and especially the need for unitization of all oil and gas fields.

The states and the industry have the means of taking this message to the proper and responsible leadership in each oil-producing state who should underwrite such a program of unitization education.

Why is such a program of information necessary?

Landowners and royalty owners do not know that, in many fields without unitization, they are losing twice as much oil as they are recovering from below their land.

Wildcatters do not realize that they cannot afford to drill unnecessary wells under present cost conditions and that investors are hardly interested in supporting exploration projects that have little chance of success and little return on their investment if they are successful.

Some state leaders do not realize that, without unitization, they are losing revenue potentials from oil and gas left in formations, never to be recovered.

Industry leaders, including integrated companies and various industry associations, seem to regard unitization as a hopeless cause and have apparently abandoned its promotion.

The consuming public does not know enough about oil and gas production, much less reservoir engineering, reservoir control, or the importance of conserving oil and gas.

Sooner or later, statutory unitization will apply to all oil and gas fields, both old and new. Unless states act now, the federal government will be forced to do so. The various bureaus of the government have long advocated unitization of oil and gas reservoirs.

Recently Federal Power Commissioner Carl Bagge addressed a municipal utilities association meeting in Kansas City on utility regulations. His ideas are pertinent since under the Phillips decision, any producer of gas today is considered a utility. He said:

> Leaks now exist in the dike of regulation . . . and new breaches will occur in the future.
>
> As new areas of social concern arise, one of us regulators . . . state or federal . . . is going to put his finger in the dike. States must immediately explore these areas and must act with dispatch if a local governmental response is required. OTHERWISE FEDERAL INVOLVEMENT IS INEVITABLE.

Unitization by the states is the most important element in the salvation of the independent. This salvation is unquestionably necessary, as statistics prove. Since the ranks of the independents started to thin out 10 years ago, the number of exploratory wells has been diminishing when the figure should have been going up. The only way to alter this course is to recognize the importance of the independent wildcatter.

In addition to providing greater recovery at lower costs, unitization will also attract the risk capital the independent needs. In many instances, unitization will deny the explorer some of his pride, but today pride is a luxury he can ill afford.

Unitization offers a hidden plus. It could be valuable in protecting operators from unrealistic price postings which often require selling oil below cost. Such a system could produce constructive competition, as opposed to destructive or chaotic competition.

The oil industry must use every means available to take the message of total conservation to the reluctant operators, landowners, royalty owners, and state officials; to consumers of petroleum, the collector of taxes, and the public which, after all, is most affected by the lack of conservation.

We must do this alone or in concert with other organizations, governmental entities, companies, or individuals.

But we must act now. In every day that passes, untold treasures of crude oil and natural gas are being lost, never to be recovered.

Conservation And The Public Interest

*"Oil would sell for a dollar today and a dime
tomorrow. Gasoline could be 30 cents a gallon one day, and the next day a customer
would get a fried chicken dinner to fill up
his tank on six-cent gasoline."*   October 20, 1966

Conservation of oil, as we know it today, did not exist before
1930. Wells were drilled as close together as possible, with no
specific drilling pattern, all producing to their utter capacity for
those lucky enough to have an outlet.

Oil was running over the ground into fresh water streams
and lakes. Storage tanks were spilling over; patches of dried salt
spotted the area from the overflow of salt water. Oil was deterio-
rating into a viscous glue that had to be burned. Fires, floods, and
the hot sun destroyed millions of barrels of oil, and the air was
foul with sulphur gas.

False-front buildings and dirty shacks existed in every oil
town. Camp followers, gambling dens, and bawdy houses were
abundant. Bootleg joints, crumby dance halls, greasy short-order
houses, thugs, and occasional shoot-offs also abounded.

A din of overactivity, wild wells, fires, explosions, and a sea
of mud were everywhere. Trees and shrubs were dead or dying
in all directions from the fumes and gases and loose oil.

The great boom and then the dull thud of the death of a
field became a stark reality. It was always the same; the signal
was when the girls moved out and the pullers moved in. Derricks,
used equipment, and abandoned shacks were left to rust and
crumble. The field became a sea of gutted wells—with no pressure
—pumping two or three barrels. There was no order, only chaos,
from the time the discovery well came in until the atmosphere of
death settled over the field. Thereafter, the boom town became
as bright and cheery as an abandoned cemetery.

What happened in these fields is exactly what happened to
the people who inhabited them. They prospered beyond their wild-
est dreams for a few months—maybe years—then they lost all
they had, except an appetite for high living which they could no
longer satisfy.

The parallel extended to the economy at all levels. The local community of the oil field typified what was happening to the state and national economy as far as the oil business was concerned. It was feast today and famine tomorrow. It was boom, and then it was bust.

In short, it was no good for anyone except the occasional and rare individual who happened to escape with a bundle, and who, more often than not, became a blight on the social scene of America and a disgrace to the industry.

The petroleum engineer and the geologist eventually began attempting to lead the errant industry and the suffering public into a better way of life through conservation.

There was nothing new about conservation. Laws had been passed to prevent the destruction of forests, the pollution of streams, the wanton killing of wild game, and the senseless erosion of soil. Even in the oil industry, individuals and companies were joining together in rare cases to practice a voluntary type of common sense about mutual interests.

As far back as 1878, the first idea of oil conservation was introduced in Pennsylvania. In 1900, the United States Supreme Court upheld the right of the states to exercise their police powers in the oil fields in the interests of conservation. Yet, for another 30 years after the Supreme Court's decision, there was only token conservation.

In those days a man could not borrow a dollar from a bank with his oil in the ground as collateral, regardless of how much he claimed, because he did not know what he had. His income was that of the moment from a well or wells that might produce 5,000 to 50,000 barrels a day.

His only banker was a supply house. Or he could sell stock if he were willing to tell the purchasers things he did not know were true and risk the penalties of the law. In reality, few operators besides a handful of major companies knew whether or not they were going to survive a month or a week or even 24 hours.

No bank or financial institution would dare loan a dime on oil in the ground. A big gusher could turn to salt water in a matter of hours. A well could blow out, explode, or burn up, and destroy an entire field in a flash. A man could be surrounded by wells, which could reduce his pressure and production to almost nothing.

If he owned 10 acres of land in an oil field, he might have to drill a dozen wells, first to protect himself from drainage, and second under the theory that the more wells he had, the more oil he could recover.

Oil would sell for a dollar today and a dime tomorrow. Gasoline could be 30 cents a gallon one day, and the next day a customer would receive a fried chicken dinner to fill up his tank on 6-cent gasoline.

The turnover in oil-field equipment and supply firms was just as rapid as it was in hot-shot oil companies. They were here today and gone tomorrow, with few exceptions.

Few communities welcomed the discovery of oil. They knew they would suffer the indignities of a boom for a while and the inevitable desolation of a bust.

The Bureau of Mines constantly warned the nation would soon run out of oil. Today we look back on these gloomy prognosticators with scorn. I do not think we should. I think they were right. We would have reached the pinnacle of oil and gas production in this country long ago had not comprehensive conservation arrived when it did.

The events which brought about comprehensive conservation were the discovery of the Greater Seminole field, the Oklahoma City field, and the East Texas field over a period of months, overlapping each other. These occurred right at the beginning of the greatest economic depression in the history of the country.

Another factor which forced petroleum conservation was the National Industrial Recovery Act. But the act was declared unconstitutional and thrown out, fortunately, or our industry might have been nationalized.

In the meantime, the states had started, with the help of the federal government and enlightened forces within the industry, to do something about comprehensive conservation.

The big testing ground was the East Texas field. Texas had started conservation as early as 1899. In fact, a proration and shut-down order was issued as early as 1919 at Burkburnett.

Four remarkable incidents happened in 1929. An oil well came in flowing 202,000 barrels per day in the Yates field, bringing about voluntary proration mostly because pipeline outlets were limited. The Van field in Van Zandt County came in and was the first major unitized project in the country. Finally, Secretary of the Interior Wilbur suggested an oil states compact. Also the American Bar Association passed a resolution demanding federal control of the petroleum industry.

Not all the drilling and production practices in the old days were bad. There was just little knowledge and much competition. Conditions were far different from today. Most people thought that oil and gas sources were inexhaustible and cared little about conserving them.

Greedy and ignorant individuals of influence blocked progress in conservation for their own benefit. Nothing was worse than the old Rule of Capture which encouraged the drilling of hundreds of thousands of unnecessary wells and contributed to the loss of billions of dollars.

Yet, this practice continued even after we knew it was wrong. Until recently unnecessary wells added to the mounting costs the domestic industry had to bear. This practice laid us wide open to the evils of excessive imports of foreign oil.

The East Texas field marked the end of the oil boom days. Since that field, there has been none of the old-fashioned boom and bust. With the beginning of proration and other good conservation practices, the flambuoyant boom town, which lived through the raw flush days of discovery and high productive rates, became a thing of the past. The blight these corrupt and filthy communities created was eliminated. In their place came clean, prosperous, lasting towns.

Through the application of geology, geophysics, and reservoir engineering, it could be determined how much oil was in a certain field, the rate at which it could be produced, what percentage of it could be recovered ultimately, and how long the field would last. Oil in the ground became money in the bank. An operator could use his reserves as collateral to borrow money and develop his property. He did not need a gusher producing 10,000 barrels of oil a day.

Banks hired engineers and geologists to evaluate oil and gas properties. The banker was protected from fluctuations and gyrations in the price of crude. Oil took its place beside other necessary commodities in normal supply and demand price adjustments.

Since comprehensive and effective conservation practices under good state regulations have been in effect, there have been no wild ups and downs in crude oil prices. Physical and economic waste prevention has resulted in a plentiful supply of crude oil and natural gas at low prices. In fact, gasoline prices have remained steady over the past 12 years while costs and all other commodity prices have increased. This is remarkable since oil is found at greater depths each year, making drilling more difficult, more hazardous, and more expensive.

Modern highway systems, airlines, and the great fleets of trucks and busses—all direct results of oil conservation—have had an unparalleled impact on the economy of this country.

Farmers, ranchers, landowners, states, and the federal government have been the beneficiaries of higher bonus and royalty income from their lands and expanded markets for products.

And they all owe an incalculable debt to those who demanded and pioneered conservation of oil and gas in this nation that eventually spread to the rest of the world.

Today the United States has about 10 per cent of the world's oil and about 90 per cent of its oil wells. Production outside the United States averages 245 barrels per day per well while the average in this country is 12 barrels. Foreign reserves per well amount to almost 4.5 million barrels and little more than 50,000 barrels per well in the United States. In the history of our industry, the world has produced about 150 billion barrels of oil. Half of that has come from American wells.

We cry today about imports killing the independents. If we had had good conservation laws in 1900, if we had drilled wells on proper spacing, if we had protected reservoirs, oil imports would be no worry today. Now we are paying for the unnecessary wells and the oil and gas reserves that were lost due to the absence of conservation. Foreign fields, aided by conservation knowledge, produce oil for a fraction of what it costs us.

In Texas alone there are more than 200,000 producing oil and gas wells. Probably three-fourths of them were unnecessary. So, we drilled 150,000 wells we did not need. It must have cost an average of $100,000 per well to lease, drill, maintain, and keep these wells in production. That means we have squandered $15 billion, not counting the thousands of abandoned producers or unsuccessful exploratory wells. That is 25 per cent of the value of all crude oil produced in the history of the oil industry in Texas. If we had saved what we wasted in unnecessary wells alone, the effect of foreign imports in this country would be greatly diminished.

When Henry L. Doherty first advocated conservation, his prime objective was the unitization of reservoirs. Unitization is practiced, of course, in all fields on government lands and in most foreign countries. The economic benefits are amazing.

Serious thought might be given to the unitization of all oil and gas fields as the next logical step in the advancement of petroleum conservation. Through complete unitization of all reservoirs, we can add tremendously to the ultimate recovery of oil and gas.

We must take advantage of every possible practice of total conservation. Doherty set the guidelines for conservation when the industry and the people did not understand what he was trying to achieve.

It took a hard-hitting, dynamic, and persevering Texan to enlighten the public and the industry to the full meaning of conservation and to force the issues of conservation upon them when it was necessary.

That man was General Ernest O. Thompson, the first great advocate of petroleum conservation in the world. He had no peer. He was effective and constructive.

Conservation in this country could not have succeeded without him. He faced the fight with courage. He knew no fear. And he was clever, imaginative, and resourceful.

He stood up to vilification, threats of bodily harm, charges of corruption by the corrupt; and he worked long hours at poor pay to bring about conservation. He fought in the fields, in the court rooms, in the state legislative halls, in Washington, and wherever the battle was set. And he fought until he won.

Thompson stressed that the role of state conservation of minerals is not limited to protecting the proprietary interests of the operators and mineral owners. It is much broader. It must consider the public welfare in terms of all the state's citizens, the state and local governments, and other economic interests.

If the state legislature had not adopted sound conservation practices and authorized disciplined producing rates, Texas would have long since squandered its oil and gas birthright. It would never have become the prosperous, industrial state it is destined to be. Conservation preserved this birthright and multiplied its bounty for all to share.

The effects of conservation in Texas are typical of the benefits to be expected from national acceptance of conservation practices:

(1) Initial conservation was drastic and arresting. It slowed an uneconomic development rate long enough to make possible the acceptance and application of new knowledge in reservoir exploitation techniques. It established a new economic climate necessary for the development of sophisticated geological and geo-

physical skills needed in Texas to solve the complexities of the state's deeper structural and stratigraphic oil provinces of the 1950's and 1960's and to give long-term stability to the economy.

(2) Since the 1930's, the state's population has about doubled. The state's budget has increased fifteenfold, and the value of oil and gas production, over thirteenfold. The state's population characteristics have changed from rural to urban.

(3) Conservation practices preserved the Texas oil and gas resources that were to become, in the postwar era, the cornerstones for a vast Texas petrochemical industry and a national network of gas transmission pipelines.

(4) Conservation made possible the expansion of the state's educational system at all academic levels. It permitted the orderly leasing of the state school lands; it maximized the bonus, rental, and royalty income from these lands to the enduring benefit of all Texans.

(5) Conservation made possible higher production tax income needed to balance the state budget and stabilized the flow of such tax income to predictable rather than chaotic rates of flow.

(6) County and city tax collections were stabilized and real estate values preserved in many areas because the oil boom town passed from the scene with conservation.

(7) Stability made possible by conservation permitted a long-range program of highway construction and improvement of waterways.

(8) Conservation in Texas opened new sources of oil financing. With conservation, Texas banks could make loans with confidence because prices were stabilized, producing rates were certain, and reservoir data were made dependable. Oil financing was made even more flexible in the postwar period with the advent of the "ABC Deal." This device permitted oil operators to sell properties and pay only the capital gains tax rate on their capital gains. Without conservation, both routine development and speculative exploration drilling would have been sorely pressed to find adequate capital.

(9) It is difficult to assess what economic contribution conservation has made to the growth of the state's other industries. Manufacturing, transportation, communications, utilities and the service industries, financial institutions, and insurance companies have all shared in the growth and stability made possible by oil conservation. Farmers, ranchers, and timber owners have been the beneficiaries of higher bonus and royalty income from their lands

and an expanded market for their agricultural, stock, and timber production.

(10) Conservation, further implemented by the new pooling bill, has provided a sound economic base for Texas' future over the next 30 years or more. Crude oil, natural gas liquids, and gas reserves are at an all-time high. Railroad Commissioner Langdon estimates that Texas oil wells could produce 1.75 million additional barrels a day of crude oil above current rates if called upon. This would place total daily output capability at about 4.5 million barrels a day.

(11) The year 1966 marks the centennial of the first oil discovery in Texas, near Nacogdoches. In this 100 years, the wellhead value of the crude produced in Texas was over $65 billion. This value was improved many billions of dollars more by manufacturing. Without conservation these values would have been much less. All of the Texas economy and its citizens would have paid a staggering price for squandering its most valuable and irreplaceable mineral.

Conservation has been a good custodian of Texas' future. It can create similar changes in other states and thus multiply the contributions of the oil industry to the nation. It is up to the industry to implement sound conservation practices before the government decides to do it for us.

5
HALBOUTY
AND THE PRESS

News Articles
Editorials
Dialogue

Introduction

This section contains a sampling of press and public reaction to the positions of Michel Halbouty and, in a few instances, his reaction to theirs.

Reprinted here are news stories and editorials from papers throughout the state of Texas, along with the prestigious Los Angeles Times and the Christian Science-Monitor, and such trade publications as Drilling and The Oil Daily.

And there are letters that reflect the deep impression Halbouty's speeches made on the industry and the nation, including one from a then United States senator, Ralph Yarborough.

News Articles

. . . a wide range of press coverage and comment

Port Arthur News
September 9, 1958

"Last Oil Frontier"
GEOLOGIST IS SOLD
ON ALASKAN FIELDS
by Nell Gillman

At least one Texan is completely sold on Alaska—especially as concerns that area's importance to us as a source of oil, a commodity we must have to compete in today's atomic age.

He's Michel T. Halbouty, Houston geologist, independent oil producer, petroleum engineer, and discoverer of the Port Acres Field who spent some time in Alaska last summer traveling in the remotest regions of that country.

Halbouty spoke to some 100 Desk and Derrick Club members and their guests at their third anniversary and guest night dinner Tuesday night in the Country clubhouse. In addition to the Port Arthur and Beaumont Clubs, Desk and Derrick in Lake Charles, La. and Houston was represented.

Halbouty cited Alaska's oil potentiality as far greater than that of the Middle East, South America, our own continent, and the Phillipines, all areas in which he has worked as one of Texas' most noted oil and gas finders. He said Alaska has everything from a geological standpoint to assure us that one of the greatest oilfields in the world lies in our prospective new state.

Oil Frontier

"Alaska is our last great oil frontier—an oasis of oil potentiality," he said.

He attributed the spirit of competition between the independent and major oil producers as the major factor in making the oil industry what it is today. He termed the field a "native" industry and oil a commodity that man has kept up a constant search for, even in the remotest places, since the discovery of the Titusville field in 1859.

The Beaumont native stressed the importance of geology, stating that he thought the subject should be taught in school the same as the three Rs.

"Everything is affected by geological principles," he said.

Corpus Christi Caller-Times
October 28, 1958

GULF COAST AREA TO REMAIN TOPS IN OUTPUT, RESERVES

Regardless of the demands for petroleum in this country, the Texas-Louisiana Gulf Coast will continue to top the rest of the nation in supplying the majority of the needs and producing the major share of new reserves.

This is true because of the existence of salt dome features in the great oil and gas province, according to Michel T. Halbouty of Houston, independent oil operator.

In 1901, the world's annual production was about 138 million barrels. Russia was the leading oil producing nation with an annual output of 68 million barrels. The United States was second with 58 million barrels and the remaining 12 million barrels was divided among countries such as Rumania,

Austria, Hungary, the Dutch East Indies and Borneo.

Of the 58 million barrels produced in the United States 95 per cent or 53 million was from the "oil region" of Ohio, West Virginia, Pennsylvania, Indiana and New York. Four million or six per cent was from California and the remaining one million or two per cent was produced in Texas, solely from the Corsicana Field.

Geology professors and big time operators paid little attention to new oil possibilities of other areas. When a new field such as Corsicana was found, it disturbed the thinking of the young industry. As far as the Gulf Coast was concerned, the best brains in the business said the area would never produce any oil and that the region as a whole was unworthy of testing with the drill.

Most of the released research and studies on domes in recent years have been by independent geologists and the majority of deep wells drilled to test the extreme outer flank of these structures have been by independent operators such as Mecom, Richardson, Burton, Abercrombie and others.

As of January, 1957, there were 2,385 land fields along the Texas-Louisiana Gulf Coast within a 100-mile belt.

"I believe that with new geological thinking, improvement in deeper drilling techniques and equipment, that this same land area will produce as many new fields in the next 56 years as have been found in the past 56 years," Halbouty said.

Tidelands

There is no question that the tidelands area will add much more wealth to this area and that many more oil and gas fields will be found. It is highly probable that if drilling activity in the tidelands approximates that on land, equally as many fields will be found offshore.

Forecasters have given the oil industry something to think about. By 1965 the United States is supposed to consume 13 million barrels of petroleum a day against the present rate of just over seven million barrels. These forecasters place our output in 1965 at 10 million barrels a day against the present rate of 6.8 million barrels a day. If this is true, the United States will have to depend on other sources for the three millions a day deficit.

"Providing we continue to have the incentive for hunting oil, the oil industry in the United States can produce its maximum required national demand through 1965 and beyond, if necessary," Halbouty said.

Will Meet Demands

"I will not subscribe to the belief that there is no more new oil to be found in this country. Forecasters have been singing the same song since 1917 when production was barely enough to meet the World War I demand.

"Geological and engineering thinking has always met the challenge and will continue to do so in the future. The geologists must quit thinking of what has been and start thinking of what has to be done. The engineers are capable of supplying the necessary tools to help in exploration as well as in deeper drilling.

"A strong and binding coordination by management of the geologists, geophysicists and engineers will not only find more new reserves, but cut down on the overall costs," Halbouty concluded.

The Houston Post
December 2, 1959

OILMAN HALBOUTY PLEADS FOR TOTAL CONSERVATION
by Billy G. Thompson

Houston Oilman Michel T. Halbouty Tuesday night called for total conservation in the petroleum industry if federal controls are to be presented and further losses in oil investments in Texas halted.

Halbouty made the plea in addressing the annual meeting of two Houston petroleum groups. He advocated a new state law which would require mandatory pooling on established spacing patterns in Texas oil and gas fields as one step toward achieving total conservation.

The oil operator, geologist and petroleum engineer spoke before the Houston chapter of the American Petroleum Institute and the Gulf Coast Section of the Society of Petroleum Engineers at the Houston Club. His remarks were among the most vigorous ever expressed on the conservation issue.

ARTICLES   252

Halbouty proposed three additional steps toward total conservation to erase the industry's vulnerability to attacks from proponents of federal controls and for maximum benefit of the public:

1) Discontinuance of the use of "arbitrarily selected allocation formulas" for wells. He urged an allocation formula adopted for each field that would give to each well and tract "its fair share of the oil or gas underlying the tract but no more."

2) Temporary spacing rules immediately upon the completion of the discovery well in a new field and before offsets are commenced. Such rules should continue in effect until the field is sufficiently developed to determine the best spacing for the field.

3) A shoring up of conservation laws in all petroleum states and modernized to meet existing problems.

Halbouty differentiated between mandatory pooling, which he identified as being on an established unit basis, and fieldwide compulsory unitization.

Compulsory unitization, under federal laws, is a strong possibility unless steps are taken to correct present "inequities" in conservation laws and regulations, he asserted.

He charged that many great gas-distillate reservoirs in Texas were being prematurely destroyed by unnecessary wells made possible by "unfortunate" field orders and court decisions which uphold them. He said a recent book, written under a direct grant from the API, actually advocated "mandatory unitization of all pools in this country under federal law.

"This is fuel for the fire of federal control—even the eventual public utility status for our industry," Halbouty said. "The best protection lies in shoring up our state conservation laws and regulations, in Texas and elsewhere, if we are to avoid federal control."

Halbouty said the public outside the oil industry must be made aware of the need for avoiding preventable physical waste of irreplaceable natural resources, especially oil and gas. He asserted that petroleum conservation laws, rules, regulations and application in Texas—"the most experienced and advanced state on the subject —are behind conservation needs.

"In an ever growing number of instances," said Halbouty, "some of the 1930 conservation laws when applied to modern gas fields, actually encourage rather than prevent waste of gas and liquids."

He attributed much of this to a misinterpretation of the law of capture, which provides that any producer is entitled to any production that comes out of his oil or gas well.

"The law of capture is court-made law," said Halbouty. "It was not passed by the Legislature and is not contained in rule or regulation."

Thus, said Halbouty, "this rule is nothing more than a declaration of non-accountability to adjoining owners for production from wells located upon an owners land."

The simple rule, continued Halbouty, has come in for serious misunderstanding with some contending it confers an "absolute" right on a well owner to drain oil and gas from his neighbor.

Halbouty said the thought is widespread that a proration formula had to guarantee operators the cost of their well and a reasonable profit, even though that amount is not originally in place and will have to be drained from adjoining tracts.

Halbouty said that no court has decided or held that a well on a segregated tract must be assured cost plus profit.

The Houston Post
December 3, 1959

HALBOUTY
MAY CARRY PLEA
ACROSS STATE
by Billy G. Thompson

Industry associates of Houston Oilman Michel T. Halbouty Wednesday suggested that his plea for total oil conservation be presented personally in other sections of the state.

Halbouty Tuesday night called for all-out oil conservation to ward off federal controls, half the stream of oil investments from Texas and to save oil and gas resources for future generations.

More than 500 petroleum engineers and oilmen from other segments of the industry heard Halbouty's call for total conservation at the Houston Club. The turnout at the annual joint meeting of the Houston sections of the API in the Society of Petroleum Engineers was the largest on record.

Halbouty proposed a new statute which would require mandatory pooling on established spacing patterns in Texas oil and gas fields as one phase of total conservation effort.

After the address Halbouty was besieged by members of the audience, urging him "to take the speech to the people—not just oil people—all across the state."

A source close to the operator-engineer-geologist asserted that Halbouty was giving serious consideration to touring the state with his message.

Halbouty departed from his prepared remarks Tuesday night to declare that the problems presented by "outdated" conservation rules, orders and practices in Texas have become of more concern to him than his own business activities.

"Mike's sincere message should be carried throughout the state," one of his listeners insisted Thursday.

The Houston Chronicle
December 2, 1959

HALBOUTY FLAYS
DRILLING WASTES

Michel T. Halbouty Tuesday proposed a new interpretation of the law setting up oil and gas allowables in Texas.

He addressed a joint meeting of the Houston Chapter of American Petroleum Institute and the Gulf Coast Section of the Society of Petroleum Engineers.

He said Texas' conservation laws discourage drilling because the wells allowed on small tracts raise the cost of producing the oil.

Halbouty referred to Article 6008 of the Texas statutes on gas allowable from a reservoir, which, he declared, directs that each well be given its "fair share" of the gas to be produced from the reservoir.

He declared that "The courts have repeatedly said fair share means the approximate amount of gas underlying a particular tract.

A misinterpretation of the law of capture, Halbouty said, has led to the idea that any producer is entitled to whatever he can get from his oil or gas well.

Calling the law of capture a court-made law, he said it permits an operator to drain oil from beneath his neighbors' land.

To protect his property from oil being drained away, an operator must drill more expensive wells than would be necessary under proper production regulations, Halbouty said.

The solution, he said, is a state law which would require mandatory pooling on established spacing patterns in oil and gas fields.

San Angelo Standard-Times
December 2, 1959

HALBOUTY ADVOCATES UNITIZATION

Houston—A new state law which would require mandatory pooling on established spacing patterns in Texas oil and gas fields was advocated Tuesday night by Michel T. Halbouty, prominent Houston oilman, in a forceful and significant speech before the annual joint meeting of the Houston chapter of the API and the Gulf Coast section of the Society of Petroleum Engineers of AIME.

Halbouty differentiated between mandatory pooling, which he identified as being on an established unit basis, and fieldwide compulsory unitization. He said, however, that compulsory unitization, under federal law, was a strong possibility in this country, unless steps were taken soon to correct present inequities in conservation laws and regulations.

He said he was convinced that compulsory unitization could solve a great number of problems under present conservation laws and that he was certain it would come in time. But, he added, it is those who are taking advantage of the weaknesses in petroleum conservation regulations today who will make it come sooner than expected.

Halbouty said the citizens of this state and nation outside the oil industry must be made aware of the need for avoiding preventable waste of irreplaceable natural resources, especially oil and gas. He said the industry is vital to our economy and freedom. Total, not partial, conservation is important to every American, he asserted.

Allocation formulas for each new field should be based upon facts developed at a hearing and that the "fair share" principle should be strictly adhered to, he added. He also recommended that temporary spacing rules be adopted immediately upon the discovery of any field rather than be postponed until six or more wells are drilled as at present.

Halbouty has extensive oil and banking interests in San Angelo and West Texas.

The Oil Daily
December 4, 1959

HALBOUTY SAYS FEDERAL OIL CONTROL IS 'RISK'
by Max B. Skelton (AP)

Houston (AP) A Texas oilman believes oil states must modernize petroleum conservation or risk federal control.

"Partial conservation is a made to order vehicle for the proponents of federal control," said Michel Halbouty, an independent operator.

"The best protection lies in shoring up state conservation laws and regulations in Texas and elsewhere if we are to avoid federal control."

Waste Said Encouraged

The Houston geologist and petroleum engineer who recently expanded his operations to include explorations in Alaska said some current conservation laws actually encourage rather than prevent waste of gas and liquids when applied to modern gas fields.

"We know that within a very few years it will take twice as much oil to meet the requirements of the people in this country as it takes today," he said. "Therefore, petroleum conservation is far more vital today than it was in the 1930's when most of the present laws on the subject were placed on the books."

State Control Attacked

Halbouty said an attack on state level conservation of oil and gas was made in a book published last month under a direct grant from the American Petroleum Institute. "Integration and competition in the Petroleum Industry" was written by two economists, Melvin de Chazeau and Alfred Kahn.

Halbouty said the book should be accepted by oilmen as a warning in that it advocates mandatory unitization under federal control for all pools throughout the nation.

Halbouty objected particularly to two paragraphs in the book.

The authors said:

"It is clear that state control under prorationing has failed to achieve attainable standards of efficiency in the development of oil reservoirs.

"In our view, these goals stand a better chance of attainment if a uniform federal statute governing oil development is substituted for the present multiplicity of state regulations."

'Popular Pastime'

Halbouty said such views are being supported by some of the

leading business publications of the nation.

"Attacking our system of conservation by states has become a popular national pastime," he said. "These attacks should make us all realize that unless the conservation laws, the application and interpretation of these laws, and the rules and regulations adopted under these laws are modernized to meet the needs and demands of the industry in 1960 as opposed to 1930, we are in real danger of having bureaucratic federal control imposed from Washington."

The Oil Daily
December 2, 1959

URGES STATE LAW FOR COMPULSORY POOLING OF UNITS

Houston, Dec. 1—A change in Texas law to allow compulsory pooling of leases to form drilling units was proposed formally here tonight by Michel T. Halbouty, of Houston.

He warned that federal control of the petroleum industry is "a real danger" unless state conservation statutes are overhauled and modernized.

Addressing an annual joint meeting of the Houston chapter of the American Petroleum Institute and the Gulf Coast section of the Society of Petroleum Engineers of AIME, Halbouty distinguished pooling on a unit basis from fieldwide compulsory unitization.

He said a book recently written on a direct grant from API actually called for compulsory unitization of all domestic oil and gas reservoirs under federal control on grounds that the states had failed to develop reservoirs efficiently.

The speaker said he was convinced that compulsory unitization will come in time, but declared it ought to be imposed by the states, not by Washington.

In advocating new Texas laws, Halbouty went a step further than some operators who have been advocating reforms but have felt these can be achieved without a trip to the legislature.

Besides compulsory pooling and revision of conservation laws, he recommended:

1) Discontinuance of "arbitrarily selected allocation formulas" in favor of formulas which would give each well "a fair share of the oil or gas underlying the tract, but no more."

2) Adoption of temporary spacing rules in each area after completion of the discovery well instead of waiting until a cluster of wells is drilled.

Declaring that the public interest must be paramount to any individual's hope for special gain, Halbouty traced much of Texas' conservation troubles to alleged misuse of Texas Railroad Commission Rule 37, which permits spacing exceptions, and to alleged misinterpretation of the so-called "law of capture."

Asserting that rule 37 is silent about allowables, he said a body of practice nevertheless has grown up about a judicial aside on allowables in the so-called Hawkins Case. He said the "aside" has been interpreted to guarantee each small tract operator enough production to pay the cost of his well plus a profit.

The Houston Chronicle
December 6, 1959

OIL CONTROL LACK
TOLD BY HALBOUTY
by Max B. Skelton (AP)

A Texas oilman believes oil states must modernize petroleum conservation statutes or risk federal control.

"Partial conservation is a made-to-order vehicle for the proponents of federal control," said Michel T. Halbouty, an independent operator.

"The best protection lies in shoring up state conservation laws and regulations in Texas and elsewhere if we are to avoid federal control."

The Houston geologist and petroleum engineer who recently expanded his operations to include explorations in Alaska said some current conservation laws actually encourage rather than prevent waste of gas and liquids when applied to modern gas fields.

"We know that within a very few years it will take twice as much oil to meet the requirements of the people in this country as it takes today," he said.

"Therefore, petroleum conservation is far more vital today than it was in the 1930's when most of the present laws on the subject were placed on the books."

He said an attack on state level conservation of oil and gas was made in a book published last month by Yale University Press and under a direct grant from the American Petroleum Institute. "Integration and Competition in the Petroleum Industry," was written by two economists, Melvin G. de Chazeau and Alfred E. Kahn.

Halbouty said the book should be accepted by oilmen as a warning in that it advocates mandatory unitization under federal control for all pools throughout the nation.

The Houston Post
December 7, 1959

HALBOUTY WARNING ON
U.S. CONTROLS TIMELY
by Jim Clark

When Mike Halbouty warned oilmen at a meeting here last week that there was a danger of federal control in trying to fit the 1960 petroleum conservation picture into a 1930 frame, he wasn't (as the fellow says) just whistling Dixie.

There is a definite movement on foot to get the oil industry under federal control. The central government people want it because it would result in federal control of the source that provides 70 per cent of the energy in this nation. The centralizers have about given up on the high hopes they had that federalizing the gas producers would work for the whole industry. So, they are trying the conservation route. And it's a promising one.

Halbouty, who believes that under proper conservation an operator or a landowner is entitled to the minerals below his land, also spoke out in favor of mandatory pooling, especially in gas fields. He said such a plan would enable voluntary unitization (pooling is unit-wide, unitization is field-wide) to work in Texas fields. And he said that compulsory unitization was probably down the road. This, he said, is obvious in view of the fact that unless good voluntary unitization under equitable rules can be enforced by the regulatory bodies, then mandatory unitization under federal law is bound to result.

He blamed the prospect of mandatory or compulsory unitization not on the big companies or the big independents, but on those who continue to abuse Texas conservation laws, and he hinted that unless the Railroad Commission starts writing better orders in the interest of what he calls "total conservation," it will also have to bear some of the guilt for compulsory unitization, possibly under federal control.

Another thing Halbouty touched on was that discrimination in favor of what some call "the little man" in Texas is chasing oil and gas investments out of this state. He pointed to recent laws in North Dakota and Montana designed primarily to attract risk capital not just to those states, but to divert it from coming to Texas.

Halbouty said such Texas Railroad Commission rules as the exception to Rule 37 (which permits a man to drill one well on any size tract) and the Law of Capture (which says that a man is entitled to any oil he gets out of a well on his land) are being abused and that the commission was not doing enough to discourage the abuse. Halbouty said the abuse to the Rule 37 exception is that the Railroad Commission permits sufficient oil or gas to be produced from wells on segregated (small) tracts to make a profit. He says the law simply says a man must be permitted to drill a well on such a tract and that the law says no more about him making a profit out of the well than it says about an operator on a full-sized tract making a profit out of his well.

He says this confusion over the law is compounded by the commission's attitude toward the Law of Capture. Halbouty says the Law of Capture simply means that a man is entitled to the oil or gas that comes out of his well. That doesn't mean, he said, that he is entitled to all of the oil he can get out of the well, or even enough oil to assure him a reasonable profit. In most cases, Halbouty pointed out, a reasonable profit for such a well means injuring a reservoir or taking oil or gas that belongs to someone else. And, he said, that is one reason oil investments that might be made in Texas are finding their way to Montana, North Dakota and other states with a more realistic and modern outlook toward conservation.

Halbouty had a lot more to say and he said it well. He said some things that will not endear him to the Railroad Commissioners and that took courage since the commission regulates almost every move he makes.

But when you have known the gentleman as long as I have you will know that he has no fear of anyone when he feels he is right. He really has great respect for the commission, but he thinks oilmen should speak out when they see something they think is wrong about the way their business is regulated.

Dallas Times-Herald
January 29, 1960

COMPULSORY POOLING OF OIL FIELDS URGED

An arbitrary allocation formula for well allowables by regulatory authorities completely ignores the protection of correlative rights in oil and gas fields, Michel T. Halbouty, Houston independent oilman, told members of the Petroleum Engineers Club in Dallas Friday.

Mr. Halbouty, who is staging a campaign against what he calls some antiquated rules and regulations applied to petroleum conservation in Texas and elsewhere, advocated compulsory pooling of oil and gas fields in Texas.

Public Interest

He said the public interest in conservation is far greater than the average citizen realizes. He said that from the standpoint of cost alone the drilling of unnecessary wells and the loss of hydrocarbons in reservoirs was adding to the public burden.

It is his contention that the Texas Railroad Commission's arbitrary allocation of one-third of an allowable for a well and two-thirds on an acreage factor disregards the principle of ratable take and equitable production in many fields.

"The most damaging and destructive result of these arbitrary, inequitable formulas is that they encourage, or even force, unnecessary drilling of wells just to get an allowable," he said. "These unnecessary wells are a curse imposed on the people of this state, our industry, and the nation as they contribute absolutely nothing. They find no new oil or gas nor do they increase ultimate recovery from the reservoir. In fact, in the majority of cases, pressure from the reservoir is prematurely reduced and physical waste occurs."

Ft. Worth Star-Telegram
March 3, 1960

SPEAKER WARNS SMALL TRACT DRILLING PROMOTES WASTE

Dallas, March 3 (Spl)—Certain oil regulatory practices of the Railroad Commission are political expedients which promote waste, disregard sound engineering principles and may cause exploration capital to be diverted to other states, Michel T. Halbouty, Houston independent operator charged Thursday.

Halbouty made a militant attack on the commission's Rule 37 which permits drilling on small tracts in an address before the southwestern district, division of production, of the American Petroleum Institute.

The Houston operator warned that failure on the commission's part to alter its approach to small tract drilling may help to bring on federal control of oil production. He said the commission's failure to enter a pressure maintenance order for the Port Acres gas-condensate area in Jefferson County would lead to a waste of 7,000,000 barrels of hydrocarbon liquids through retrograde condensation with a loss of $22,000,000.

The Houston Post
March 4, 1960

TOOL-OF-MAJORS TAG SPIKED BY INDEPENDENT HALBOUTY

Houston independent Michel T. Halbouty Thursday denied reports that he has become a tool of the major oil companies in his campaign "to improve conservation practices" in Texas oil and gas fields.

Halbouty, in addressing the Southwestern District meeting of the American Petroleum Institute at Dallas, said he had received "reports" that he had joined forces with the majors and had become their standard bearer.

"This is nothing but an attempt to link what I am trying to do with an irrelevant issue," asserted Halbouty. "The fact that many of the major oil companies happen to agree with what I am saying does not in any way tie my efforts to improve conservation practices in Texas with any major company campaign or policy."

The Houston Post
March 27, 1960

THOMPSON AND HALBOUTY GIVE SPACING VIEWS TO PRODUCERS

WICHITA FALLS—(Sp)— Texas conservation chief and a Houston oil operator who is waging a state-wide campaign for "better conservation rules" Saturday outlined their views on the controversial well-spacing issue before North Texas oilmen.

Gen. Ernest O. Thompson, chairman of the Railroad Commission, declared that the initiation of spacing rules is not the job of the state's petroleum regulatory board.

"We hear the facts then set the rules," declared Thompson in addressing the annual meeting of the North Texas Oil and Gas Association.

Houston Independent Michel T. Halbouty, who spoke earlier asserted that important Texas exploration money is going to other states that have adopted "wider spacing" policies.

Halbouty said that investors cannot "risk exploring in a state where, under completely erroneous and arbitrary interpretation of good laws they will be subject to unnecessary losses and waste to good reservoirs to accommodate those who plunder and destroy them in the name of justice to the 'little man' ".

Thompson told the North Texans that "if broad spacing of wells is desired the thing to do is to space the wells the way you feel will adequately drain the alotted acreage."

Thompson advised hearings be asked "to have prescribed proper spacing rules and other necessary field rules after five wells have been drilled in a field and the characteristics of the producing strata ascertained."

Halbouty urged the substitution of an allocation formula based on the total number of acre feet underlying each tract in an oil or gas field for the present one-third well and two-thirds acreage formula. He said there was no need for any change in Railroad Commission Rule 37 which governs field spacing "if the regulatory authorities put fair, enlightened and modern interpretations to those rules."

Halbouty said that what he was advocating was what two state independent producers organizations—one of which is the North Texas association—have recommended or endorsed.

Christian Science Monitor
March 30, 1960

OIL CONSERVATION VIEWED BY TEXAN
by Bicknell Eubanks
(Staff Correspondent)

DALLAS—A long look by the oil industry at state conservation laws is urged by an independent operator who expects the industry to be called on to produce twice as much oil in a few years just to meet the needs of the United States.

Michel T. Halbouty of Houston, a well-known independent and consultant, says that "total conservation" is the great need. He spoke to the spring meeting of the southwestern district of the division of production of the American Petroleum Institute.

Unless the states bring their conservation rules and regulations up to date, federal intervention or perhaps even federal control might result, according to Mr. Halbouty. Mr. Halbouty spoke especially on the problems of conservation in Texas, which pioneered in regulating production in the 1930's. Most of those rules still govern the production of oil and gas in this state, the largest producer in the United States and one of the major production areas in the world.

Changes Observed

But times have changed. And Mr. Halbouty cautions that what served the state well in the 30's when strong action was needed to curb runaway production, does not exactly fit the needs of the 60's.

"We know that within a very few years it will take twice as much oil to meet the requirements of the people of this country as it takes today," he said in his talk, which he entitled "Conservation—Total or Partial?"

Oil production has gone through many technological changes since the 1930's. For example, oil fields once considered "workcd out" have become important producers again through secondary recovery processes. And those processes have been adapted to improve primary production.

Because of technological changes many oil operators including Mr. Halbouty, consider that present conservation laws, rules, regulations and applications are behind conservation needs. Therefore, according to Mr. Halbouty, "our citizens should be made to realize that we need total conservation—not just partial conservation."

The Houston Post
April 8, 1960

CULBERSON CONFIDENT FORMULA WILL STAND
by Billy G. Thompson

Texas' formula for prorating gas well production will stand indefinitely despite attacks from the platform and in the courtroom, a member of the state oil and gas regulatory agency predicted here Tuesday.

Railroad Commissioner Olin Culberson expressed belief that any change in the formula—pegged to a one-third well, two-thirds acreage factor—will come about only through constitutional amendment. He indicated doubt that even an approach in that direction would succeed.

There have been some recent moves within industry circles—notably a state-wide speaking campaign by Houston Independent Michel T. Halbouty—for a revamping of Texas' conservation

rules "to bring them up to date." The gas allocation formula has been a major topic with opponents contending it encourages "wasteful, small-tract drilling."

The Houston Post
April 24, 1960

COMPULSORY POOLING LESSER OF 'EVILS', SAYS HALBOUTY

Houston Independent Michel T. Halbouty asserted Saturday that if compulsory pooling or compulsory unitization ever came to Texas it could not be blamed on oil operators who practice and plead for total conservation.

"If that happens we can blame two things," he asserted. "First will be the so called 'little man' who insists on drilling wells on small tracts regardless of how much he takes from his neighbors and second will be that arbitrary interpretation of sound laws which ignores the best conservation practices . . ."

Halbouty reiterated a position he took early last week in addressing petroleum engineers in the Midland area. There, he declared that he favored compulsory pooling on as the "lesser of two evils."

"It would, of course, be far better to have nothing compulsory," Halbouty said.

"If the Railroad Commission of this state set a spacing pattern for a field based on sound engineering principles and stuck by it, and at the same time adopted a formula based on such data, there would be no necessity for compulsory pooling."

The Houston Post
May 22, 1960

ACTION GROUP TO PUSH CRUSADE FOR CONSERVATION AIMS URGED

by Billy G. Thompson

Leading figures in operating and technical ranks of Houston's petroleum industry applauded at week end a state wide "crusade against oil and gas waste" just concluded by Houston Independent Michel T. Halbouty.

They expressed hope that an action committee would be formed by Texas oilmen to press through recommendations which Halbouty outlined in a nine-speech tour that carried him to all major oil centers in the state.

Halbouty wound up Thursday night a six-month-long plea for modernization of state conservation laws to prevent petroleum waste and to avert federal controls over the oil industry.

"There should be a statewide committee of independents and average citizens to follow through on the great work that Halbouty has started," urged Earl Hankamer, prominent independent oilman.

"I am ready to join such a committee, or, in fact join the leadership in forming a committee," he volunteered. "The Railroad Commission needs a show of strength and unity on this subject in order to act on the Halbouty recommendations."

Halbouty waged a militant attack on the Railroad Commission's Rule 37. It permits drilling of wells on small tracts and the subsequent assignment to the wells of a high allowable which causes drainage from adjoining properties.

The president of the Houston Geological Society — Edd R. Turner, Jr.—hoped there would be a "follow through" based on Halbouty's campaign.

"I know many geologists recognize inequities in present conservation regulations because some of the rules are not abreast of scientific development," Turner said.

He expressed confidence that geologists would wholeheartedly support any action that could result in getting together with the commission to develop conservation changes that would be workable under modern conditions."

Belief that most petroleum engineers would support an action committee was expressed by Pete Cawthorn, Jr., president of the Gulf Coast section of the Society of Petroleum Engineers.

"It is a feasible suggestion and I know it will have great value from the standpoint of conservation and petroleum economics," he stated.

Oil and Gas Journal
June 13, 1960

HALBOUTY'S CRUSADE PICKS UP SUPPORT

Houston Group organizes to give permanence to their fellow independent's conservation program. They plan to apply pressure on Railroad Commission and Texas legislature for action. Chief aim of campaign is to eliminate small tract drilling and get allowable based solely on acreage.

Sharp-tongued Michel T. Halbouty has been evangelizing throughout Texas for 6 months on behalf of a conservation program that many oil men believe Texas needs.

His "crusade" over, what happens next?

The vocal Houston independent told the Journal last week that if the Texas Railroad Commission refuses to adopt his program, the legislature will be asked to spell it out by law.

Halbouty's fervor on behalf of a plan to eliminate small-tract drilling and to write an allowable formula based solely on acreage is unabated today. And while he considers his personal job of arousing public opinion finished, he is aware privately that it is just beginning.

He has spoken nine times in 6 months in Texas, and there are preliminary plans for a tenth speech—probably the most important of his campaign.

New plan . . . A committee is forming in Houston to give some permanence to his program and carry it to Austin for a showdown before the Railroad Commission and, if necessary, the legislature.

Earl Hankamer, another Houston independent is the driving spirit behind the move to put the Halbouty program into action. Hankamer's plan is to organize a local committee first and then spread out to other cities.

By autumn there should be enough interest to hold a widely publicized meeting, perhaps at Victoria, Tex., to hear Halbouty speak again and then move on Austin.

The approach . . . Even in private conversation, Halbouty's voice hits an emotional pitch as he promotes his cause.

He scorns the argument that "little people" will suffer by a plan that eliminates small tract drilling. He speaks of the "leeches" of the oil industry who thrive on speculation and take advantage of loopholes in the law.

He rails at "political expediency" on the Railroad Commission that disregards expert testimony on what it takes to produce a reservoir without waste.

The "little people," says Halbouty, are the citizens who suffer when the resources of the state are subject to "wanton waste" by unwise interpretation of the state's conservation laws.

While he does not single out individuals, there is no doubt that Halbouty's chief targets are the three members of the Railroad Commission—Ernest O. Thompson, W. J. Murray, Jr. and Olin Culberson. Thompson and Murray are both long-time friends of Halbouty, but it is no secret today that the Halbouty campaign has strained this relationship.

The program . . . Halbouty wants, first of all, to make pooling on the established spacing pattern compulsory.

This is essential if a regulatory body is going to prevent waste and protect correlative rights. It would eliminate drilling of unneeded wells in small-tract areas, such as townsites.

With pooling compulsory, unitization on a field-wide basis probably could be achieved voluntarily in almost every proper instance.

Halbouty concedes that compulsory pooling is "the lesser of two evils" and would prefer that no operator be forced to do anything.

Who's in charge? . . . The Halbouty campaign has created some embarrassment in Texas among oil men who have worked with the Oil Industry Conservation Forum, an organization of independents and majors formed in 1958 to promote wider spacing and other conservation practices. Halbouty himself is a member of the forum.

But the forum, even its leaders admit, has failed to develop in 20 months a plan of action that will put pressure in the right places and get results. While fundamentally Halbouty and the forum are compatible, the forum has come forward with no concrete proposal.

It is possible that the Hankamer committee and the forum eventually will join forces, but Halbouty is not waiting for that.

"I left part of my life on that rostrum," he said fervently last week. "This thing has cost me at least $32,000 and 6 months of my time. I don't want anybody saying the majors or anybody else paid for it, and I've had plenty of offers. I'm fighting City Hall. This is a dedicated thing."

San Antonio Express and News
October 23, 1960

TEXAN IN OIL CRUSADE

by Nancy Heard, Oil Editor

Petroleum conservation in Texas today is regulated by 30-year old laws and this isn't as effective as that in some of the newer producing states such as Colorado and Nebraska.

This was part of the message from Texan Michel T. Halbouty—at the Friday session of Rocky Mountain Oil & Gas Assn. in Denver.

Halbouty is a consulting petroleum engineer and geologist as well as an independent operator (among those pioneering oil in Alaska) in Houston.

For the last year he's been crusading over Texas, talking mainly to petroleum professionals, for improved conservation in this state, particularly in curbing of unnecessary drilling. Now he's in the second phase of his crusade, and its an open secret that organizational work is to start soon.

Until Texas has a statute to eliminate unnecessary drilling—"or even compulsory pooling for drilling units—" this state will have only partial conservation, and partial conservation is not only ineffective, but wasteful, Halbouty said in Denver Friday.

Halbouty urged the oilmen at Denver to remember that "overdrilling forced Texas to pass a market demand law," and that other states would have to do the same if they allow drilling of unnecessary wells. He believes the unnecessary wells result in over-drilling, then overproduction, creating curtailment of exploration, and jeopardy to future reserves.

The Texan said he agreed in principle with the Utah state oil official who at a recent Interstate Oil Compact Commission said people of Utah would rebel against any out-of-state suggestion for curbing production in that state.

Los Angeles Times
November 4, 1960

INDEPENDENT OIL FIRMS SEEN IN MAJOR CRISIS
by Robert Sullivan, Oil Editor

"Independent oil producers in this country are facing a crisis," Michel T. Halbouty told a convention of West Coast petroleum geologists Thursday at the Ambassador.

He ticked off several reasons.

"In the energy market we are stealing from ourselves with under-priced natural gas. There is also the almost sudden slow-down in industrial expansion. Petroleum conservation practices are below what they should be, and imports of foreign crude oil are excessive."

Imports plus gas and gas liquids, exceed domestic crude oil production in total energy supply by more than 1.5 million barrels a day, the independent oil operator from Houston said.

In a Nutshell

"That's our domestic oil production plight in a nutshell. With the addition of heavy imports to our surplus oil situation, we are in something of a peck of trouble."

Having far more crude oil in this country than we need affects all of us he said.

"As an independent operator, I find it increasingly difficult to continue to invest in exploration under these trying circumstances."

Thousands of oilfield and refinery workers are out of jobs, along with steel workers and others directly affected, Halbouty said.

'Appalling Situation'

"This is an appalling situation. It's like a boxer cutting off his right arm and still expecting to win."

He blamed unfair price competition of imports, in part, for the present situation. With refiners running more oil to stills than they can sell, and with importers cutting prices, the industry can look for continued price reductions, Halbouty said.

Another solution, he said, would be for importing companies to start converting profits from foreign oil into domestic exploration.

"By such an act, they would not only be saving the professions represented here today, they would also be serving their country," he concluded.

Los Angeles Mirror
November 4, 1960

ECONOSCOPE by David Rees

SOLUTION SUGGESTED FOR OILMEN NOW ON HORNS OF DOUBLE DILEMMA

Our domestic oil industry is on the horns of not one but two dilemmas.

How it resolves them will likely determine how quickly the industry will pull out of the depression now afflicting oilmen and whether we'll have adequate supplies in another 10 years.

When Michel T. Halbouty outlined the industry's problems here Thursday, he didn't stop there. He also suggested a possible answer in his talk before the 37th annual meeting of the American Assn. of Petroleum Geologists, Pacific Section.

The first dilemma involves "excessive" imports of foreign crude oil, according to the Houston consulting geologist, petroleum engineer, independent producer and operator and commercial banker. On the one hand, he suggested, we must continue to import foreign crude to help support such free world producing countries as Venezuela and Saudi Arabia.

On the other hand, though, these low-cost crude imports are depressing domestic prices, production and exploration. And this situation, he warned, likely will get worse with Russia now competing for world markets with low-priced oil.

We can look for some more reductions in Middle East crude prices . . . Venezuela also, he continued "will be forced to meet all reductions . . . Inevitably, those falling prices are going to extend to our shores and widen the already punishing margin between domestic crude and imported crude prices.

"So, with the importers cutting prices and the refiners running more oil to stills than they can sell at the pump, we can look for continued price reductions."

Halbouty conceded imports are not the only item contributing to the current petroleum depression here. He also ticked off: "under priced natural gas," the almost sudden slowdown in industrial expansion," "petroleum conservation practices are below what they should be."

He put the plight of the domestic oil industry in a nutshell: "From a relative position of dominance 10 years ago, when domestic crude production exceeded its two major competitors—imports and gas—by 1,200,000 barrels a day, it has fallen behind them by 1½ million barrels."

The second dilemma sees us now on the one hand with a great oil glut, resulting in depressed prices which discourage further domestic exploration and new discoveries here.

On the other hand, industry experts such as David T. Searls, general counsel of Gulf Oil Corp., predict natural gas consumption within the next 10 years will be about double thus requiring a tremendously increased exploration and drilling program.

Halbouty figures 925,000 new wells must be drilled in the next 10 years. That would be an average of 92,500 new wells a year to meet future gas requirements vs. the 44,000 wells expected to be drilled this year and the record peak of 57,110 new wells in 1956.

"We all should start looking for new domestic reserves with a vengeance now," Halbouty asserted.

But how to stimulate such drilling activity in the face of the current oil glut and depressed prices? Halbouty warned not to look to government for the solution.

"We are constantly running the risk that national political action, not state political action, will control the future of the industry. If this happens, the big will get bigger and the small will get smaller, which would result in the eventual elimination of the independent.

"And if that happens, who will drill the wildcat wells in this country?" Halbouty asked, noting independents drill nearly 85% of this country's exploratory wells.

Halbouty's suggested solution is two-fold:

1) Natural gas prices must be raised. Currently, he observes, crude sells for about $3 a barrel at the wellhead, but an equivalent amount of energy in the form of gas sells for only 68 cents.

At such a price differential, it's little wonder production of natural gas and gas liquids, expressed in oil equivalents, increased by 3,-790,000 barrels a day within the past decade while domestic crude production increased by only 2 million barrels a day.

2) The oil industry must use "today's profits from relatively cheap foreign oil to explore for and find domestic oil and gas we know we will need tomorrow," Halbouty explained.

"Should the importing companies start converting profits from foreign oil into domestic exploration, and this seems a per-fectly logical and wise thing to do, they not only stimulate the industry which made them all big and successful corporations, they could also utilize the services, the genius and the know-how of the men they are laying off, retiring early and terminating.

"They should prepare now for the drilling of 62,000 or 92,000 wells annually by finding the places to drill with the greatest possible dispatch."

San Antonio Express and News
November 27, 1960

OIL SAVING PLEA WINS CONVERTS
by Nancy Heard, Oil Editor

Not everyone agrees with Michel T. Halbouty, who thinks we have more oil wells than we need in Texas. But like his ideas or not, those who are objective must admit that the Houston oilman is converting more and more in his crusade for modernizing petroleum conservation regulations in this state.

A considerable number of these converts are in the professional ranks of the petroleum industry. More important, when it comes to possible legislative changes, are the conversions among the "people"—the people, that is, who have no income from oil or gas.

Some of these are fortunate enough to own land, but not fortunate enough to have oil or gas production on it. They have no direct connection with petroleum, but they have more knowledge of and more interest in Texas oil and gas than most oilmen (and also most of us in the communications industry) realize or admit.

These and other surprises became apparent in San Antonio last week after Halbouty spoke to a trio of San Antonio professional petroleum groups, and then made an un-advertised appearance on WOAI-TV.

Favorable Opinion

Halbouty's talk to the oilmen seemed to create a majority of favorable opinion from the generally conservative local groups. It even stimulated a considerable number to voluteer to make similar speeches and take other "action".

Biggest surprise came later, though, after a four-minute TV tape program, which brought a response indicating the non-oil public is (contrary to some opinion) vitally interested in at least some of the more technical aspects of the petroleum industry.

(Not one oilman had commented on the TV program to this writer but during a three-hour period Wednesday, following the Tuesday night talk, 19 others, including several women, an Air Force officer and a Kelly Field worker, called this newspaper for additional information on the same subject.)

"Billions, not millions of dollars have been wasted by drilling unnecessary wells in Texas," Halbouty told his television audience. "I am urging that rules, laws, if necessary, be changed to stop unnecessary wells in the future and

cause this unnecessary expenditure to be diverted to searching for new reserves which will help all the state."

Three-hundred-odd oilmen turned out the first week to hear Halbouty condemn the wide spacing and Rule 37 (spacing) exceptions allowed in Texas. The size of the crowd was considered significant in itself.

Oil
February, 1961

REGIONAL FORUMS FOR INDEPENDENTS AND MAJORS NOW ADVOCATED BY HOUSTON OILMAN HALBOUTY

Houston: A recommendation that independent and major oil producers create regional forums wherein they can informally discuss mutual problems was made by Michel T. Halbouty, Houston oilman, in an address before the Oklahoma Independent Petroleum Association in Tulsa.

Halbouty said the idea was not original with him, but that it had been suggested recently by L. F. McCollum, president of the Continental Oil Company, during a conversation between the two men enroute to the Interstate Oil Compact Commission meeting in Phoenix.

The speaker said he believes 99 per cent of all misunderstandings between independents and integrated companies stem from ignorance of each other's problems.

Oil and Gas Journal
February 26, 1962

PORT ACRES
REACTION VARIES

Halbouty rejoices over outlawing of small-tract drilling in Texas field, but there's a hint the fight may not be over.

Two extremes of opinion were represented last week in Houston on the state Supreme Court decision kicking out small tract drilling in the Port Acres field (OGJ, Feb. 19, p. 63).

Michel T. Halbouty, who conducted a "one-man crusade" against small-tract drilling last year in Texas was jubilant.

Stanley C. Woods, president of the Texas Landowners and Independent Oil and Gas Producers Association, said the decision will be fought by defendant landowners to the U.S. Supreme Court, but the principal attorneys in the case said no decision has been reached on this point.

Halbouty, a Houston independent, said the Port Acres ruling "substantiates and adds to the Normanna ruling and may eliminate for all time the legal basis for small-tract confiscation—something the precedent-setting Normanna decision failed to do.

"The Railroad Commission is now free from limitations of early antiquated interpretations of the conservation laws handed down before the development of our industry into its present complex form. These unfortunate limitations have cost the people of this state and our industry literally billions of dollars. The commission is now in a position to prevent . . . this waste," he said.

San Angelo Standard-Times
March 23, 1962

API BACKING URGED
ON JFK TRADE PLAN
Interior Official
Speaks in Odessa

Odessa (SC) Southwestern oilmen Thursday were urged to support the national trade policy of President Kennedy by John M. Kelly, an assistant Interior Department secretary. Kelly was keynote speaker as the production division of Southwestern District of American Petroleum Institute opened its meeting here.

The President is challenging the American people to rise to support "a national trade policy designed to meet the needs of today's world," Kelly said.

"You must do this, not only because it is your collective self-interest, but also because it is in the collective self-interest of the people . . ." he said.

Michel T. Halbouty of Houston, independent operator who also is chairman of the board of San Angelo's First National Bank, also was a speaker here and mentioned a December talk made by Kelly at a meeting of the Interstate Oil Compact Commission.

"In his talk . . . Kelly made no threat of federal control, but there were those of us who read an "or else" implication in his remarks," Halbouty said.

"For years we have been handicapped in this state by regulations that have permitted the drilling of unnecessary wells," Halbouty said. "This has resulted in an economic loss that has been every bit as devastating to those of us trying to continue to exist in this industry as excessive imports have been." The federal government, Halbouty said, wants states to modernize conservation and regulatory practices to make domestic oil competitive with foreign oil.

The Oil Daily
October 4, 1962

TEXAS SLANT-HOLE SCANDAL LINKED WITH SMALL-TRACT DRILLING
(Dallas, October 3)

Michel T. Halbouty, Houston petroleum scientist and oil operator, today linked Texas' slant-hole scandal with its long tolerance of small-tract drilling.

Addressing the Fourth National Institute for Petroleum Landmen he said it is probable "that East Texas slant-hole drillers fully observed that small-tract operators were legally taking somebody else's oil and gas, and probably justified their actions in thinking it is just as legal to illegally take somebody else's oil through slanted wells.

It is ironic that the slant-hole scandal attracted immediate widespread attention and demands for remedies, he said, because it took 22 years of massive effort to obtain action on the small-tract problem.

Fort Worth Star-Telegram
March 6, 1963

OIL MEN SAY POOLING ECONOMIC NECESSITY
by Harry Heinecke, Oil Editor

Austin, March 5—Pooling is an economic necessity and one of the basic principles of conservation, two oil authorities told a House committee Tuesday night.

Two leading advocates of HB 510, which provides for compulsory pooling, were L. F. McCollum, Houston, president of Continental Oil Company and board chairman of the American Petroleum Institute and Michel T. Halbouty, Houston, consulting geologist, petroleum engineer and independent producer.

Halbouty, a member of the CEDOT steering committee, said "Pooling is a means for every land owner to get exactly and precisely those minerals that lie beneath his property—no more and no less."

Pooling is one of the most elementary of all conservation practices and "is working in the vast majority of the oil producing states in this country," he added.

Halbouty said, "There is no violation of the principles of free enterprise or legal tradition in the pooling of small tracts to drill a single well that will do the work of several."

The Houston man said the principle of pooling protects both private and public interests; permits the use of technical knowledge; conserves capital and enables the consumer to receive oil products at low prices.

Halbouty added the measure would halt the flow of capital from Texas into other states, would enable Texas oil men to compete better with foreign imports and would offer "some measure of protection against the threat of federal control."

The Houston Post
March 18, 1963

HALBOUTY ASSAILS SADLER STAND ON OIL POOLING BILL
by Billy G. Thompson

Land Commissioner Jerry Sadler's open alliance with opponents of a controversial oil and gas bill before the Legislature came under sharp attack Sunday from a Houston oilman and leader in the ranks of advocates.

Michel T. Halbouty, vice chairman of the Committee for Equitable Development of Texas Oil & Gas Resources charged Sadler had aligned himself with a small minority of misguided oil producers in a most disappointing action by an elected state official of his stature.

Halbouty further contended Sadler had made "incredible" and "shocking" claims in a statement he sent to a legislative committee that held hearings on the hotly-disputed proposal.

Sadler announced Saturday he had accepted the chairmanship of the newly formed Committee Against Forced Pooling at the request of a group of landowners, taxpayers, veterans and small oil producers.

The Halbouty committee, made up of independent and major company leaders throughout the state, seeks a solution to the small tract drilling problem in Texas through HB 510. The measure was introduced by Rep. Wayne Gibbons, but is the handiwork of the committee.

HB 510 would permit the Railroad Commission to establish oil and gas drilling blocks by force if voluntary efforts proved unsuccessful.

Halbouty said the bill is "the most important piece of constructive oil and gas conservation legislation offered in this state in almost 30 years."

The Houston oilman, a widely recognized petroleum engineer and geologist, predicted:

"If Mr. Sadler and his organization should succeed (in defeating HB 510), the diligent efforts of hundreds of thousands of good and honorable oilmen of this state to re-establish our leadership in our most important industry would be thwarted."

The continuation of small tract drilling will mean continuation of problems which are destroying the Texas oil industry, Halbouty contended.

In a statement read for him last Tuesday night at a House Oil, Gas and Mining Committee hearing, Sadler said he opposed the bill in its present form and that its passage "would certainly affect the interest of some 3 million school children, 30,000 veteran purchasers (of Texas under the veterans land program) . . . and millions of taxpayers."

Halbouty charged Sunday that Sadler's comment about "protecting millions of little school children . . . is an incredible, shocking and demagogic statement which I consider unworthy of a man whom the people of Texas have time and again honored with high public office."

Among the good results the pooling bill would bring, Halbouty said, is "the protection of our institutions, including our schools, churches, charities, local, county and state governments."

The Houston Post
March 18, 1963

POOLING BILL HAS MERIT
by Jim Clark

What is probably the most important oil and gas conservation legislation offered in the Texas Legislature in 30 years, a bill to permit the forced pooling of drilling blocks, was sent to a House subcommittee after both sides of the issue presented their arguments.

Of course, the action of the House and the Senate on such a complicated and controversial measure cannot be anticipated, but it is evident that the proponents of the measure, House Bill 510 by Representative Wayne Gibbens, presented the most cogent arguments.

In the hearing last Tuesday night opponents of the bill had their day in court. Their best case was one presented by Alwyn King, eloquent and persuasive former president of the Texas Independent Producers and Royalty Owners Association.

Yet it seemed that even King's arguments failed to offset the most convincing arguments of the proponents.

King said the major companies, which generally support the bill, continued to import foreign oil which is detrimental to the state. Proponents had previously said that imports are stimulated by unnecessary drilling which keeps domestic crude prices higher than they should be, and thereby less competitive.

He pointed to the fact that "little men" were being forced to sell out or were in the process of selling out. The week before Michel T. Halbouty said this, but he attributed the condition to the self-imposed unnecessary high expense of drilling thousands of unnecessary wells. He said this was a burden that he and few other independents could long afford to bear without eventually being forced out of business.

The Oil Daily
December 4, 1963

JFK ASSASSINATION SEEN AS POLITICAL CALL TO OILMEN

Houston—The assassination of President Kennedy "should have left us all with some feeling of guilt in the sense that we have participated too little in public affairs."

Michel T. Halbouty, independent Houston oilman and earth scientist, said so here Tuesday night in an address to Gulf Coast sections of the Society of Petroleum Engineers and the American Petroleum Institute's Division of Production.

Oil industry professionals have left too many things to be done by the other fellow, who too often has turned out to be a screwball, he asserted.

"I am not saying that we can eliminate assassins and misfits . . . but that collectively we can change the thinking and courses of un-savory groups that don't care about anything but themselves," he asserted.

The Houston Chronicle
December 3, 1964

COMMISSION RULING RAPPED BY HALBOUTY

Houston oilman Michel T. Hal-bouty said today some action will be taken to halt the "shocking and appalling order" of the Railroad Commission in hiking gas allow-ables for small tract owners in the Port Acres field.

He said the 326,000 cubic feet daily allowable given 22 small tract wells in the Jefferson County field more than double the more realistic 150,000 cubic feet daily currently allowed.

"(The order) flaunts the de-cision of the Texas Supreme Court", he declared.

He added that, "This is the first time that a state regulatory agency has openly declared that it was appropriating unto itself the authority to take property belong-ing to one person and arbitrarily give it to another."

The Houston Post
December 3, 1964

ALLOWABLE REVISION BLASTED BY PRODUCER

A new Railroad Commission order revising upward the special gas production allowables for 22 wells in the Port Acres Field drew sharp criticism Wednesday from an independent producer who led the lengthy fight against allow-ables favoring small tract opera-tors in the Jefferson County area.

The Texas regulatory agency boosted the allowables for the Port Acres wells to 238,000 cubic feet daily from 150,000 cubic feet in an order issued Monday. The latter flow rate was set in Novem-ber 1963 after the State Supreme Court voided commission rules which allocated production one-third equally among all producers and two-thirds on the basis of tract size. The court found such formulas deny each operator his fair share of a reservoir's gas.

Blunt criticism of the new Port Acres order came from Michel T. Halbouty, who led the court fight to overturn the one-third/two-thirds allocation formula.

"This is a shocking and appall-ing order," stated Halbouty.

"It flaunts the decision of the Texas Supreme Court in the Port Acres case."

Halbouty continued:

"The people of this state should be particularly concerned because this is the first time that a state regulatory agency has openly de-clared that it was appropriating unto itself the authority to take property belonging to one person and arbitrarily give it to another."

The Houston Chronicle
January 27, 1965
OIL AND GAS POOLING LAW FOR STATE URGED
by Albert T. Collins, Bus. Ed.

Requested passage of an oil and gas pooling law by the legislature was viewed today as a means of restoring vitality to the oil and gas industry in Texas.

Gov. John Connally, in his legislative address, urged the legislature to pass a measure authorizing forced oil and gas pooling.

"Where several different individuals own an interest in oil and gas in a common reservoir," the governor said, "it is often both inefficient and uneconomical for each to drill a separate well in order to recover his fair share of oil and gas from that reservoir."

Connally said he supports a statute which would authorize the Railroad Commission to provide for pooling of "these separately owned interests in a common reservoir—so long as the correlative rights of each interest owner are protected."

Houston independent oil operator Michel T. Halbouty called the recommended legislation "a strong step forward in the direction of total conservation" for the state.

He predicted that its passage would "reverse the declining trend in oil and gas exploration because it will mean the elimination of wasteful, unnecessary wells."

Tulsa Daily World
March 8, 1965
... FORCED POOLING BILL ... PERSONAL TRIUMPH FOR CRUSADING GEOLOGIST
by Max Skelton (AP Oil Writer)

Houston (AP)—Texas oil and gas conservation statutes date back to 1899 but final action on a compulsory pooling statute was not undertaken until last week.

Gov. John Connally signed on Thursday a bill authorizing the Texas Railroad Commission to require pooling of the operation of a drilling tract when voluntary efforts fail.

In effect, the bill was designed to prevent tracts of only townlot size from receiving more than a fair share of production.

While Texas pioneered many an oil and gas conservation measure, 31 other states were ahead of Texas in adopting such pooling authority in one form or another. Kansas now is the only major oil state without such authority.

Until a year ago, a compulsory pooling bill was too controversial for Texas legislatures to handle.

But Connally's signature Thursday was something of a personal triumph for Michel T. Halbouty, a Houston independent, who launched on Dec. 1, 1959, a one-man crusade that eventually led to the new bill sailing through the Texas legislature this year with ease.

"It's not a perfect pooling bill, but it is what I wanted," Halbouty said Saturday. "It protects the big operator and the little man. No one can hurt anyone. It means adding teeth to our state's conservation program."

Halbouty ran into the small tract problem in the Port Acres Field in the southeast corner of Texas and launched the crusade at breaking up a Texas tradition that anyone had a right to drill for oil or gas regardless of how small a tract or lease he owned.

Both the railroad commission and the 7,000 member Texas Independent Producers and Royalty Owners Association long had championed such a tradition.

The Port Acres Field sprawled across two small-lot subdivisions and included more than 500 leases involving tracts of only townlot size.

Halbouty went to court—and eventually won—with an argument that drilling permits for 35 wells involving a total of only 25 acres would mean the 35 wells could ultimately produce from 20 to 25 per cent of all the reserves beneath the 4,000-acre field.

He also began stumping the state to tell anyone who would listen that such a policy meant two things—small tracts were receiving more than their fair share of production and hundreds of unnecessary wells were being drilled across the state.

"I ignored my own business affairs and health and during that one-man crusade that lasted 19 or 20 months," Halbouty said, "I was threatened to be whipped in Midland and Victoria."

By early 1961, however, Halbouty's cause had attracted a few followers, including several independents.

On May 15, 1961, Halbouty and a few friends persuaded the state's independent operators to relax their traditional stand against compulsory pooling a bit by offering to assist the railroad commission in efforts to correct inequities resulting from small tract drilling.

"That was when we got our foot in the door," Halbouty said.

The Houston Post
September 19, 1965

WATER CITED AS MAJOR CHALLENGE OF GEOLOGIST

Finding new sources of water that will avert a world-wide shortage was cited here at the week end as a serious challenge for geologists.

Michel T. Halbouty, a geologist-petroleum engineer-oil producer from Houston, stressed this point in keynoting the first annual meeting of the Texas Section, American Institute of Professional Geologists. Some 200 members and non-members attended the two-day session that had as its theme future trends in the role of the professional geologist.

Halbouty, who is president of the section, spoke on the importance of geology to mankind. He pointed out that lack of sufficient water limits economic growth, undermines and lowers living standards, jeopardizes the security of nations and endangers health of people.

"Answers must be found for this baffling and seemingly impossible problem or we face the certainty of watching the world's future multiplying population slowly but surely perish for lack of this vital natural resource," said Halbouty.

"This, I would say, is one of our profession's most serious challenges in meeting human needs of the future," he added.

Los Angeles Herald-Examiner
June 18, 1970

OIL INDUSTRY CENSURED FOR 'MISLEADING PUBLIC'

Oil industry executives were under censure from one of their own leaders for "propaganda and promotion" which has "misled the public.

Michel T. Halbouty, nationally-honored Houston geologist, told the American Association of Petroleum Landmen at the Beverly Hilton that "the crisis hanging over the petroleum industry has been created by self-serving communications from the industry."

"We have been concentrating on propaganda and promotion when we should have been concentrating on facts and the industry story," Halbouty said. "We must give the people honest light so they can find their own way."

Halbouty said he thought the time had come when the industry had to stop blaming the news media and others when the fact is that the industry itself has been ineffective in communicating objectively.

"Through our system of controlled public relations and public affairs we have answered questions that have not been raised and we have not always subjected ourselves to questions the public might want to ask . . . We have been mouthing a set of cliches about high risks, low profits, excessive imports, tax matters, and price controls. These are our problems. Now we must concern ourselves with public problems."

Halbouty said that the Soviet Union is gaining control over or favor with countries where most of the world's oil is located, such as the Middle East, Libya, Nigeria, and the rest of Africa, with South America as its next goal. He said this is a threat to every individual in the free world, but to Americans more than to others because they have more freedom to lose.

He said this country has ample supplies of energy for its own use with only half of its oil and gas discovered in the lower 48 states plus the prospect of abundance of shale oil, coal from which both gas and gasoline can be made, nuclear energy and other sources.

"But the problem is to supply friendly nations, especially Western Europe, Japan and South America," he said.

"The only place on earth outside the United States where the energy supply potential is high and where there is no direct present threat from Communist Russia is Canada," Halbouty said, "and that is why there has to be better relations with Canada in the field of oil and gas."

Halbouty advocated free trade on important items needed by both countries, especially petroleum, under a common policy.

The speaker was sharply critical of the Nixon proposal to renounce United States ownership of resources in the offshore in waters deeper than 200 meters or beyond the 3-mile limit, whichever is greater. He said 26 natural resources in addition to petroleum are covered by the proposal.

Recalling a recent proposal by a member of the board of directors of Get Oil Out (GOO) of Santa Barbara to nationalize the oil industry, Halbouty said—

"Today nationalization of the oil industry; tomorrow the other business and industrial complexes, including organized labor," he said.

"Do the average citizens of this country realize what this man is advocating? Do they want to change our system of government? Do they want free enterprise, capitalism and individual freedom to be swallowed up by nationalization, socialism or communism?"

"I can answer that and so can you. They do not."

"If the people in industry, business, the professions, and labor do not begin to speak up, educate, inform, and create a dialogue with the man in the street, if we don't end our monologue with ourselves, and our talking to instead of with the people, or answer some simple questions and give some straight answers, nationalization is what we are going to get", he warned.

Halbouty said the petroleum industry has been concentrating on its problems and ignoring the public's problems. He said the

public could not care less about industry woes, but that it would be interested in its own problems, those of the country, and the survival of freedom.

Halbouty is a past president of the American Association of Petroleum Geologists and presently chairman of the board of the Energy Research and Education Foundation.

Oilgram
June 19, 1970

OIL 'ANSWERS QUESTIONS THAT WEREN'T ASKED,' HALBOUTY TELLS LANDMEN

Los Angeles—6/18: Houston oilman-geologist Michel T. Halbouty told American Association of Petroleum Landmen today that oil industry has "wasted millions of dollars in attempts to inform the public, and in turn, the people have laughed at our antics and referred to the lot of us as a bunch of selfish, rich, arrogant bastards."

Halbouty, a former president of American Assn. of Petroleum Geologists, charged industry "for years" has been "attempting to communicate to the people through a controlled system of what we call public relations or public affairs.

"We have answered questions that haven't been raised, but we have not always subjected ourselves to the questions the public might want to ask," he continued. "We have used competition as an excuse for covering up in far too many cases."

Halbouty said "most Americans have no idea how close" nation is to nationalization of oil industry, adding that nationalization of business and industry are the goal of "the agitators and militants who are prodding young people in this country."

He called for "firm international petroleum policy" between U.S. and Canada, saying Canada is only place of high energy supply potential not facing "serious threat from the communists."

The Houston Post
June 21, 1970

HALBOUTY VIEWS SOVIET OIL TARGETS
by Max P. Skelton, AP Oil Writer

An internationally known geologist says Russia is adding emphasis to its petroleum objectives that involve political and economic pressures throughout the world.

"Russia hopes to dominate the world through petroleum," says Michel T. Halbouty, former president of the American Association of Petroleum Geologists.

The Houston independent oil operator says the Soviets are using every device necessary to get a foothold for their coming petroleum domination.

"Their interest in Vietnam is the oil in Indonesia, not in helping the North Vietnamese," he says.

"Their interest in the Arab-Israeli conflict is their plan eventually to control Middle East and African oil—not in their love for Arabs or Africans."

Halbouty believes Canada is the only place outside the United States where the energy supply potential is high and where there is no current serious threat from communism.

He predicts the United States will gradually need to import more and more Canadian crude but expresses concern about Western Europe and other areas that depend on petroleum from the Middle East, Africa and South America.

Under present conditions, Halbouty says, there is no way this country could provide its allies and friends with oil over an extended time as was the case during the Arab-Israeli conflict of 1967.

Halbouty gives this appraisal of major producing areas:

Middle East—"Today most of the countries of the Middle East are either hostile to the United States and friendly to Russia or they are under overwhelming pressure from the Kremlin and their own leftist neighbors."

Africa—"Within the past year one regime after another in the important oil countries, regimes once friendly to the free world, have been replaced by those favorable to the Russians."

Libya—"One of the most prolific oil areas of the world, a government friendly to the United States has been overthrown and replaced by a puppet of the Soviets and I would imagine that our time there is relatively short."

Nigeria—"Rapidly becoming the location of tremendous offshore oil reserves, the existing government owes much of its existence to the Soviet Union."

Indonesia—"A considerable potential for tremendous new oil reserves is being found but only the action in Vietnam has so far prevented communist control."

Venezuela—"Castro's agents are a threat to Venezuela and its great oil reserves. In fact, it is obvious that this is communism's prime objective in this hemisphere."

Halbouty says he often wonders if the American public is aware of the fact more than 75 per cent of the known proven free world reserves of oil are in the Middle East and African countries either hostile or under unrelenting communist pressure.

"The Middle East is now providing 67 per cent of our oil requirement for the war in Viet Nam," he says.

He adds that Soviet petroleum marketing arrangements have reached almost every capital in Europe.

"Their basic plan is, as most people can see once it is shown them, to make all oil consuming nations, including us, dependent on petroleum they control in any part of the world," he says.

"With that goal accomplished, the cold war will end and the communists will be the winners."

Oklahoma Journal
November 9, 1970

TEXAS GEOLOGIST CITES COMMUNIST OIL THREAT
by Guy A. Goodine

Tulsa (UPI)—North America is the last bulwark against Communist hopes to control the world's oil resources, a Houston producer and geologist says.

To offset trends he feels threatens North American security, Michel T. Halbouty, president of his independent oil firm by the same name, wants the federal government to give a little on its policy of restricting import of Canadian oil.

"Greater importation of Canadian petroleum into the United States under a common policy of free trade on important items needed by both countries is necessary," Halbouty said.

Noting a growing Soviet influence in most oil producing countries in the world, and recent moves to nationalize the oil industry in many countries, Halbouty said, "the only place on the Earth outside the United States where the energy supply potential is high and where there is no present serious threat from the Communists is Canada."

"In this regard," he added, "it is an enigma to me that the U.S. and Canada have not, long ago, entered into a firm international petroleum policy."

He blamed recent action by the Nixon administration in limiting imports of Canadian crude for causing "some misunderstanding," but said he feels that move will be little more than a short-term deterrent in arriving at a common energy policy.

"We should encourage the best of relationships and free trade on important items needed by both countries," he said, "especially on petroleum. Under a common policy I feel that incentives to find additional crude for U.S. and Canadian security would be forthcoming."

This is not the first time the elderly oilman has expressed concern for the future of the oil industry in the free world.

In 1965, he set off on a "domestic exploration explosion" program in which he was seeking increased oil and gas reserves within the U.S. He said it was to ease U.S. dependency on foreign oil and gas.

He began that campaign at his own expense and was credited recently with being the first American independent oil operator to find gas in Alaska.

He has often urged European markets to take a stronger attitude toward their stake in a dependable U.S. source of supply.

Halbouty is a former president of the American Association of Petroleum Geologists, the world's largest geological society, and is now an honorary member of that organization based on his contributions to the profession and the association.

Ruston, (La.) Daily Leader
November 10, 1970

U.S., CANADA NEED TREATY, SAYS OILMAN

Tulsa, Okla. (UPI) — Houston oil producer and geologist Michel T. Halbouty said Monday the United States and Canada should sign an oil treaty because North America is fast becoming the last bulwark against communist attempts to take over oil producing countries.

"We should encourage the best of relationships and free trade on important items needed by both countries, especially on petroleum," he said. "Under a common policy I feel that incentives to find additional crude for U.S. and Canadian security would be forthcoming."

Halbouty, president of an independent oil firm and former president of the American Association of Petroleum Geologists said the Nixon administration is to blame in limiting the imports of Canadian crude.

"Greater importation of Canadian petroleum into the United States under a common policy of free trade on important items for both countries is necessary," Halbouty said.

EDITORIALS

*. . . regarding Mr. Halbouty's views and
positions on the issues*

The Beaumont Enterprise
January 21, 1960

A CALL FOR CONSERVATION

Michel T. Halbouty, geologist, engineer and independent producer and operator knows the petroleum and associated industries up one side and down the other. When he speaks, therefore, he speaks with authority, and even those who disagree with some of the ideas he has on the complicated operation of a complicated business have tremendous respect for the sincerity and ability of this highly successful figure in Texas oil and natural gas. This is because so much of his great store of knowledge has been accumulated through actual experience.

In an address before the Spindletop Section of the Society of Petroleum Engineers, the Beaumont native, who now lives in Houston, spent a great deal of time in discussion of a subject very dear to his heart—more effective efforts toward conservation of petroleum resources and more orderly and common-sense development of oil and natural gas fields.

Stating that $30 million worth of petroleum liquids may be lost at the Port Acres gas-distillate field alone unless the Railroad Commission of Texas amends spacing regulations, to prohibit the drilling of unnecessary wells, Mr. Halbouty made this highly significant statement:

"We cannot have partial conservation. We must have total conservation." He also warned that unless Texas and other oil and gas producing states shore up their regulatory statutes to insure the maximum recovery of underground oil and gas supplies, the industry is threatened with federal regulation which would destroy the independent operators and injure the major oil companies.

It is not surprising that the Houston man feels that the complexity and contradictory nature of the state's conservation laws have made a great contribution to the confusion that now exists. And, it is not surprising that he proposes a general shoring up of these statutes, with a modernization program to meet today's pressing problems. It stands to reason that such a streamlining process would be in the interest of order and understanding in the relationship of government to operations. In fact, this is the situation in a great many other Texas fields of activity.

Mr. Halbouty sees the responsibility of officials of cities and towns in which oil or gas is discovered as being twofold: Conservation of natural resources and protection of the lives and rights of their citizens.

Oil Magazine
March, 1960

Editorial

The pseudo-intellectuals ensconced in some of our leading universities and on the staffs of some of the most prominent business publications, including larger daily newspapers, who criticize petroleum conservation and call it a price-fixing gimmick, are steeped in abysmal ignorance. Either that or they are outright socialists who want to see the American petroleum industry under complete federal control as a major step in changing the form of government in this country.

The best bet, of course, is that they are stupid rather than subversive. But they are making a pretty fair case for the subversive and should be answered. Fortunately here lately, they are being answered by such groups as the Mid-Continental Oil and Gas Association, the American Petroleum Institute, the Independent Producers Association of America, the American Association of Oilwell Drilling Contractors, the Petroleum and Equipment Suppliers Association, and a few effective individuals.

The attack on conservation ignores history. In the 1930's, when effective conservation was first instituted in this country through good conservation laws in Oklahoma, Texas, and other states, this country was facing the end of the line as far as petroleum reserves are concerned. In other words, if there had been no conservation there would now be no domestic oil.

The conservation attack always includes calling the market demand laws, proration, spacing and even the Interstate Oil Compact Commission as price fixing gimmicks. Without these things there would be no conservation and without conservation there would be no domestic oil. And without domestic oil there is little doubt that we would be paying much more than we are now paying for foreign oil. And we would be paying it without benefit of a vital and virile domestic industry which is the highest taxpayer in the United States and which has one of the biggest payrolls and pays out money in lease, rentals, and bonuses that generates more taxes and more jobs.

Of course, conservation is no price-fixing gimmick, but if it were, it would certainly be a worthwhile one in view of the facts in the preceding paragraph.

But what all of this is getting around to is that today there is a great need to bring conservation up to date. If we don't then we are going to be wide open to attack. The attack could lead to federal control, then monopoly, followed by socialism—the ultimate goal.

Organizations like the West Texas Oil and Gas Association and individuals like Houstonian Michel

T. Halbouty are trying to show the way. They are advocating sane conservation laws that will deprive the racketeers in the industry of an unfair advantage which enables them to siphon off oil and gas which does not belong to them. This injustice is a perfect argument for federal control as Halbouty has so eloquently pointed out.

. . . It is high time that more attention be paid to the West Texas Oil and Gas Association and Michel T. Halbouty. This country stands to lose too much otherwise. Halbouty says that political and partial conservation will lead to ruin.

There can be absolutely no doubt about the truth of that statement.

Kilgore (TX) News-Herald
April 4, 1960

JIM CLARK COMMENTS

For several months now Michel T. Halbouty, Houston independent oilman, has been making the rounds of the state in a sort of one-man campaign for what he calls "Total Conservation" of oil and gas.

Starting with a well-written and documented speech in Houston, he has moved to Beaumont, Tyler, Dallas and Wichita Falls. Later this month, he will go to Midland. Therefore, most of the state has heard his pleas. Wherever his talk has been made it has been well received, not only by the industry, but by the press and public.

Halbouty has taken steps to make sure the press and the public got his message. He started out by saying the industry talked to itself too much and that his plea was not only in the interest of the industry but in public interest.

He has been critical of several policies of the Texas Railroad Commission even while praising the commissioners for their great contribution to oil and gas conservation. He thinks it is time to change a few policies to meet modern conditions and to follow technological advancements, especially in natural gas.

Halbouty has been particularly critical of the arbitrary formula for allocating oil and gas allowables. This formula is based on one third of the per well allowable for the well and two thirds for acreage. The commission thinks this formula is fair. Halbouty thinks it is arbitrary and confiscatory. He has used illustrations to prove that in many areas an exception to the field spacing rule under the present allocation formula provides certain operators and landowners with a legal weapon to confiscate the oil or gas that rightfully belongs to an adjacent operator and landowner.

It has been suggested by Halbouty that the commission adopt a new formula based on the number of acre feet beneath any given tract. Acre-feet is the equivalent of the number of surface acres multiplied by the number of feet of productive oil sand. No new law is needed to accomplish this, Halbouty says, simply a new and enlightened policy.

The Houston Post
May 29, 1960

OIL CONSERVATION CRUSADE: HALBOUTY'S SERMONS HAVE WON CONVERTS

by Billy G. Thompson,
Post Oil Editor

One night last December an independent oilman finished a dramatic speech before a combined group of two professional societies here.

His audience had sat spellbound for well over an hour. He was perspiring in spite of the coolness of the weather. His eyes still flashed as he reclined into his chair. There was a moment of prolonged silence.

Then came a thunderous ovation, almost unheard of in the dignified group of scientists and technologists. The audience of nearly 600 rose to its feet in unison and the applause became louder. Then the speaker stood again. His flashing eyes turned soft and warm in a smile of deep appreciation.

The evening and the speech marked the beginning of a half-year long trail across Texas for Michel T. Halbouty. His passage may well mark him as the trailblazer of a new philosophy about the state's most important industry.

To the north, east, west and south went the multi-careered Houstonian, preaching a message of total conservation of Texas' rich petroleum resources—rather than "partial" and what, charged Halbouty, is sometimes "political" conservation.

In the memory of other oilmen and Texas business leaders, never has one man launched himself on such a strenuous, controversial and "one-aganst-the-field" task.

Tagged as "Crusade"

Early in what developed into a nine-speech stumping of the major oil centers of Texas, Halbouty's campaign was described by a newspaper as a "crusade for conservation." The term stuck and at each and every stop on his travels, his introduction invariably mentioned "crusader" or "who is conducting a one-man crusade." From start to finish, Halbouty's campaign was epitomized by his declaration that:

"Conservation is more important to the public interest and the public welfare than it is to the petroleum industry or to any geologist or engineer or manager in the industry," he told his Houston audience last December.

"It supersedes the proprietary interest of any landowner, oil operator, or oil company. The public interest supersedes any personal interest in wealth or power.

"I would like to plead with this industry and the citizens of the petroleum states that we shore up our conservation laws—modernize them to meet existing problems—before we are faced with federal laws on this subject that could and would lead to federal control of our industry."

He raised this warning on the night of December 1, 1959, at a joint meeting of the Society of Petroleum Engineers and the Houston chapter, American Petroleum Institute.

4 Recommendations

The warning was repeated at every halt along with four recommendations to update conservation laws and practices:

1) Through legislation that would make pooling on the established well spacing patterns compulsory. Such a law would be helpful, if not essential, to the regulatory body in discharging its duty to prevent waste and protect correlative rights.

2) Through discontinuance of arbitrarily selected allocation formulas to establish producing allowables for oil and gas wells.

3) By early adoption of temporary spacing rules in newly discovered fields.

4) By adoption, by towns and cities, of ordinances to protect the life and property from the hazards accompanying exploration for and production of petroleum.

The persevering operator-engineer-geologist—some of his associates say—has undertaken his "mission" with such sincerity and zeal that "he is actually sacrificing his health and his business."

Actually, Halbouty asserts, the campaign—a personally conceived and supported endeavor—was sparked by his intense concern for the conservation of oil and gas.

In advocating modernized conservation practices, Halbouty has gone against some traditional philosophies. He bucked the standard rules and regulations of the regulatory authorities. He moved out in defiance of what others said were established court decisions. And he invaded "the private do-main of a handful of oil operators who have always lived on small tract operations because they were either unwilling or unable to get into larger lease plays before oil was discovered."

What makes a man turn his mental and fiscal resources against such seemingly overwhelming odds?

Halbouty sums it up this way:

"For 30 years—ever since I was a little shaver out of college—I have been practicing conservation. In the last 15 of those years, the (Railroad) commission has become more lax toward conservation."

Views are Accepted

From petroleum engineers and oilmen, his views appeared to have overwhelming acceptance.

There are voices of opposition and objection but they are marked by their low volume and infrequency. Likely, they will become inaudible as well pressures hit bottom.

He has probably become the most widely heard independent oilman in the state.

He has received numerous suggestions, with encouragement to make the supreme effort for total conservation—run for a position on the Railroad Commission, or even governor.

The irrepressible Halbouty leaves you believing that he would do just that, if it becomes necessary for his crusade to achieve its goal.

This, then, is the story of one man and his crusade. It shows that the power of the individual is not dead.

Halbouty has already stirred thousands to action. His mail proves that.

Whether Halbouty is right or wrong or whether his campaign is a success or failure, it has been something to spark the imagination and revive the spirit of individual action.

The Houston Post
November 7, 1960

HALBOUTY GETS HIS 'IRISH' UP
by Jim Clark

Somewhere in his background there must be a little Irish mixed up in Michel T. Halbouty. You could see it coming out in Los Angeles last week as he addressed the American Association of Petroleum Geologists.

What Halbouty was stirred up about was the way many of the oil companies have been laying off geologists, geophysicists and other earth scientists and members of the oil finding trade in the past year or so.

He said he was puzzled when one major oil company economist after another goes before big audiences and puts out press releases about all of the oil and gas this country will need in the next 10 years on the one hand, and their companies continue to eliminate the very people who can find the necessary reserves on the other hand.

Really it doesn't make much sense. Big companies, particularly the integrated companies, are supposed to be long range organizations as contrasted with the short range activities of the independents in the oil and gas business. When the market or the price for oil drops, the independent is in immediate trouble and is forced to act. But the same thing wouldn't seem to apply to bigger companies, especially when they can see enough optimism in the future to send speakers around the country quoting statistics that make you wonder how the industry is going the measure up to its requirements.

So, Halbouty offered a suggestion to the bigger companies in Los Angeles last week. He said that while he believes imports in this country today really exceed the point where they do more than supplement domestic production that he recognized the necessity of imports. He based this on the thesis that it is better for American companies to be in control of most foreign oil operations than it would be for the Russians to have that control.

But he added that it was a burden on domestic producers to have to compete with foreign oil that was somewhere around $1 a barrel cheaper than domestic oil.

So, he suggested that the extra dollar being made on each barrel of imports might be well utilized in putting oilfinders back to work to look for the oil and gas the petroleum economists say we will need in the next decade to meet our domestic requirements.

Pointing out that in any emergency, foreign oil, even that in

American hands, could become unavailable, Halbouty suggested that all importers are primarily and basically domestic companies.

He said that if these companies would start converting foreign oil profits into domestic exploration they could not only stimulate their industry but they could utilize the genius and the know-how of the men they are now laying off and retiring early.

The Houston Chronicle
January 8, 1961

DRILLING TRACT MEET POSES QUERY: 'WHAT ARE UNNECESSARY WELLS?'
by Tom Lester, Oil Editor

Every oilman is opposed to drilling unnecessary wells, but when it comes to mandatory pooling, unitization or spacing rulings, it's a different matter to a large number of Texas producers and royalty owners.

That fact was brought out at a meeting here of Texas Independent Producers and Royalty Owners Assn. members last Friday. The meeting was called chiefly to discuss possible changes in T.I.P.-R.O.'s traditional stand against any type of mandatory unitization or pooling.

After a number of the members had expressed their opinions for and against the issue and the meeting was near adjournment, Houston oilman Johnny Mitchell, member of the unitization committee and chairman for the session said he thought there should be an expression from the members.

"Everybody who favors compulsory pooling, rise," he suggested.

Few for Pooling

There was a stir of a handful of men among the some 100-odd present and it was hard to tell whether those standing were merely getting up to leave, when Michel Halbouty, arch foe of small-tract drilling, leaped to his feet and shouted:

"That's not the way to put it. All of you who are opposed to drilling unnecessary wells, please stand."

It appeared unanimous.

Oil
February, 1961

EDITORIAL

The fact that there might be a way to end the sometimes bitter and always unnecessary misunderstanding between various segments of the petroleum industry was expressed in a landmark speech by Michel T. Halbouty, Houston independent oilman, in Tulsa last month.

Halbouty had a simple plan—an informal forum. He said the suggestion came to him from L. F. McCollum, president of the Continental Oil Company, while the two men were traveling together on a plane to the Interstate Oil Compact Commission held in Phoenix.

The title of Halbouty's talk, which was a masterpiece of simplicity, was One Step Toward Survival. The Houston oilman, like oilmen all over the country, are concerned with the survival of small independent oilmen. Halbouty is not himself a "small" independent. He is probably in a little higher bracket of independents. But he was once small and his preoccupation over the fate of small independents is deep seated.

Halbouty recognized that both independents and majors are at fault today, but he dismissed the idea that the reasons included selfishness or greed. He said the biggest reason was a lack of understanding of the problems of each other. He listed several of the complaints majors have against independents and viceversa. So, he said, no one is without sin.

But he added that by a simple act of sitting around and discussing mutual complaints with each other most of them may be either eliminated or explained to the satisfaction of the other side.

The Houstonian did not advocate the formation of another association or club or organization of any kind. He simply said there should be regional discussions where majors and independents with similar operating conditions could meet and iron out their differences.

He said the industry had enough problems today without continuing to add any more that could be avoided. He thought the traditional rivalries between independents and majors were feeding the enemies of a free domestic oil industry too much fuel with which to fight the industry. Halbouty said there were justified complaints by both sides against the other, but they should be kept in the family until such a time as they were beyond solution and until the public interest became involved.

Halbouty was critical of associations that spend their time getting their membership worked up against the major companies. He said he thought associations were necessary but that with conditions like they are today there were certainly better things for them to do than stir up unnecessary fights that break out into the public print and put the whole oil industry in a bad light.

Maybe something as simple as sitting down, breaking bread, and talking things over in private can eliminate many problems and leave the industry with sufficient energy to meet its real enemies head on.

Oil Magazine
March, 1962

PORT ACRES— A SIGNIFICANT DECISION

Two significant decisions by the Texas Supreme Court in the past year, one of them less than a month ago, have apparently put a quietus on the practice of drilling unnecessary wells in that state.

The decisions were made in appeals to the high court in the Normanna and Port Acres suits, brought by operators of large tracts who had drilled on state prescribed acreage patterns, in most cases after cooperative landowners had entered into voluntary agreements with oilmen!

In Normanna, the Supreme Court said that there would be no further drilling on tracts of less than the prescribed acreage under exceptions to the state-wide drilling law simply to permit a landowner or small leaseholder to get a well on his property. The decision did point out, however, that consideration would have to be given those who had already drilled such wells and that in the future when a small tract owner could not get a fair deal from others in the pooling area that they would be permitted to drill their own well.

In the Port Acres case, brought by Houston oilman Michel T. Halbouty and other operators in the field, the court said: ". . . To infer that the rule of capture gives the landowner the legally protected right to capture the oil and gas underlying his neighbor's tract is entirely inconsistent with the ownership theory." The court then put a definition on the rule of capture that many leading oilmen, since the late Henry L. Doherty, have claimed is proper when it said: "The rule of capture can mean little more than that due to their fugitive nature, the hydrocarbons when captured belong to the owner of the well to which they flowed, irrespective of where they may have been in place originally, without liability to his neighbor for drainage. That is to say that since the gas in a continuous reservoir will flow to a point of low pressure, the landowner is not restricted to the particular gas which may underlie his property originally, but is the owner of all that he may legally recover."

The court put high emphasis on the word legally and described the rule of capture as one of accountability.

In addition to bringing the landmark Port Acres case, Halbouty carried out a one-man crusade for the modernization of Texas conservation laws last year. In his lectures made mostly to professional geological and engineering groups, and petroleum associations over the state, Halbouty stressed many of the points contained in his lawsuit. The Supreme Court apparently agreed with practically every important point Halbouty brought up. Texas conservation leaders contend that Halbouty's crusade had as much to do with enlightening the court as the evidence in the case. The vigor of the crusade and the fact that the state press gave it so much attention undoubtedly brought it more emphatically to the court's attention. This seems to prove the point that a vigorous program of information and education can have important impact.

Halbouty's crusade, incidentally, started long before even the Normanna decision. The Port Acres case, which directly involved the Halbouty properties, confirmed and added strength to the Normanna decision. Now most Texans believe the fight for modernized conservation in their state has been won.

Whether it has been won or not, a new organization known as the Committee for Equitable Development of Texas Natural Resources (popularly the CED) has been formed. One of its leaders is Halbouty. It is composed of leading independents and integrated companies in every section of the

state. The chairman is Charles Al-
corn of Houston, Falcon-Seaboard
Oil Co. executive and long-time
leader in both the API and Texas
Mid-Continent Oil and Gas. Assn.
affairs.

Oil Magazine
November, 1962
**MIKE HALBOUTY
EXHAUSTS THE SUBJECT
OF CONSERVATION**

Michel T. Halbouty, Houston independent, is one of those rare
birds who combines the dedicated
zeal of the true scientist and the
shrewd acumen of the business
man. As a geologist he has discovered many new fields in Texas
and Louisiana—as a business man
he had the ability and the industry to develop them.

Mike's talent is such that it was
necessary for his alma mater,
Texas A&M, to create a special
degree with which to honor him.

Mike has a good many hobbies.
One is that of collecting, not bird
eggs or postage stamps, but
banks!

Mike's pet subject is "CON-
SERVATION"—and it may be
that he has made himself something of a nuisance to those authorities and interests opposed to
any such thing.

In a speech made at the National Institute for Petroleum
Landmen at Dallas in early October (a meeting sponsored by the
Southwestern Legal Foundation)
he gave the most thorough and
convincing treatment of the subject that we have read to this
date.

The title of Mike's speech was
"Present Trends in Well Spacing
and Possible Effects of Normanna
and Port Acres Decisions."

Following the introduction Mike
presented a chronological background of petroleum conservation
in Texas beginning with the association of producers formed at
Spindletop to deal with blowouts
and fires. The head of the association was J. S. Cullinan (founder
of the Texas Co.) and his committee was authorized to wear and
use guns for enforcement.

The next time conservation became a problem was when several
of the old salt dome fields started
producing salt water and the
farmers, ranchers and citizens in
the surrounding communities became increasingly alarmed over
the problem of pollution. These, of
course, were simply measures by
operators to protect themselves
from losses and damage suits.

Mike brings us to the saga of
east Texas: "It was the last wild
wasteland of oil production. It was
the 'Last Boom'."

Then Mike proceeds to tell us
about the effect of partial conservation in Texas . . .

"Probably the most telling blow
to Texas' hopes for conservation
progress came in the Hawkins
case when a Court of Civil Appeals on April 10, 1946, handed
down a decision upholding the
arbitrary rule of thumb allocation
factors established by the Railroad Commission and went even
further by establishing, in a
judge's dictum, the rule that anyone drilling on a tract of land
under an exception to the state-
wide spacing rule had the right

to not only drill the well, but to make a reasonable profit therefrom."

In his own fashion, Mike deals with the "waste of recoverable reserves:

"In addition to the commission's duty to protect the correlative rights of the owners in oil pool, it also has the duty to prevent waste. Unless the commission handles the allocation problem within a pool on a proper basis so that the rights of all owners are protected, it disturbs or realigns the ownership of the pool. This becomes important not only in the primary stages of production, but also in the secondary recovery projects also at the income rates which are greater than their fair share of the properties.

"Other responsible owners in the pool often refuse to make this concession and as a result efforts to effect secondary recovery projects are thwarted. Thus oil may be left abandoned in the ground, which is a loss to the state, which means the taxpayer, as well as the owners in the pool. It is also a loss to national security and the consumers of oil and gas products. Moreover, it is a direct and often significant loss to land and royalty owners, among others, including the local community, its merchants and farmers and professional men, and the county, school districts, and other taxing authorities."

The meat of the Halbouty speech is contained in the following discussion of *"decisions based*

on political and emotional factors create inequities."

"There can be little doubt that some political considerations became roadblocks to good conservation in Texas, both in the Railroad Commission and in the courts. Because of the voluminous amount of technological data supporting their views the big companies always get on the side of justice in matters of conservation. The small independents who also favor similar views find that at times it is really a little difficult to carry the big companies on their shoulders while expressing the same views."

Mike pointed out that two court decisions open a new approach for a policy of total conservation, that is, the possible effect of the Normanna and Port Acres decisions on future trends in well spacing.

With the incisive probe of the surgeon's scalpel Mike touched on the east Texas slant-hole scandal which has recently preoccupied the thoughts of Texas oilmen.

In conclusion Mike said "we are facing a new era of conservation in Texas."

Mike may be one of those infernal optimists who are always seeing better days just around the corner—but more power to him, anyway. His Dallas speech was a masterful contribution to current oil literature and should be in every oilman's library, whether he is a conservationist or slant-hole driller who must do his reading in a Texas prison until paroled for good behavior.

Odessa (TX) American and
Wichita Falls (TX) Times
March 31, 1963

TALES OF
THE OIL INDUSTRY
by Jim Clark

It is so rare that a man doggedly pursues a policy and a program which has the potential of costing him more than a million dollars, just for the purpose of standing by a principle, that the story deserves telling.

Such an individual is my old and good friend, Michel T. Halbouty, the champion of the one-man campaign for more equitable well spacing in Texas and presently a leading advocate of legislation which will eliminate the drilling of unnecessary wells in this state.

Halbouty, an engineer and geologist first and an oil operator second, was incensed about the fact that town lot operators could receive allowables which enabled them to drain minerals from beneath the property of others. He decided to make his one-man campaign across Texas to take the story to the people.

He had worked on his speeches and reworked them and had accepted his first date at a meeting of the API in Houston. His attack on what he called an "iniquitous policy of legalized theft contrary to the philosophy of the protection of correlative rights of all property owners" was regarded by most who read it before its presentation as a masterpiece.

Among those to whom Halbouty sent the speech for final comment was Harry Jones, Sr., of the firm of Andrews, Kurth, Campbell and Jones who was representing him and others in the now famous Port Acres case, as well as his own personal attorney and his own geologists and engineers.

At this particular time the Port Acres field was in the process of being developed. Halbouty had interests in some 1000 to 1500 acres. Geological information indicated that his acreage, on the east side, was on the fringe edge of the field where the sand thickness was at a minimum compared with the sand in the center of the field.

So, Halbouty's advisors felt obligated to warn him that if the pure engineering and scientific approach to the subject of spacing and allowables, which he was advocating, were to be adopted, that he stood to suffer considerably.

In fact, it was pointed out, that even the litigation he was engaged in at the time could have the same potential result. Most oil operators or other prudent businessman would have paused to think about this high priced advice to use caution.

Halbouty is not that prudent. He didn't quibble a moment. His answer, according to his attorney, was to go ahead with both the lawsuit and the one-man campaign.

This is why, in the closing statement by Jones before the Railroad Commission on behalf of

Halbouty and Meredith and Company, Jones said:

"The proof shows that Halbouty will be among those who are hurt as a result of limiting each operator to the reserves underlying his units. Despite this fact, he has fought for recognition of reserves in the prior hearing before this commission, in all of the proceedings involving the validity of the $\frac{1}{3}$-$\frac{2}{3}$ formula and is still fighting for it in this proceeding."

By the time the argument was made it was absolutely certain Halbouty's position in the pursuit of what he calls "total conservation in the public interest" would probably cost him no less than $1 million, and possibly twice that amount.

Some people engaged in the fight to bring about equitable development of oil and gas fields in Texas—on one side or the other—may be thinking about their own financial well-being. But such has never been the case with Mike Halbouty. His interest is in equity and good conservation practices based on sound petroleum engineering.

This may not be a rare occurrence. The oil industry is filled with others of similar high principles. But it does prove to a sometimes doubting public that there really are men who consider principle above profit, and in these days when great doubt is sometimes cast upon the moral attitude of modern man such stories might help to revitalize our sagging faith in our fellow man.

The Houston Chronicle
November 21, 1964

DEPLETION IS DESIGNED FOR ABUNDANCE— NOT FOR PROFIT

by Jim Clark (Editorial)

When Michel T. Halbouty, the Houston oilman, told fellow petroleum engineers in Los Angeles recently that he thought oil producers should stop their public pleading for the percentage depletion, he caused quite a stir within the industry.

Shortly after his speech, Halbouty went directly to Chicago to attend the American Petroleum Institute annual meeting. There he was confronted with fellow oilmen from throughout the country on the very day the story of his Los Angeles talk appeared in newspapers and the trade press.

He found an interesting reaction to his remarks. Most of the oilmen, weary of the age-old fight, agreed with him. A few, quite frankly, were shocked.

Halbouty had said he thought the oil industry should tell congressmen to do whatever they please about depletion, but the industry itself should keep quiet on the subject unless called on to supply congressional committees with facts and statistics.

He pointed out that the depletion provision was a creation of the congress in the public interest and not a law passed for the specific purpose of making oilmen rich and oil companies excessively profitable.

Yet, he said, many oilmen treat the provision as if it were the industry's private possession. At least, he said, their loud and long defense of the provision made it appear to taxpayers that that was the case.

Halbouty said that he believed 27.5 percent depletion is necessary, that it has kept U.S. oil and gas supplies abundant, but he added, this has been done in the interest of the consumer. The consumer, he believes, depends on the continued healthy existence of the domestic oil industry.

If the consumer can be taken in by the demogogues who continually attack depletion from seats in congress, then it might be well to forget depletion. The most likely results of changing the depletion provision would be higher product prices, far less exploration for oil and gas, a growing shortage of domestic supply, a dependence of foreign sources for oil, the complete exhaustion of gas in this country, and a shattering blow to the entire national economy, which is based on energy.

But that, Halbouty seems to think, is for the people and the congress to consider. In fact, he thinks the gravest danger to depletion might be the continual cry for its retention in paid advertisements signed by oilmen, by a constant din of press releases, pamphlets and public speeches coming from oilmen and oil companies, and from no one else.

This, he says, conveys the erroneous and harmful impression oilmen are seeking the continuation of some kind of tax gift which benefits them and them alone. Let the public and the congress accept responsibility for the depletion provision, he says.

If percentage depletion is reduced, eliminated or tampered with in any respect, it is true that few independents could continue to operate and that many changes costly to the public would result. But that is the price the public and the congress would have to consider, Halbouty reasons.

The suggestion that oilmen stop their pleas, which Halbouty says sound selfish and self-serving when they are not, is a good one. If all that has been said about the benefits of depletion has not convinced congress and the people, maybe some silence on the subject will be more helpful.

Oil Magazine
September, 1965

DUBIOUS RELATIONSHIP OF MAJORS AND INDEPENDENT

The current controversy of Mike Halbouty, Houston independent, and Malcolm Abel, President of the Texas Independent Producers and Royalty Owners Association, is deeper in its significance and implications than may be apparent on the surface.

We do not question the motives and sincerity of either party, who stand high in the esteem of the industry at large, but we do question the soundness of the methods employed to bring about better relationship between independents and major companies.

By reason of his long association with the major companies, Mike Halbouty is naturally in sympathy with their objectives and their methods. His own far-flung operations as a successful geologist and producer have brought him in contact with many of the leading executives of major companies and undoubtedly this has influenced his attitude and views with respect to their policies and programs.

The Houston Chronicle
September 19, 1965

PETROSCOPE ON
THE OIL AND GAS INDUSTRY
by Albert T. Collins, Business Ed.

Geology Needs New Image

Michel T. Halbouty, the Houston oilman who heads the Texas Section of the American Institute of Professional Geologists, figures the nation's geologists have two important "image" tasks confronting them.

One of the tasks he told the institute at its first annual meeting Friday in San Antonio, is improving its public relations.

"I am told," Halbouty remarked, "that geologists have done the worst job of communications of any profession or science on earth with the possible exception of the medical profession."

The other task is promoting geological education in the nation's schools in an effort to attract brilliant young men and women into the profession.

"Ours is one of the most vital and essential sciences on earth. It is also one of the most attractive and fascinating," Halbouty said. "But the fact is the public knows little about geology or its achievements. This, I believe qualifies all of us for the dunce cap."

The Houston Post
October 24, 1965

OIL TODAY
by Billy G. Thompson, Oil Editor

Halbouty plea in keeping with his all industry approach to issues

Too few men in the Oil Country today exercise 20-20 foresight and stick with straight talk in dealing with the multiple problems and controversies within the petroleum industry.

One of the dwindling few with panoramic vision when it comes to petroleum is Houston's Mike Halbouty.

Last week in Fort Worth, Halbouty was presented one of the industry's highest honors—the Texas Mid-Continent Oil & Gas Association's Distinguished Service Award—for his work in the oil industry and for community, state and nation. At each annual meeting, the association presents service awards to an outstanding independent and a major company oilman.

Halbouty, an independent who has distinguished himself as a petroleum engineer, geologist, oil producer and banker, has been presented many awards from industry groups. None, however, were more deserved than the one an old Beaumont school chum and fellow-oilman, Randolph Yost of the Pan American Petroleum Corp., handed Halbouty in Fort Worth.

Halbouty has never been one to rely on sophisticated semantics to keep him in good graces when dealing with oil controversies and issues. Pro or con, his position on pooling, small tract drilling, and other thorny issues in the oil industry is never in doubt.

He is often at odds with other independent oilmen, for Halbouty is an all-industry oilman.

His all-industry stand was pointed up vividly as he accepted the Texas Mid-Continent citation.

Halbouty made the occasion an opportunity to raise a plea for efforts to develop an area of understanding between independents and major company oilmen.

". . . there is no difference between the men who operate as independents and those who manage for major companies," declared Halbouty. He insisted:

"We are all cut from the same cloth. Most of us have the same type of simple, uncomplicated backgrounds. None of us are trying to do anything to the other except in the sense of true, American competition."

Oil Magazine
November, 1965

(Letter to Editor)
OIL
"INNOCENT BYSTANDER"
IN HALBOUTY-ABEL TILT

Houston, October 20, 1965
Dear Mr. Brannan:

This is with reference to your September editorial entitled "Dubious Relationship of Majors and Independents."

I would like to point out that in your second and third paragraphs you have placed Mr. Halbouty in the role of a spokesman for major oil companies and Mr. Abel as a sort of champion for independents. I have known Mr. Halbouty for a long time and have never felt that he was a spokesman for anyone but Mr. Halbouty. As independents, all of us have natural associations with major oil companies and from time to time are receiving dry hole money, bottom hole money and other kinds of support in our day to day operations. I do not think the major oil companies would assume that Mr. Halbouty is their spokesman. I know Mr. Halbouty has been a member of the TIPRO organization for a long time, a member of the executive committee, board and a vice president. I think he only pointed out that harassment of major oil companies is not getting our job done. He noted that during all of this harassment the majors were getting bigger and the independents were getting smaller, so he tried to suggest a more positive course of action. He also suggested that the misrepresentations, all of which he documented, were hurting TIPRO's effectiveness instead of helping it. He also felt that hundreds, even thousands, of TIPRO members were not being heard.

Mr. Halbouty suggested that opposition or seeking an investigation into foreign depletion was suicidal in that it would open the whole question of depletion, domestic as well as foreign to debate, ridicule and possible elimination or reduction.

Maybe you don't recall that when Stanley C. Woods, the one and only president of the so-called Texas Landowners and Independent Oil and Gas Producers Association, was in Washington a year or so ago, he advocated elimination of foreign depletion.

Senator Douglas, assisted by Senator Proxmire, is the most avowed and outspoken opponent of depletion. Douglas and Proxmire recognize that the greatest obstacle they have had in the past to eliminating depletion is the united front of the oil industry. That is why Douglas was elated with what Mr. Woods said.

Riley Wilson of the TULSA WORLD carried this dialogue for the testimony in his column:

Douglas is questioning Mr. Woods.

Douglas: "Let me ask you this. Would you oppose removal of the depletion allowance from foreign oil shipped in by American oil companies?"

Woods: "I would not oppose it."

Douglas: "Would you favor it?"

Woods: "I would almost advocate it."

Douglas: "Good. Now we are together. Now the united front of the oil industry is being broken."

It is Mr. Halbouty's contention in his letter that TIPRO's opposition to or investigation of foreign depletion endangers the entire fabric of percentage depletion in oil and every other extractive industry in the country. It is his contention that this action by

TIPRO is a disservice to the industry as a whole, but particularly to the independent producers, royalty owners, landowners, workers, state governments and the consumers of oil products, as well as natural gas. So, it was his feeling, I am sure that he was echoing a majority of the members of TIPRO in his "vicious letter" as Mr. Abel called it. Mr. Abel should have immediately taken Mr. Halbouty's side instead of opposing him. Yet you call Mr. Abel a fighter for the independents and imply that Mr. Halbouty is a spokesman for the big companies.

I am told that you favor elimination of depletion of foreign crude. Therefore, it is obvious that you are biased in this respect. I hope you can think this thing through and see fit to look at it more objectively.

For your information, I have been a member of TIPRO for many years. I have also been an executive committeeman, vice president, have been active in the IPAA, and have also been a director of the Mid-Continent Oil and Gas Association. I have many friends who are executives among major oil companies and have many more who are independent oil men, and I think I am very independent.

Incidentally, you didn't comment on the fact that Mr. Abel did not respond to a single statement made by Mr. Halbouty in the exchange of letters. I thought this was most significant.

Yours very truly,
J. R. Butler

Houston, October 15, 1965

Dear Mr. Brannan:

In your September 1965 issue the letter of Michel T. Halbouty, criticizing the TIPRO policies, and the letter of Malcolm Abel, in answer, were presented to the readers. The editorial on page 5 commented on the controversy.

It should be fairly obvious to all that both Halbouty and TIPRO are interested in advancing the common cause of the independents in the oil business.

Halbouty's remarks, while rather severe, contained much helpful criticism with constructive suggestions. Because of his established and well recognized background, any remarks of his should be considered. Abel's answer, instead of facing the issues raised by Halbouty, merely attempted to brush aside the business by criticizing Halbouty for his tactics and questioning whether his source material was accurate.

Anyone can plainly see that there is great need of more and better public relations work, and in great need of improving the TIPRO image so that it can be more effective.

The greatest need of the independent today is money. Money, which he needs badly, is being withheld from the oilman, because of his unhealthy public image. It is being put into stocks. Why not take a tip from the stockbrokers who act in accord with one another to shout to the housetops about stocks rising and how healthy the market is, etc. (when every day the over-all average rise of stocks after paying the broker when buying and selling, is little or practically nothing, and in some cases an actual loss). But in this manner, the brokers keep people running to the stock market every day like bees after honey.

Why not spend some time getting across to the general public the facts that the oil business is a good, sound business, and that money can be made in it, and that money is actually being made in it today, and cite specific examples (there are many). Money can not be attracted to the oil business by showing the small operators as in despair and mistreated, no matter how militant they make themselves.

How much better a course of conduct would be that tended to show the independent in a healthy light, instead of the current publicity constantly reflecting the independent as mistreated, maligned and slowly dying on the vine.

Yours cordially,

E. T. BURTON, Jr.

Editor's Note:

The accompanying letters from two Houston oilmen undoubtedly reflect the sentiment and views of a considerable segment of the oil industry, mostly larger independents, who have taken exception to an editorial in our September issue titled "Dubious Relationship of Majors and Independents".

So far as Mr. Halbouty is concerned we did not mean to suggest or imply that he is a spokesman for the major companies, who already possess a plethora of more authentic spokesmen. We appreciate the fact that he is a true independent and only interested in the welfare and advancement of the entire industry. What we did mean to suggest, however, is that his long association with the majors would naturally give him a more sympathetic approach to their problems and a better understanding of their common interests.

While OIL is an independent publication, serving no special interests, it is our considered opinion that the industry would fare better in its public relations and influence with government agencies if it would close ranks and present a solid front. As to the methods employed in achieving this happy Utopia we will not venture to criticize any important group, whether API, IPAA or Tipro but continue to offer an open forum for their discussions and debate.

San Angelo (TX) Standard-Times
April 22, 1966

OIL ALLOWABLE BOOST
GOOD NEWS FOR STATE

Action of the Texas Railroad Commission in raising the oil allowable to the highest level in seven years could mean an extended period of good times ahead for the oil industry.

And good news for the oil industry is good news for the Texas treasury, the pocketbooks of the thousands of Texans employed in the industry and related fields—and good news for the American war effort in Viet Nam.

Several factors probably dictated the decision of the Railroad Commission to raise the allowable. Not the least of these is the increased demand for oil occasioned by the escalating war in Viet Nam. The nation must be assured of adequate reserves of gasoline and other oil products important to the war effort; stimulating production and the search for oil is necessary to this assurance.

And oil exploration is not a one-shot brief stimulus to the economy. The development of new fields, new wells, new locations is spread over a number of years.

Certain far-sighted individuals —the name of Michel T. Halbouty comes readily to mind—for years have been expounding the vision of an expanded oil industry. They have been urging more young persons to enter the fields of study related to oil—geology, chemical engineering and the like—forecasting increased demand for the services of such trained personnel. It begins to look as though the promise which they have foreseen is about to be realized.

Longview (TX) Journal
June 17, 1966

INDEPENDENTS ARE NEEDED

The independent who explores and drills for new sources of oil and gas, far from being outdated by new developments, is needed as much or more so today than at any time in history.

Neither is the independent a "vanishing American" as so many people in and out of the petroleum industry believe, says Michel T. Halbouty of Houston, who is president of the American Association of Petroleum Geologists.

Mr. Halbouty, a widely known oilman and consulting geologist, believes that the independent oilman today needs to develop and put into practice new concepts of exploration which have come about in the industry in recent times.

The time has passed when independents can sit back and coast along with yesterday's exploration methods. Halbouty said in an address at the mid-year meeting of the Independent Petroleum Association of America in Los Angeles.

He said the nation is facing immediate challenges to find more reserves in this country, and this means it is imperative that the industry increase its exploration activity.

It is apparent in the United States that "we are barely holding our own in the discovery of new oil and gas reserves, and because of this fact this nation could be facing a very serious petroleum crisis within 10 years— not 50 years or 100 years from now—but just around the corner."

He described the 32 billion barrels of proved reserves in the United States as "piddling" when compared to much greater proved reserves in foreign lands.

To maintain adequate reserve positions against increases in demand for the next 10 years, Halbouty said the petroleum industry is required to find in this country 50 billion barrels of oil and 300 trillion cubic feet of gas.

These new reserves couldn't be found by employing exploration philosophies and methods, he said, but "as a new era of exploration is entered," he said two facts will emerge:

(1) The independent operator will dominate domestic exploratory activity.

(2) The geologist, both independent and major, will have greater stature than ever in formulating and establishing the policies for oil and gas exploration activities in the future.

In undertaking a positive and forthright view of his position, Halbouty said the independent oilman will have to maintain bold, unorthodox thinking—a kind of reasoning that "incorporates an attitude of progressiveness which applies to the explorationist but more so to management. To be bold is to have courage—and to have courage is to have the proper enthusiasm, optimism and incentive," he said.

Oil Magazine
September, 1966

MIKE HALBOUTY AND HIS AAPG "LIAISON" COMMITTEE

Mike Halbouty, the "dynamic" (IPAA label) Houston independent, has taken time out to devote some of the energy and enthusiasm which have made him so successful in his own business, with over forty field discoveries to his credit (like so many scalps in the Indian's tepee) to the ills and problems that beset the industry at large.

As President of the prestigious AAPG, Mike has organized a liaison committee of prominent oilmen to assist AAPG in solving some of the more urgent and acute problems of the industry.

In this issue of OIL we publish a list of the members of this liaison committee and it will be noted that a good many are top-flight executives of major companies. This of course assures the prestige and influence of the committee, whatever may be its objective.

"The major objective of this important committee", Mr. Halbouty said, "is to promote better liaison and understanding between AAPG, the world's largest geological association, and the top management men of the industry it serves . . .

"Without successful exploration resulting in finding the needed reserves of the future, the companies could not continue to exist as petroleum suppliers. The geologist is the key to a successful exploration effort."

This is quite true. The geologist is the "key"—but the operator himself, whether major or independent, is in the final analysis the one who must unlock the door to the buried treasure. It is noted that there are a large number of important independents on Mike's list and we venture to hope that they are in sympathy with the efforts of other independents in other groups to provide an "incentive" for the smaller producers to stay in the business and put

their shoulders to the wheel. This will mean more in increasing production and reserves than countless volumes of technical knowledge.

If we had the wisdom of King Solomon, which we haven't, we could tell you what will come out of Washington as a result of some needling by Mike's Committee.

The Tulsa Daily World
September 11, 1966

WORLD IN OIL SLANTS
by Riley W. Wilson, Oil Editor

The Independents Role in Modern and Future Exploration

Michel T. Halbouty, that enthusiastic president of the American Association of Petroleum Geologists, made possibly the best speech of his AAPG career Saturday at Abilene, Tex. It was a typical Halbouty speech, but it was unusual for a couple of reasons.

First, it was made in the midst of independent country and Halbouty gave his views on independents, both geologists and producers. Second, the speech showed that Halbouty hasn't been stifled in his enthusiasm for the geological profession and in his uninhibited style of speech making.

Halbouty's enthusiasm, dash and intenseness as AAPG president has brought some color to the highly professional and sedate organization. This has been cheered by some, but has brought official frowns from others in the AAPG leadership.

His comments on industry problems have not been limited strictly to geology and his public challenges to the geological profession have perhaps hit too close to home with some individuals.

But any move to put a damper on the incomparable Halbouty hasn't entirely succeeded, as his Abilene speech showed, and the AAPG is better for it. He is saying some things that need to be said, and he should keep saying them even if they ruffle a few feathers.

At Abilene, Halbouty wasted no time in taking a pot shot at the sacred cow of every independent producer in the nation—the mandatory oil import program. He followed with a blast at further requests for federal government aid, including import quotas for producers and then ripped into the individual independent geologist and producer.

In the process, however, he gave sound reasons for his belief that independents have as great an opportunity for growth now as at anytime.

Here are some of Halbouty's comments:

"The more we ask for governmental help, the more liberties we will lose. Bear in mind one indisputable fact: nothing will be given to us without something being taken away from us.

"I want to cite an example. A few years ago we had voluntary import controls. The system was not perfect, but at least it was controlled by our own industry. But independents kept complaining that the importers were ruining the domestic oil industry, and they kept going to Washington in droves and insisting on mandatory import controls.

"Well, we finally succeeded in getting mandatory controls. Now we have two and a half times as much foreign oil and products coming into this country as we had under the old voluntary plan.

"In addition, mandatory import controls also accomplished exactly what the left wing element in this country wanted. It indirectly gave the government the right to control crude prices. We have crude oil prices controlled by an Office of Price Administration. Price increases which would have been affected by the variation of supply and demand in crude oil are nullified by the control of imports out of Washington.

"We are now about to urge Washington to extend mandatory imports controls by giving domestic operators a portion of the import allotment as a 'drilling incentive.'

"Do you realize what this is asking for? This is asking for the federal government to control, lock, stock and barrel, our entire oil and gas producing industry.

"If the government is going to give you a share of the foreign imports for drilling wells, it will eventually take control of the way you drill those wells, where you drill them, how you produce them and how much you produce. In fact, the government will plan and run your business in accordance with its own rules and regulations.

"Let's begin helping ourselves by believing in ourselves and acting accordingly. The time has passed when we can sit back and coast along with a smug attitude about yesterday's exploration methods.

"It is evident that we couldn't possibly find these new reserves needed to meet future demand by employing our present exploration philosophy and methods.

"Therefore, as we enter this new era of exploration, two facts will emerge: (1) The independent operator will dominate domestic exploratory activities; and (2) the geologists, both major and independent, will have greater stature than ever before becoming the accepted leader of the exploration team in formulating and establishing the policies for exploration activities in the future.

"The most necessary of all the factors affecting exploration success is bold, unorthodox thinking. This kind of reasoning incorporates an attitude of progressiveness which applies to the explorationist but more to management. To be bold is to have courage—and to have courage is to have the proper enthusiasm, optimism and incentives.

"It is in this field of courage that the independent will assume his role as the forerunner—as the leader in this new exploration era. The independent is imbued with the spirit of boldness and daring, and it is these characteristics which mark him as vital to our industry and nation.

"One fact is certain: The independent of the future must either be a well-trained and dedicated geologist, or he must employ the very best of geologists to create for him the new, bold exploration ideas and concepts for finding oil and gas.

"To find the new giant reserves of the future in this country, the geologists must replace the unenthusiastic and yielding attitude of the past nine years with bold and progressive thinking associated with a strong courage of conviction and determination.

"This will require us geologists to reassert ourselves and revert to the best tool we have in our possession: Sheer Brain Power!! We must once again become dedicated geologists! We must once again employ bold geological deduction and imagination.

"And, above all, we should restrain ourselves from depending too much on the 'magic black electronic box' and other such equipment which have placed our cranial substance under sedation for more than 35 years.

"The independents of the future will assume a more vital role in exploration. In addition to finding and drilling his own prospects, he will be sought after to drill major company farmouts more than ever before.

"Eighteen years ago, most of the major companies came to the sudden conclusion that to really find petroleum their explorationists should be located in district areas . . . Now, after all these years . . . most of the majors have now concluded that decentralization is a mistake and that the only way to find oil and gas is to centralize.

"So, district offices are being closed and the exodus has begun. Because of family ties and personal investments in property, many of the geologists refuse to move from the area, and, consequently, the majors are losing a great many of their good oil finders to the consulting and independent segments of the geological profession.

"What will this change in exploration philosophy mean to the independents? I am sure that the independents will gradually move into these vacated districts and begin drilling the cream of the prospects worked out by the geologists who chose to remain in the area as consultants and/or independents. Therefore, the activity of most independents will spread beyond the restricted area he had previously outlined for himself.

"The independents who modernize their own operations and update their own thinking are the independents who will survive in the evolutionary weeding out process.

"Some of the self-help must be done collectively by the independents. I suspect we'll see evidence of that soon, not necessarily through any single formal group or geographic area, but through a real grass roots awakening to the need for collective and unselfish action on the part of a large number of thoughtful men to explore together, drill together, produce together and operate together.

"The oil man who stands still will not remain independent. The times move too rapidly. The independent oil man who adjusts to

his environment will gain strength from it . . ."

The Houston Chronicle
Wednesday, September 14, 1966

HALBOUTY FLIES AGAINST OIL-SUBSIDY GIMMICKS
by Norman K. Baxter

One of the stormy petrels of the oil industry, Michel T. Halbouty, is flying again.

The Houstonian, an independent oilman, has never been hesitant about expressing his opinion and more often than not it has turned out that he was on the right side (the eventual winner).

He is classed as one of the "good guys" in the industry who is not only interested in finding oil and making money, but also in improving methods and conditions in the oil business. When he takes on a cause it is with evangelistic fervor.

His newest crusade is against those who are seeking "subsidies, free incentives and handouts," to spur exploration activity in the domestic oil business.

As Halbouty points out, there is only one place to get these gimmicks—from the federal government—and "the more we ask for government help the more liberties we will lose. Nothing will be given to us without something being taken away."

As president of the American Association of Petroleum Geologists, the major compiler of exploration statistics, Halbouty is well aware of the decreased oil-hunting activity in the United

States and the need for finding lots of oil to meet growing demand for petroleum. But he doesn't believe subsidy gimmicks are the answer.

He is a member of the executive committee on one oil group which has been promoting a drilling subsidy, the Texas Independent Producers & Royalty Owners Assn. This organization plans to hold a meeting in Houston, October 11 to decide if it should formally support some type of drilling incentive. Halbouty's criticism in a speech made last Saturday of the "great deal of noise made lately by some independents and organizations" for a subsidy certainly has a connection with the coming TIPRO meeting.

As indicated by Halbouty's protest, not all oilmen are willing to go along with the subsidy idea. A questionnaire sent to all 125 members of the Independent Petroleum Association's import policy committee produced the following results:

All of those answering said that more exploration is needed as well as additional incentives. But 78.9 per cent believed that the incentives should be provided by competitive market forces (an abstract way of saying higher prices).

Those polled were also asked what type of incentive they would recommend. Some named more than one incentive but the undisputed favorite at 63.4 per cent was adequate prices. The next highest was "strengthen the import program" with 31 per cent.

The Sunday Oklahoman
January 28, 1968

"HERE'S WHAT OILMEN NEED"
OIL DESK by Deacon New

A geologist, by nature, is as optimistic as a riverboat gambler holding a pat hand.

And one of the most optimistic —with the fame and fortune to support it—is Michel T. Halbouty of Houston, immediate past president of the American Association of Petroleum Geologists.

The AAPG, at its annual meeting in Oklahoma City in April, will focus the spotlight on the giant oil fields of the past. This will prompt some critics to accuse the geologists of reveling in the glory of the past, because there are no more big oil reserves untapped in the U.S.

Halbouty, not one to mince words, disagrees by stating: "I will not subscribe to the belief of the pessimists that there are no more large fields to be found in our nation. I believe that there are many billions of barrels of oil and trillions of cubic feet of gas to be found in large, giant, yet untapped fields."

He also happens to have some ideas on what the nation's independent oilmen need to help find those new fields.

"We need to re-establish the old wildcatter's optimism, which unfortunately has frequently been superseded by dark pessimism," he says.

"We need the majors to give up or drill some long-held untouched acreage, to give more farmouts on just and equitable terms, and to encourage the independents to drill more wells and to back this encouragement with substantial 'bottom hole' dollars instead of with meager 'dry-hole' support.

And Halbouty thinks the independents "need the sustained courage to resist trends in government control and the character it requires to demand government cooperation with us."

He adds: "No good earth scientist will deny the fact that the oil and gas are here to be found, but only by employing bold, creative and unorthodox thinking."

Halbouty didn't say so, but he's a walking example of that last statement. The odds are he'll be in on some of the big discoveries of the future.

The Houston Post
March 16, 1968

**TALES
OF THE OIL COUNTRY:
OIL ERAS TRACED
BY MIKE HALBOUTY**
by James A. Clark

The story of oil is one of the oldest and most fascinating in the world.

Take, for instance, the first recorded report of oil production. It was by Herodotus, the father of history. He came home and said there were some oil springs on the Island of Zante in the Adriatic.

That was in the fifth century. The oil springs are still producing. Mike Halbouty was telling several hundred neurologists (doctors) and their wives about it Thursday night. In his inimitable and enthusiastic manner, Halbouty seemed to consider Herodotus the first real oil reporter.

What Halbouty was doing was setting up the oil history so he could trace its three important eras. He told about Marco Polo, the Venetian traveler, also. Old Marco, it seems, really discovered Baku, the great Russian oil region, in the 13th century.

His report was a little faulty, but Marco said you could probably get a hundred shiploads of oil out of Baku with little trouble. They have taken probably a hundred million shiploads out of there since.

. . . One thing Mike wanted to tell the doctors (but didn't) was that they shouldn't be such suckers for promoters.

But you can't really tell them that. Several have already hit it too good being suckers.

Mining Record
Denver, Colorado
May 9, 1968

**IS OIL SHALE
ISSUE DEAD?**

The Mining Record has concluded the reprinting of a series of articles which comprised an official government report on the oil shale reserves in this country and the possibility of their development.

The series points up the complexity of the legal question involved in settling who owns what claims, along with the high cost of developing the oil shale reserves, but does leave the hope that within 10 years there might be some production.

Last week an independent oil producer and geologist, Michel T. Halbouty of Houston, gave the keynote address for the Fifth Annual Oil Shale Symposium in Denver.

Halbouty blasted the government inaction, and asked that private industry be given an immediate opportunity to determine whether or not oil from shale is economically feasible. He fears that if not given the opportunity, private industry will turn its efforts to other sources of supply and the reality of large oil reserves from shale may never occur.

The oil producer also labaled as "sheer nonsense" the specter of another "Teapot Dome Scandal" and the statement that "every man, woman and child of our country owns a share of the vast resources of recoverable oil and the values to each in terms of total sales volume is at least $25,000." He said that by similar reasoning each of us could take an axe into the national forest, mark off our personal trees, chop down our share and put the lumber to our own use.

Tipro Reporter
Austin, Texas
Winter, 1968

THE HALBOUTY PLAN

A plan for a Presidentially-appointed board of review to deal with basic policy of the manda-

tory oil import program advanced a year ago by Houston independent Michel T. Halbouty, has been adopted as part of recommendations by outgoing Interior Assistant Sec. J. Cordell Moore.

Halbouty's plan was first proposed at a meeting of the Oklahoma Independent Petroleum Association a year ago. It came under considerable fire from various quarters, including several associations. Ironically, Moore used the occasion of the OPIA meeting this December to offer a closely related suggestion. He said such a board "would afford those responsible for decision on oil import policy the benefit of a broadly based, technically competent, dispassionate counsel on the troubling aspects of the program."

Moore agreed with the Halbouty idea that such a board or committee could lessen the heat and pressure which makes administration of the controls program so difficult. It would serve as "a filter by which the valid points could be separated from the vast amount of irrelevant argument."

Halbouty greeted the Moore announcement by noting: "In view of the many criticisms which were directed at me by the IPAA, the OIPA and TIPRO, it is indeed satisfying to know that I was not way out in left field."

The Tulsa Tribune,
January 16, 1968

OIL COMMENT
by Marion Cracraft

They may not have liked it, but at least Michel T. Halbouty of

Houston gave Oklahoma oilmen something to think about with his luncheon speech Monday before the Oklahoma Independent Petroleum Association.

The speech urged oilmen to quit running to Washington to solve their problems, with particular reference to their present demand that Congress set—by law—the ratio of oil imports instead of leaving this to the executive branch of the government.

RCC Newsletter
July 6, 1970

OIL—THE SOVIET UNION'S SECRET WEAPON? BUSH, OTHERS THINK SO

Rep. George Bush, Chairman of the House Republican Task Force on Earth Resources and Population, warned last week that the Soviet Union seeks control of the world's principal petroleum sources as a major weapon in winning the cold war.

Bush cited the Soviet disruption in the Middle East, in Libya and the Arab countries which, he said, is producing increasingly hostile reactions against the United States, making these sources of petroleum less dependable.

The Texas Congressman, who spent 18 years in the oil business, said he agreed with a statement by Michel T. Halbouty of Houston, former president of the American Association of Petroleum Geologists, that "Russia hopes to dominate the world through petroleum."

Also in agreement with Halbouty was Raymond Ewell, vice president for research and professor of chemical engineering at New York State University, Buffalo. Ewell, among the natural resources specialists who testified before Bush's task force told the Newsletter that the Soviets are moving toward control of the Persian Gulf whose refineries are supplying much of the oil used by American forces in Vietnam.

Drilling—DCW
October, 1970

WORLD WAR III— IT IS ALREADY UNDER WAY

The Communist aim is world domination through control of petroleum energy sources. The U.S. objective is to stop them. And we're getting whipped. By Michel T. Halbouty

Public relations efforts of the U.S. petroleum industry have been arrogant, incompetent and ineffective—a multi-million dollar mouthing of cliches that have done more harm than good. Largely because we've failed to acquaint the public with the true nature of the petroleum industry and its role in modern society, the entire free world stands today in very serious danger. We'd better do something about it. Fast.

That's the view of Michel T. Halbouty of Houston, a past president of the American Association of Petroleum Geologists and one of the world's best known geologists, petroleum engineers and independent oil operators.

The peril in which the free world stands—and what we, as oil people should do about it—were the substance of a hard hit-ting address which Halbouty presented in mid-June at the annual meeting of the American Association of Petroleum Landmen in Los Angeles.

Dialogue

... statements, interviews and letters, in which Mr. Halbouty has more or less the last word.

The Houston Post
March 25, 1958

**HALBOUTY REPLIES
TO IMPORTS CUT CLAIMS**
by Billy G. Thompson

Houston Independent Oilman Michel T. Halbouty Monday declared that criticism of efforts to cut U.S. oil imports voiced by Former Undersecretary of State Will Clayton was an "irresponsible and unfair" attack on the domestic producers who are seeking relief from "excessive crude oil and product imports."

Halbouty said statements appearing in a pamphlet last week by Clayton, an elder statesman and Houston businessman, compelled him to reply.

In the pamphlet entitled "What Price Oil?" Clayton declared that efforts to restrict imports should be recognized as promotions of the short-term special interest of certain producers against the national interest.

"The national effort demands that such efforts be defeated," Clayton said.

Halbouty said he interpreted the comments in the pamphlet to infer that Clayton thinks the U.S. should permit an unlimited supply of foreign oil to come into the country without regard to the domestic producing industry.

He denounced Clayton's statement that the effort to reduce imports was "just to maintain high prices and big profits for oil producers" as irresponsible, unfounded, unfair, and misleading claim."

Contrary to Clayton's contentions, the national interest demands that imports should be reduced to the point where they supplement domestic production, the independent oilman stated. Halbouty termed oil imports now supplant domestic production.

"When they begin to supplant, they begin to destroy the initiative necessary to a healthy domestic industry," said Halbouty. "That in turn kills off required risk capital, puts men out of work and causes economic distress if not, in fact, upheaval."

Halbouty stated that most oilmen recognize that their present oil depression is not due to excessive imports alone. "But they believe such imports, in excess of the amounts necessary to supplement domestic production, amount to the straw that broke the camel's back," he observed.

"Most oilmen . . . recognize an obligation to other industries and business and recognize the necessity—of maintaining the best relations with all countries," Halbouty noted.

"With unlimited foreign imports the market for domestic production will be so curtailed that no new reserves will be found and we will become a 'have not' nation," Halbouty observed.

He pointed out that the American oil industry has consistently maintained the lowest prices on oil products to be found in the world. "Oil product prices in all other countries of the world usually more than double the price Americans pay," he stated.

Partly because of oil imports that supplant domestic production, Halbouty said, "rigs are down, the flow of oil investment capital has come to a halt, men are out of work, all industries suffer, and this nation is in economic trouble."

Halbouty declared that the best service the U.S. can do for iself and its allies in the Free world is to stay strong economically.

"If we impair the economic health of the industry that provides us with two-thirds of our energy fuels, I believe it will begin to undermine the entire economic structure," he said.

Halbouty said he personally favored a continuation of voluntary controls over oil imports, "but with a tighter rein on those who would ignore the President's pleas." He also urged an elimination of the overseas purchases of oil products with American dollars and a quota on imported products.

Halbouty rejected any type of mandatory controls "because they carry the threat of unlimited federal control of the domestic oil industry."

"American producers who are permitted 13 barrels of oil daily, eight days a month cannot compete with foreign producers who are permitted up to 8,000 barrels a day for 30 days a month," Halbouty said. "The President's voluntary plan—with the shoring up I have suggested—would protect us."

The Houston Chronicle
March 25, 1958

OILMAN DISPUTES CRITIC OF INDUSTRY

America's undiscovered oil reserves are greater than all that has been found in the past, according to Michel T. Halbouty, one of the world's foremost authorities on crude reserves. But unlimited oil imports may prevent much of that oil from ever being found," he declared.

Halbouty spoke out Tuesday in reply to a pamphlet distributed last week by W. L. Clayton entitled, "What Price Oil?"

Clayton spoke of the furor over oil imports as one of "producers whose interests are being promoted against the national interest," and "just to maintain high prices and big profits for oil producers."

Halbouty called that statement "an irresponsible, unfounded, unfair and misleading claim."

Speaking for Self

Pointing out that he was only speaking for himself as an independent producer of oil and gas, Halbouty refuted the implication made by Clayton that to halt or curtail oil imports would raise the cost of oil.

"The American oil industry has consistently maintained the lowest prices in the world," Halbouty said. "Mr. Clayton must know this. Gasoline today costs no more in this country than it did in 1925, not counting taxes. Oil product prices in all other countries of the world usually are more than double the price Americans pay."

Oil Magazine
April 1, 1958

HALBOUTY VS CLAYTON
Subject: Oil Imports

Editors Note: On this page we publish the answer made by Michel T. Halbouty, Houston independent operator, to the widely discussed pamphlet "What Price Oil", written by W. L. Clayton, one of the founders of Anderson, Clayton and Company, world's largest cotton firm.

While OIL has consistently opposed the mounting tide of oil imports, for the past several years, we feel that in all fairness to Mr. Clayton he should be credited with sincerity in his conviction that the national interest is best served by the unrestricted flow of foreign oil into the United States. He is a man of high character and high standards wherever cotton is bought and sold, the world over.

We believe that Mr. Clayton's approach to the subject may be inflenced by the fact that he has been an internationalist for many years, that he is accustomed to thinking in terms of reciprocal trade, so essential to the free movement of cotton which has always depended on a world market for its surplus of U.S. production.

We are living in a new area, however, and we believe our readers will agree that Mr. Halbouty makes out a strong case for the domestic oil producers.

In passing it might be mentioned that both Mr. Clayton and Mr. Halbouty have given some years to government service, Mr. Clayton as Under Secretary of State and Mr. Halbouty as Chief of Petroleum Production in the planning division of the Army-Navy Petroleum Board in World War II.

Halbouty's Statement:

Last week Mr. W. L. Clayton released a pamphlet entitled "What Price Oil?" which received important attention in the daily press and other media. It was an attack on the domestic oil producers who are seeking relief from what they consider excessive crude oil and product imports from foreign countries.

While I have deep respect for Mr. Clayton as a businessman, citizen, and elder statesman, I feel compelled to speak out. Mr. Clayton wrote of "producers whose interests are being promoted against the national interest." I am a producer of oil from the definition of such producers to be inferred from the news stories, I could be included among those referred to, hence this statement.

First, let me say that I speak for no company, association, or group. I speak only for myself. As an independent producer of oil and gas I am in a position to do so.

I gathered that Mr. Clayton thinks that this country should permit an unlimited supply of foreign oil to come into the United States without regard to the domestic producing industry.

He said the National interest demands that the efforts to cut oil imports should be defeated. The opposite is true. Oil imports are now supplanting domestic production. They should be reduced to the point where they supplement. When they begin to supplant, they begin to destroy the initiative necessary to a healthy domestic industry. That, in turn, kills off required risk capital, puts men out of work, and causes economic distress, if not, in fact, upheaval.

Most oil men recognize that their present oil depression is not due to excessive imports alone. But they believe such imports, in excess of the amounts necessary to supplement domestic produc-

tion, amount to the straw that broke the camel's back.

Most oil men I know recognize an obligation to other industries and businesses and recognize the necessity of maintaining the best relations with all countries, especially those in which vast amounts of American capital is invested in the oil industry.

Mr. Clayton's own words defeat his intended purpose in my opinion. He says (in defending unlimited oil imports) that "Every man, woman, and child is a consumer of energy in one way or another", and that "it is highly important to every citizen and to our national economy that nothing be done to lessen our energy supply or arbitrarily raise its cost."

I most wholeheartedly agree with that. But this nation must not become dependent on outside sources for its energy fuels, as it would surely cause it to lose its position as a world power and cause its people to suffer as a consequence. If imports are limited (and not supplanting) domestic production, we can maintain a healthy domestic oil industry always capable of meeting the demands of our people without ever having to depend on any monarch, dictator, commisar, or foreign cartel.

Since 1900, with the exception of five years during the depression periods of the early twenties and early thirties, the domestic petroleum industry has discovered more oil than it has produced. There is no reason to believe that this trend will not continue if the domestic industry is furnished with a market for this oil. Kill the market, and you kill the incentive to drill wildcat wells in an effort to discover new reserves. With unlimited foreign imports, the market for domestic production will be so curtailed that no new reserves will be found, and we will become a "have not" nation. The hunt for new reserves must go on constantly since it takes time to find and develop such reserves. In times of need such as in World War II, the nation must have available the immediate productive capacity with which to defend itself. Only a healthy domestic industry which annually discovers as much oil as it produces can assure the nation of this potential.

As for the cost of all products, the American oil industry has consistently maintained the lowest prices in the world. Mr. Clayton must know this. Gasoline today costs no more in this country than it did in 1925, not counting taxes. Oil product prices in all other countries of the world usually more than double the price Americans pay.

Mr. Clayton points out that we have only a fifth of the world's oil reserves and that we consume over half of its oil products. He speaks of proven reserves. How does any man know what our potential reserves are? I am one who contends that we have only begun to find oil in this country. As a petroleum geologist I believe we will find in the future far more oil than we have found in the past. That is, unless our incentive to explore is dulled by govern-

ment interference, excessive imports, or any of the other roadblocks now being thrown at us.

I believe there are really only two reasons for any imports of oil. First, American capital is invested in great fields of foreign oil, and second, we are obligated to do business with friends of ours who trade with us. We really don't need much imported oil. Cut out most imports and, from a supply standpoint, this country might be better off. There would be enough oil to be found in this country to take care of our demands provided we had the incentive—such as a market—to keep searching for it.

Today, due partly to oil imports that supplant domestic production, rigs are down, the flow of oil investment capital has come to a halt, men are out of work, allied industries suffer, and this nation is in economic trouble. All of this economic trouble is not due to the plight of the oil industry but part of it is, and that is an important part.

I contend that the best service this nation can do for itself and its allies in the free world is to stay strong economically. If we impair the economic health of the industry that provides us with two-thirds of our energy fuel, I believe it will begin to undermine the entire economic structure. That could be what is happening right now.

As for import controls, I personally favor a continuation of voluntary controls but with a tighter reign on those who would ignore the President's pleas, an elimination of the buying of oil products abroad with American tax dollars, and a quota on all imported products. I oppose any type of mandatory controls because they carry the threat of unlimited federal control of the domestic oil industry.

American producers who are permitted 13 barrels of oil daily eight days a month cannot compete with foreign producers who are permitted up to 8000 barrels a day for a 30 day month. The President's voluntary plan—with the shoring up I have suggested—would protect us.

I wish Mr. Clayton knew more oilmen and the oil industry or would talk with someone who did before making such statesments as the one that we are doing all possible to injure Venezuela and Canada "Just to maintain high prices and big profits for oil producers."

That is an irresponsible, unfounded, unfair and misleading claim.

But I respect Mr. Clayton's right to say what he thinks as long as there remains the right to reply.

CORRESPONDENCE
A Personal Letter
from Sen. Ralph W. Yarbrough
Washington, D. C.
August 31, 1959

Honorable Michel T. Halbouty
Michel T. Halbouty Building
911 Westheimer Road
Houston 27, Texas

Dear Mike:

It was a pleasure to put the little article about you in The Congressional Record, because you are one of the few men of wealth in Texas who has worked to advance the cause of education, and not repress it.

You are one of the few men of wealth in Texas in this past decade, who had the courage to support a candidate who stood for honest, more progressive government in our State. Frankly, I put the article in The Record because I thought you deserved it. Unlike so-called smart politicians, I do not put articles in the Record about enemies to progress in the hope that by honoring them, they will be won over to the decencies of our civilization. I think such course of conduct gives apostles of intolerance an even firmer hold of the massive forces of ignorance abroad in the world. I do not knowingly use the money of us taxpayers by wasting copy space on advocates of regression.

I am often charged with being too free with the taxpayers money. Using it up for the advance of ignorance is not one of my weaknesses.

You deserve the space. I didn't give you something for nothing. You had proved your right to every inch of it.

With warmest regards, I am
Very sincerely,
Ralph W. Yarborough

Oil Magazine
December, 1959

MANDATORY POOLING ADVOCATED

Houston—A new state law which would require mandatory

pooling on established spacing patterns in Texas oil and gas fields was advocated here by Michel T. Halbouty, prominent Houston oilman, in a forceful and significant speech before the annual joint meeting of the Houston Chapter of the API and the Gulf Coast Section of the Society of Petroleum Engineers of the AIME.

Halbouty differentiated between mandatory pooling, which he identified as being on an established unit basis, and fieldwide compulsory unitization. He said, however, that compulsory unitization, under federal law, was a strong possibility in this country unless steps were taken soon to correct present inequities in conservation laws and regulations.

He said he was convinced that compulsory unitization could solve a great number of problems under present conservation laws and that he was certain it would come in time. But, he added, it is those who are taking advantage of the weaknesses in petroleum conservation regulations today who will make it come sooner than expected.

"And it is they," he said, "not the operator who abides by the spirit as well as the letter of conservation law, who must bear the onus of bringing compulsory unitization about."

Reservoirs Prematurely Destroyed

After pointing out that many great gas-distillate reservoirs in Texas were being prematurely destroyed, and billions of dollars in gas liquids being lost forever by unnecessary wells made possible by "unfortunate" field orders and court decisions which uphold them, Halbouty warned also of federal control of the entire oil industry through the conservation route.

He said a recent book, written under a direct grant from the American Petroleum Institute, actually advocated "mandatory unitization of all pools in this country under federal law."

"This is fuel for the fire of federal control—even eventual public utility status for our industry," Halbouty warned. "The best protection lies in shoring up our state conservation laws and regulations, in Texas and elsewhere, if we are to avoid federal control."

He said that if mandatory fieldwide unitization ever comes, and he said the evidence was that it would eventually become necessary, "then it must come from the state rather than from the federal government if we are to avoid federalization of this industry."

Beaumont Enterprise
January 26, 1960

LETTERS TO THE EDITOR
Appreciation Expressed

Editor Enterprise:

The Enterprise, January 19, issue carried a comprehensive report of the meeting of the Spindletop Section of the Society of Petroleum Engineers in which Michel T. Halbouty, native Beaumonter and now an internationally known geologist and petroleum engineer of Houston, was quoted on the desperate situation faced by Port Acres royalty owners and gas producers. This situation coming about by the drilling of small town lots in the Port Acres townsite area.

I want to commend the Enterprise for the splendid coverage of Mr. Halbouty's talk and I feel that Mr. Ellis Sweatte presented the talk quite clearly in his story. I know that reporting technical subjects such as Mr. Halbouty's talk can be quite difficult since the average reader must be able to understand what transpired at the meeting.

The Enterprise did not rest on its laurels with the story of the Monday night meeting. The Enterprise followed this excellent coverage with a good detailed editorial reminding city officials of their duties to its citizenry.

Program Will Cause Waste

In reference to Mr. Halbouty's subject, I am of the opinion that the Port Acres gas field under the present development program will cause waste and the small gas producers should get together with the major gas producers and order a recycling gas program for the field before it is too late.

Club is Commended

In closing let me say that the Beaumont section of the Society of Petroleum Engineers, a membership of more than 350 petroleum engineers and drilling and production men, has given Beaumont an opportunity for a Beaumont dateline in wire coverage of the Halbouty talk. The club is to be commended in bringing men of the oil industry of the Hal-

bouty caliber reminding one and all that Beaumont is "Where Oil Became an Industry."

Bryan D. Beck, Jr.
395 Tenth Street
Beaumont

Drilling Magazine
April, 1960

YOU CAN'T BURY YOUR HEAD IN THE SAND
by Michel T. Halbouty

Federal Control of the Oil Industry Can Slip Up on Us Unnoticed

There is one form of political conservation that is already upon us—and it is very dangerous. I refer to those people who, in the name of conservation actually advocate that the Federal Government take complete control of the entire integrated oil industry. These people use the evils and results of partial conservation in support of their views.

I will admit that partial conservation is a made-to-order vehicle for the proponents of Federal control. It makes our industry far more vulnerable to such attacks. For instance, I want to call to your attention the most recent attack on petroleum conservation at the state level and particularly the attack on the Texas Railroad Commission.

This attack is contained in a book published, mind you, with a direct grant from the American Petroleum Institute. It was written by a couple of economics professors—Melvin G. deChazeau and Alfred E. Kahn. The book is entitled Integration and Completion in the Petroleum Industry. It was published by the Yale University Press and released this year. If the recommendations made in this book should be followed, the oil industry would soon be under federal control.

The authors contend that "it is clear that state control under prorationing has failed to achieve attainable standards of efficiency in the development of oil reservoirs" and they advocate Federal control with the statement that "in our view, these goals stand a better chance of attainment if a uniform Federal statute governing oil development is substituted for the present multiplicity of state regulations." These authors advocate "mandatory unitization for all pools throughout this country under Federal law."

This, gentlemen, is fuel for the fire of Federal control—even eventual public-utility status for our industry. Federal control is what we face if conservation at the state level is not made to meet the demands of our times. And if Federal control should occur, where would our operators who specialize in drilling segregated tracts be? I'll answer. They would be out! So would most of the rest of us. Yet that is what partial conservation can lead to, and that is why I am concerned tonight. We must help the Railroad Commission achieve total conservation in Texas.

The views of people like de-Chazeau and Kahn are being supported by some of the leading business publications of this country—Fortune, the Wall Street Journal, Barrons, and others. Attacking our system of conservation by states has become a popular national pastime!

These attacks should make us all realize that unless the conservation laws, the application and interpretation of these laws, and the rules and regulations adopted under these laws are modernized to meet the needs and demands of the industry in 1960 as opposed to 1930, we are in real danger of having bureaucratic Federal control imposed from Washington.

Mandatory unitization under federal control as advocated by these economic professors, should be a warning to us all. It is a warning as clear as a rattlesnake's warning to his intended victim. It is a warning to protect ourselves against the danger ahead. I do not need to remind you of the evils which result from Federal assumption of any state regulatory problem. Such evils would be multiplied if applied to the purely local function of regulating the production of oil and gas.

The best protection for the industry lies in shoring up state conservation laws and regulations in Texas and elsewhere if we are to avoid Federal control. If mandatory fieldwide unitization ever becomes necessary—and the evidence is that it will eventually become necessary—then it must be under state mandate rather than Federal if we are to avoid Federalization of our industry. Give us proper well spacing and more realistic allocation formulas and we can avoid Federal control.

"The Threat of Federal Control" and "What Has to be Done" were adapted especially for Drilling Magazine from the paper "Conservation—Total or Partial" presented by Independent Operator Michel T. Halbouty at the Southwestern District meeting of the API, Dallas, Texas.

Drilling
April, 1960

WHAT HAS TO BE DONE

MICHEL T. HALBOUTY suggests five vitally important steps which must be taken to assure the continued independence of the United States oil industry.

I want to emphasize that the answer to all of the critics of the oil industry is to eliminate the weaknesses of our present conservation laws, rules, regulations, and practices. These laws, rules and regulations have long served this state well. But some changes are now needed. We must recognize and respect this fact and act responsibly. To ignore this fact and remain silent is to act irresponsibly. That is why I am speaking up.

As men of science and technology, most of us know that one way is right and one way is wrong. It would seem that conservation based upon truth could lead only the right way. Sometimes it is difficult to determine or find the true or right way. But once found, it is wrong to go in any other direction.

Some definitions are necessary for an accurate understanding of my first recommendation. The word "unitization" as commonly used in Texas, refers to an entire field and I will use it here. On the other hand, the word "pooling," as commonly used in Texas, refers to forming units of less than fieldwide area. Pooling, as I use the term, simply means the combining of smaller surface tracts into a larger tract equal to or approximating the acreage pattern or proration unit area set by the regulatory body.

Herewith are a few of my recommendations:

Compulsory Pooling

My first recommendation is that, as the initial step in modernization of our laws, one should be passed which would make pooling on the established spacing pattern compulsory. Such a law would be helpful if not essential to the regulatory body in discharging its duty to prevent waste and protect correlative rights. It would eliminate the over-drilling which now prevails in townsites and other areas where there are segregated small tracts. With compulsory pooling as an aid, I believe that voluntary fieldwide unitization ultimately could be achieved in almost every proper instance.

New Allocation Formula

Second, I recommend that the use of arbitrarily selected allocation formulas be discontinued. I recommend that an allocation formula be adopted for each field that will give to each well and tract its fair share of the oil or gas underlying the tract, but no more. Such formulas should be in accord with known technological and engineering data for each particular field.

Better Well Spacing

Third, on the subject of spacing, I recommend that, immediately after completion of the discovery well in a new field and before offsets are commenced, temporary spacing rules be adopted for the particular producing formation encountered until the field is sufficiently developed to determine the best spacing for the field; and that, in general, wider spacing be adopted for all fields.

Protection for Towns

Fourth, I recommend that any town or city in which or near which, oil or gas is discovered should immediately consider and adopt an ordinance which would protect the life and property of its citizens from the hazards which accompany the exploration for and production of oil and gas.

Modernize Conservation Laws

Fifth, I should like to plead with this industry and the citizens of the petroleum states that we shore up our conservation laws—modernize them to meet existing problems—before we are faced with Federal laws on this subject that could and would lead directly to Federal control of our industry.

Wallace E. Pratt
Post Office Box 209
Carlsbad, New Mexico
October 5, 1960

Mr. Michel T. Halbouty,
Consulting,
Michel T. Halbouty Bldg.
Houston, Texas

Dear Mike:

I have just read of your successful completion of a big gas well on Kenai Peninsula in Alaska. I want to tell you that this news cannot give you much more satisfaction than it gives me. I have been keenly aware of your two previous failures and they have discouraged me. But they did not discourage you! I have long felt that in you are combined two traits of character, both extremely valuable, that seldom go together. It is said that all men may be divided into two classes: (1) the thinkers and (2) the doers. Your papers on salt dome geology and salt dome oil occurrence long ago convinced me that you are a first-class thinker. Your success as a producer in the Gulf Coast Region has led me strongly to suspect that you are also a doer. Now your fine achievement in Alaska confirms my suspicion and leaves me no longer any alternative but to class you as both thinker and doer.

I hope you are not embarrassed by fan mail! Congratulations and warm good wishes.

s/   Wallace E. Pratt

Petroleum Week
Dept/Opinions

VIEWS THAT
MAKE NEWS

Dear Sir:

I have been out of my office for a few weeks and your Inside Slant, "It's the Law that Rules" (PW-Aug. 12, '60, p.3), has just come to my attention.

Before our conservation laws were adopted, an operator could drill as many wells as close together as he desired. If a neighbor was draining him, this operator could simply drill enough wells to stop that drainage. He had the remedy of "unlimited self help". However, in those days fields were rapidly drained of their flush production, reservoir pressures were prematurely dissipated, and many fields were abandoned in a very short period of time.

Our conservation rules and regulations contain a famous provision known as Rule 37. It is the statewide spacing rule and simply says, first, that no well for oil or gas shall be drilled nearer than 933 ft. to another well completed in or drilling to the same horizon on the same tract or farm, and second, that no well shall be drilled nearer than 330 ft. to any property line, lease line, or subdivision line. In a particular field, the pattern as set by special field rules may be larger, and thus these distances may be greater.

In order to make Rule 37 constitutional, the rule contains an exception. This exception provides that in order to prevent waste or to prevent confiscation of property, the Railroad Commission may grant exceptions to permit drilling within shorter distances than those prescribed in the rule.

Rule 37 is absolutely silent as to how much oil or gas may be produced from any well drilled, either under the spacing pattern adopted for a field or as an exception to Rule 37. This is very important to remember, for much confusion arises over the contention of owners of segregated small tracts that in some fashion Rule 37, when taken with the Law or Rule of Capture, requires that the operator who drills on a segregated tract be allocated a quantity of oil or gas sufficient to pay for the well and return a profit.

As fantastic as such contention sounds in the light of simple exception to Rule 37, it is repeatedly made. It is contended that if such allocation is not made, then the exception is meaningless and confiscation results despite the exception. I would like to make it clear that I am not opposing Rule 37 or the exception thereto.

The confusion that exists as to just how much oil or gas the owner of a well should be entitled to produce from a segregated tract is further compounded by misinterpretations of the "Rule of Capture." The Law or Rule of Capture is court-made law. It was not passed by the legislature and is not contained in a rule or regulation. But let me say that I consider the Rule of Capture a profound and useful conservation measure.

The courts have defined this rule or law very clearly as follows: "The Rule of Capture is simply this—that the owner of a tract of land acquires title to the oil (or gas) which he produces from wells drilled thereon, although part of such oil or gas may have migrated from adjoining land." In other words, the owner whose well the oil is produced through or from does not have to account to his adjoining owners for such oil, although it may have migrated to the well from the adjoining tracts. However, this very simple rule has come to mean many things to many people.

The most serious misunderstanding in the application of this rule presently current is the assertion by town-lot and segregated small tract operators that the rule means more than non-accountability to adjoining owners. These people contend that it confers an affirmative absolute right of a well owner to drain oil and gas from his neighbor. These people contend that the allocation formula must afford the single well on a segregated tract enough production from that well to pay for the well plus a profit, even though that amount is not originally in place under the tract and will clearly have to be drained from adjoining tracts. Such language of the court contained in the Hawkins case is pointed to as authority for this fallacy.

The courts have repeatedly said that "fair share" means the ap-

proximate amount of oil or gas underlying a particular tract. Therefore, according to the interpretation of the courts, an allocation formula is confiscatory and unlawful if it does not allocate to all wells in a reservoir approximately the oil and gas in place under the tracts upon which such wells are located. Yet this interpretation is misconstrued and is not taken into consideration by those who have the power to use it, namely, the Railroad Commission.

Michel T. Halbouty
Independent Producer
Houston

San Angelo Standard-Times
March 10, 1963

HALBOUTY EXPLAINS MERITS OF PROPOSED POOLING BILL

Michel T. Halbouty, Houston Independent oilman and banker, told a House Committee Tuesday night that a proposed oil and gas pooling bill is needed to keep the Texas oil industry from withering away.

He was one of a long line of witnesses appearing for and against a measure which would lead to pooling in irregular or small oil or gas tracts.

The bill, House Bill No. 510, sponsored by Rep. Wayne Gibbens of Breckenridge, would continue to allow voluntary pooling if well and royalty owners could agree. If not, the State Railroad Commission would have the authority to set up a drilling block to govern proration of the wells.

Halbouty, a member of the Steering Committee for Equitable Development of Texas Oil and Gas Resources said, "Pooling is a means for every landowner to get exactly and precisely those minerals that lie beneath his property—no more and no less."

Pooling is one of the most elementary of all conservation practices and "is working in the vast majority of the oil producing states in this country," he added.

Halbouty said, "There is no violation of the principles of free enterprise or legal tradition in the pooling of small tracts to drill a single well that will do the work of several."

The Houston man said the principle of pooling protects both private and public interests; permits the use of technical knowledge; conserves capital and enables the consumer to receive oil products at low prices.

Halbouty added the measure would halt the flow of capital from Texas into other states, would enable Texas oil men to compete better with foreign imports and would offer "some measure of protection against the threat of federal control."

San Angelo Standard-Times
February 14, 1965

**DRILLING
OF 60,000 TESTS YEARLY
URGED BY HALBOUTY**

"We should drill at least 60,000 U.S. wells a year for the next 10 years if we are to meet demands for the next 20 years and at least 25,000 of those wells each year should be exploratory tests."

This was the opinion of Michel T. Halbouty, Houston and San Angelo oilman, author and banker, in the lead article in this month's issue of Drilling International, Dallas, a leading oil publication established in 1939.

"We can do the job," says this industry authority, "but to do so we must launch a sound scientific search for the vast reserves awaiting discovery.

"Soaring energy requirement will tax the oil and gas finding abilities of the domestic industry during the next decade, for petroleum is still the world's most important energy source and no serious challenger is yet in sight.

"At present, we simply are not finding oil and gas at the rate we need to find them if we are to meet demand and maintain reasonable reserves, even through the next 10 years." Halbouty said we found some 60 million barrels less crude oil than we produced in 1962 and again in 1963. We have found more gas than we have used each year up to now, but there is a major indication of trouble ahead; the life expectancy of existing reserves is dropping. In 1945, we had 30.8 year's supply; in 1960, although reserves were 116 trillion cubic feet higher than they were in 1945, they represented fewer than 20 years' supply. Today we have less than 17 years of gas supply in present reserves.

"Since federal controls, imposed by the Supreme Court in the Phillips decision, have eliminated independent competition in gas exploration and promoted monopoly in the production of gas to meet market demand in this country for the next 20 years and certainly not to the end of the century.

"We can find all of the oil and gas we need within the boundaries of the country provided unnecessary controls are removed; however, we must drill more exploratory wells than we are now drilling. In 1964, we drilled approximately 11,000 exploratory wells and it appears the number will be no higher in 1965. With such a low number of wildcats, it will be impossible to meet the requirements of the next decade much less the requirements of the second decade. Also 34,000 development wells were drilled in the U.S. in 1964, but they add little to the reserve picture; they simply prove up previous new reserves found by exploratory wells."

Oil Magazine
September, 1965

**TIPRO POLICIES
BLASTED BY HALBOUTY**

Editor's Note: We are pleased to publish verbatim the text of two letters by industry leaders who represent opposing schools of thought, in the hope that they will help to clarify the obscurity of an impressionistic picture that seems to depend for its interpre- *tation on where you are standing. No doubt our readers will be divided in their reactions, which will reflect their partnership, affiliations and associations in varying degrees of loyalty and independence.*

*Houston, Texas
August 9, 1965*

Mr. Malcom D. Abel, President
The Texas Independent Producers
and Royalty Owners Association
P.O. Box 1391

Midland, Texas 79701
Dear Malcolm:

For some time I have been concerned about the manner in which TIPRO has been conducting its business. As you will recall, several weeks ago I informed you by telephone of my concern over matters I am herewith outlining. After our talk, I held back forwarding this letter in hope that matters might begin to improve in TIPRO. However, the recent position taken in regard to foreign depletion has confirmed my decision to speak up with the hope that we might possibly avoid future destructive moves. At that time I had hoped to address this letter to your attention only. Now, I believe that it should be an open letter to counteract some of the adverse publicity TIPRO has been receiving, and consequently, I have decided to make it public Thursday morning.

I have taken much time to inventory my thoughts on TIPRO programs and pronouncements to arrive at a judgment as to TIPRO's value to its membership and to the industry. As a result of this reflection, I am now fearful that some of TIPRO's indiscretions are making it more enemies than friends and are needlessly exposing its membership and the industry to a number of mutual jeopardies. While the following analysis is quite lengthy I do feel that it merits your careful consideration.

Over the past several years TIPRO has carried on a continuous harassment of the major oil companies both publicly and internally through the TIPRO Reporter. It has been carried on at a time when the Justice Department and some economists question the market demand states' conservation practices, their inflationary effect on crude prices, the advisability of any import controls, and are claiming that these practices and controls result in the public subsidizing the high cost stripper well production.

Recently TIPRO stepped up its attack on foreign depletion which in my opinion, is one of the most serious mistakes in its history.

TIPRO has probably rightly deduced that it can attack the majors without serious recriminations, but it overlooks the fact that many of its demands and proposals play into the hands of foes of domestic depletion, the liberal economists and the professional regulators who would put the small independent producer out of business.

For example, TIPRO's May 1965 statement before the Federal Trade Commission which was inquiring into gasoline marketing practices, is just one of the many instances of TIPRO indiscretions which jeopardize its membership's interests. TIPRO called on FTC or some other governmental agency "to investigate the anticompetitive aspect of the crude oil purchasing practices of major integrated oil companies in the United States." Such an investigation would be the province of the Justice Department rather than FTC. It would in all probability accommodate not only unspecified TIPRO allegations, but also the contentions of liberal economists (Burck, Kahn, Adelman, Rostow, Hewitt, et al). The economists have recommended (a) federal unitization of all reservoirs, (b) removal of crude import controls, (c) limiting state conservation authority to setting MER's for the unitized pools and (d) termination of state market demand authorities. They say the results would be beneficial to the public as crude prices would drop about $1.00 per barrel to the world market level and this would eliminate the stripper well and small flood production and prevent the drilling of unnecessary wells. (The 6,400 Texas operators include 5,550 operators who produce a total of only 151,000 b/d or 27 b/d per operator).* I need not point out to you that the basic fallacy of this program is it would ultimately make this country dependent on foreign oil and not only would national security be jeopardized but the consuming public would have to pay the prices set by foreign governments which would be all the "traffic could bear."

About ten days after TIPRO testified before the Federal Trade Commission, Dr. Hewitt of Indiana University, on the same stand, charged that the major oil companies worked with the state conservation bodies to maintain artificially high crude prices "which preserve a place for the marginal producer." He further stated that pressure to maintain high crude price has come from the small crude owners and producers. The TIPRO witness had complained that crude prices are too low and that the majors are conspiring to drive crude prices down to recoup their losses in gasoline price wars and advance their monopolistic position (page 3 of TIPRO FTC statement and Summer 1965 TIPRO Reporter). Hewitt insisted that the ills of the oil industry are due to (a) rigid crude price structure made possible by market demand proration, (b) tax benefits for production, and (c) vertical integration. Hewitt, like a number of other economists, contends that the independents' unprorated production is subsidized under existing regulations. So both TIPRO and Hewitt have urged the Justice Department to take a look at state conservation practices, but for entirely different reasons. Justice's reasons for "taking a look" would hardly accommodate TIPRO's objectives but would undoubtedly indulge some of Hewitt's contents.

TIPRO testimony, in support of its recommendation for a crude purchasing investigation, suggests that the majors are responsible for the 1965 crude price cuts (page 5), that a serious monopoly position by the majors is threatened (oral testimony as reported in the Summer 1965 TIPRO Reporter), that majors can enhance their economic advantages by unfair trade practices (page 3), and that FTC should end unspecified, unlawful practices now designed to destroy competition (page 7).

I find that all of the Texas crude price cuts made during the first five months of 1965 were posted by independents (Permian, Suntide, Southern Minerals, McWood and Greer). Most crude price reductions of my experience, whether posted by independent or major purchasers, are a reflection of (a) oversupply, (b) quality equalization, and/or (c) changes in refining area destinations where the delivered price must be competitive with the delivered crude prices from other competing areas if the crude is to find a market.

Testimony by Marathon at the hearings indicated that few majors were even approaching domestic crude self-sufficiency which was TIPRO's implied test of threatened monopoly. The TIPRO statement offers no example of unfair or unlawful trade practices on the part of the major crude purchasers, many of whom have helped to find a home for distressed Texas crude over extended periods.

On page 3 of its statement, TIPRO charged that price wars are intended (by the majors) to "repress competition from independent refiners and producers." This, of course, was not proved by later testimony of any FTC witnesses.

On page 4, the Commissioners are told that inland refiners cannot benefit directly from refining low-cost foreign crude so they exchange their quota tickets for domestic production at a profit of $1.25 per barrel. This situation, TIPRO stated, makes the majors mad so they recriminate by squeezing the independent refiners profits at the filling station level. Such a malicious and specious TIPRO argument reflects no credit on the integrity and high principles which characterize the responsible TIPRO membership.

Equally unrealistic was its recent recommendation to the Railroad Commission for a 10-day emergency cutback of May allowables to 17% to help reduce stocks by 477,000 b/d (TIPRO Reporter, Summer 1965 issue).

Recently, TIPRO voted to ask Congress to determine whether oil companies operating overseas enjoy any tax advantages not available to domestic operators. It asked that such a study place particular stress on foreign depletion. However, your letter of July 15 and its attached staff papers leave little doubt as to the position of many of the TIPRO officers who would jeopardize their own interests in domestic depletion by proposing a reduction in the foreign depletion allowance. Your letter states that many TIPRO members believe that foreign oil investments enjoy preferential tax treatment. According to the tax

people I consulted last week, foreign production has no economic advantage because of U.S. tax laws. They say that recent IPAA studies confirm their judgment.

Your staff papers are misleading in several respects. The first one would lead the reader to believe that a reduction in foreign depletion would not endanger domestic depletion. Even though there may be some Congressmen who feel that a cut in foreign depletion would not jeopardize domestic depletion, there are many who are equally convinced to the contrary. Senator Douglas and others have been trying for years to divide and conquer the oil industry on the domestic depletion issue. Certainly, he feels that a reduction in foreign depletion would be a wedge which would help him attain his long standing goal of reducing the rate for domestic production.*

In your staff's general comments under the caption "Foreign Tax Advantages" it is stated that there is a widespread abuse of tax privileges accorded American oil companies operating abroad. Secretary Douglas Dillon was quoted as criticizing preferential treatment of foreign investment income, implying that he considered foreign percentage depletion to constitute such preferential treatment. This implication is misleading and in all fairness should be corrected. First, Mr. Dillon was talking strictly about rules for taxing income of foreign subsidi-

*Hearings before the Committee on Finance, U.S. Senate, 88th Congress, First Session, on H.R. 8363 Part 5, pp. 2394 to 2397.

aries of American companies. He was proposing some changes in the law as it existed prior to 1962 because the income of such foreign subsidiaries was not taxable to the parent company until paid out in dividends.* This was deemed to be an advantage that a foreign subsidiary had over a domestic subsidiary operating abroad. *Percentage depletion had nothing to do with these proposals.* The only advantage of foreign producers over domestic producers lies in the larger oil reservoirs, greater productive capacity, and lower costs per barrel.

I am advised that in the President's 1963 Tax Message he did suggest a minor technical amendment to prevent any excess foreign tax credit attributable to percentage depletion from being available to reduce the U.S. tax liability on foreign income from non-mineral sources. This proposal did not suggest in any way that the full percentage depletion deduction should not be allowable with respect to foreign mineral income. To the best of my knowledge, there has never been a suggestion by any president or by any administration that depletion should be reduced to foreign production only.

Your staff memorandum states that foreign income taxes are, in fact, royalties and should not be treated as "taxes" for the purposes of the foreign tax credit.

This statement is refuted by the IPAA Special Committee on Foreign Taxation, which pointed out in its report last Spring that royalties paid to foreign countries are comparable to those paid landowners in the United States and more particularly to royalties paid the U.S. government on federal lands. If IPAA is in error, I would appreciate your advice as to where they erred.

Additionally, of course, each of the foreign countries like the U.S. government has the sovereign right to levy taxes on oil and gas producers, and like the U.S., they do levy income taxes on them in addition to the royalties. The Internal Revenue Service has examined each of the tax statutes of foreign countries and has concluded that the levies are taxes that qualify for the foreign tax credit irrespective of whether the taxpayer produces oil or manufactures cars and tractors. The record of the hearings before the House Ways and Means Committee, which wrote the applicable tax laws, confirms the accuracy of this interpretation. Otherwise, this would be a double taxation of foreign income.

It is misleading to say that Americans producing oil abroad have any tax advantage over domestic producers. My understanding is confirmed by the IPAA Special Committee appointed to study the tax treatment of foreign oil and gas operations. This committee last spring concluded that "tax provisions of themselves do not give any advantage to foreign

* See Hearing Before the Committee on Ways and Means, 87th Congress, First Session, May 3-11, 1961, Vol. 1, pages 27-37.

operations over U.S. operations."

It is incorrect and misleading to argue that the balance of payments problem can be alleviated by eliminating or reducing depletion on foreign production. The only evidence about which I have knowledge indicates that in 1963 American oil companies contributed $360 million toward a favorable balance of payments. (See Hearings Before the Committee on Banking and Currency, 89th Congress, First Session, March 9-25, Part 1, pp. 519, et seq.) This testimony is surely reliable, so it seems to me that TIPRO cannot say that a reduction in depletion could help with the balance of payments predicament. It would, however, place the U.S. companies at a competitive disadvantage with the British, Dutch, et al.

If we back off and get a good perspective on this problem, it occurs to me that there is another danger in any TIPRO proposal to reduce foreign depletion. There is danger that it may create a public image of vindictiveness in advocating that a greater tax burden be placed on foreign producers just because they have a cost but not a market price advantage over domestic production.

Such a position may suggest that TIPRO is not interested in the national security when it is generally recognized that reducing foreign depletion would place American companies at a distinct advantage in competing with foreign companies. In some instances it is the foreign governments themselves that are competing

with American companies. Russia is the prime example of this kind of government versus private industry competition. In recent years the Russian govenment has won a substantial part of the market for petroleum from American interests by selling crude and petroleum products at extremely low prices. In 1962 the average price of crude oil reported by Russia to the Free World was $1.36 a barrel, compared to $2.52 a barrel for crude they sold to satellite countries. The volume of Russian oil sales to Free World countries is estimated to be over 800,000 barrels a day in 1965 and is expected to increase to as much as 1,600,000 barrels a day by 1970.*

The National Petroleum Council has stated that the Communists are not simply trying to sell oil but to undermine and destroy the private oil industry. In support of this statement the NPC cites the following from an authoritative Soviet publication:

"It should be borne in mind that oil concessions represent, as it were, the foundation of the entire edifice of Western political influence in the (less developed) world, of all military bases and aggressive Blocs. If this foundation cracks, the entire edifice may begin to totter and then come tumbling down."

Any TIPRO proposal to reduce foreign depletion can only com-

* National Petroleum Council Report titled "Impact of Oil Exports from the Soviet Bloc"

fort, not deter, communism in its stated goals.

Turning now to TIPRO's activities in the import area, we find that in five years of battling since the inception of the mandatory crude oil import program, TIPRO has not won a single, significant point with the Interior Department, White House, the Congress and the major integrated companies. Actually it has lost ground in the import arena, feuded with IPAA, castigated John Kelly, the former Assistant Secretary of Interior, and sorely tried the patience of the major crude purchaser with its many intemperate charges. Meanwhile, its membership has steadily declined.

Most people in the industry and those in government have long accepted the fact that the TIPRO proposal to cut crude imports by 300,000 to 500,000 b/d was totally unrealistic. TIPRO has finally accepted this concensus and has called for import stabilization but with a quid pro quo on higher residual imports for lower crude imports. Such a quid pro quo is also unrealistic. TIPRO does not have and never will have the political assets to cause any significant cuts in crude imports in the face of Western Hemisphere diplomatic considerations and the administration's foreign trade objectives. The majors are equally ineffective.

I submit that it is time that TIPRO quit jeopardizing the interests of its members by sponsoring unrealistic policies and exploiting them in the consistently vindictive and harassing manner.

TIPRO's divisive tactics has put it in a role of a Sampson pulling the house down on the entire petroleum industry. It is timely that the responsible leadership of TIPRO recapture its policy making and public pronouncement authorities.

There is one thing that I want to make clear. That is the fact that I have no intention of resigning my membership or my office in TIPRO.

I am merely bringing up some complaints I have with policies and practices which I believe are contrary to the best interests of our association, its membership, our state, and our industry as a whole.

It is my feeling that we, as officers of TIPRO, should direct our attention to these ineffective policies, which some of us believe are doing our members and our industry irreparable harm, and to attempt to adopt better policies.

TIPRO has made some important contributions in the past, but the opportunities to do far more good abound today. One opportunity is in the field of better internal industry relations, especially our relations with other industry associations and organizations.

Another is in the field of relations with our members, the press, and the general public in Texas. Our state is the greatest oil and gas state in the Union. It is my feeling that the image of the Texas industry can either help or or harm the whole domestic industry. Whether it is justified or not, the Texas oil industry image has not been good in the past.

This, I feel, is because no organization in this state has taken the time or made the effort to properly inform the public at home or out of the state about the Texas petroleum industry. We could do that better than any other group and with far greater effect and at a real profit to our membership.

We could continue to promote more realistic and honest conservation measures. We could devote some attention to reducing costs of exploration and production. We could continue to seek outlets and better prices for our production. We could promote intrastate sales for natural gas to avoid the deathly influence of ridiculous federal regulations on natural gas, as typified by the most recent Permian Basin rule.

I think we might be better informed about the world petroleum situation as it relates to the United States and Texas so that we could more intelligently approach the problems with which we find ourselves confronted. In short, I would prefer to see TIPRO return to the type of sound, dignified, and responsible programs that were undertaken in the association's earlier history.

These are a few things we could do, or do better, if we so directed our energies. It could be that in order to do these things we should exercise more control over the staff to prevent continuing in our present direction.

If we did these things I am certain we could avoid the resignation of great independent leaders and could attract the membership of hundreds of other solid and successful Texas independents who have, up to now, either declined to become members, or have ignored the opportunity to offer the strength of their leadership.

I hope you and the other officers of the association take these remarks in the spirit in which they are intended and not as personal criticism. I believe we have all inherited some practices that have built up in the past, possibly as a result of our paying too little attention to details ourselves and leaving too much to the TIPRO staff. The staff, I believe, is evidently of the opinion that harassment of other segments of the industry creates the atmosphere that attracts and holds members. I doubt this.

I realize I am subjecting myself to attack from some elements of our organization, but as you know, I have never been one to avoid controversy or criticism when I am convinced in my own mind that I am right.

Very truly yours,

Michel T. Halbouty

TIPRO Prexy Abel answers criticism.

August 12, 1965

Mr. Michel T. Halbouty
5111 Westheimer Road
Houston, Texas 77027

Dear Mike:

I am frankly shocked by your vicious public attack on TIPRO. I am surprised also that some of the positions you take seem to contradict former Halbouty speeches, especially on conservation.

Nevertheless I always welcome disagreements from members who claim to be very active, even though you have found time to attend very few meetings.

Mike, speaking personally, I am afraid you misunderstand the whole purpose of TIPRO when you try to change policies by attacking the Association in the press. The most hallowed tradition in TIPRO is the right of the individual to dissent, and it is through executive and policy committee sessions that we hear everybody out, and then reach the concensus judgement of non-integral domestic independents. Had you attended the San Antonio meeting, where it was announced well in advance that these issues would be decided, you know your views would have had full consideration. You also would have learned why the positions were taken. Then carrying your grievances to the press would not have been necessary. If these issues were as important to you as your public letter indicates, surely you could have arranged your business to be there.

As to foreign depletion, the only decision made at the recent session was to get all the facts out on the table. That information is just not available to us except through a Congressional study. Nor does IPAA have the necessary information needed, as their committee made clear. We need to know if the cards are stacked against domestic oil in the nation's tax policies. If so, then some change must be made for the good of the whole industry. Certainly you must agree that, however well a few independents are doing, most domestic producers are in serious trouble, and something has to be done about it.

As to TIPRO import policies, I think you have your organizations slightly confused. You may want to check your sources on that and a few other points you raise.

Concerning the staff, I can tell you as President that it is conscientiously trying to carry out Association mandates as set by the members. To change what it is doing simply requires a change in instructions to the staff.

In my own view, it is not too important whether TIPRO has "sorely tried the patience of the major crude purchasers" in its efforts to deal with price cuts, purchaser proration, and practices which are keeping the indepedent from enjoying any part of record industry prosperity. The purpose of TIPRO is survival of the independent, and not to keep the large integrated companies happy with us.

May I suggest that you make a special effort to attend future policy meetings to find out if the Executive Committee agrees that a change of direction in TIPRO is needed.

Sincerely yours,

M. D. Abel

World Oil
April 1969

THE CURRENT U.S. ENERGY CRISIS AND WHAT WE CAN DO ABOUT IT

Almost two years ago we published an exclusive interview with Mr. Michel Halbouty, one of the world's leading geologists and petroleum engineers wherein he outlined the current crisis in diminishing domestic petroleum reserves and how the United States could combat the situation.

Originally published in April, 1969 WORLD OIL *under the title: "Needed: more wildcatting to increase reserves", we are reprinting it now because we feel it still offers a concise analysis of the current energy crisis in the U.S. that is beginning to affect every American citizen.*

William G. Dudley
Publisher

Don E. Lambert
Associate Editor

The United States is facing a shortage of producible oil and gas in the 1980's. If this happens, it will be a case of famine amidst plenty. History will trace the blame to short-sighted government and management policies in the 1960's.

The status of oil and gas exploration today, how it got that way and what can be done to insure adequate supplies for the future are discussed in the following interview with Michel T. Halbouty, independent producer, geologist, petroleum engineer, past president of the American Association of Petroleum Geologists, author and world-wide lecturer.

Mr. Halbouty, are prospects for major U.S. oil and gas discoveries dying out?

By no means, I firmly believe there are large reserves yet to be found.

It is true that much of the easy-to-find oil and gas already has been discovered. But, there are many large reserves in less obvious traps which have not yet been found.

Then how do you explain the decline in the U.S. reserves position?

Geological, geophysical and wildcat activity have dropped far below levels needed to maintain a favorable reserve position. At current activity levels, there is no way we can meet this nation's needs in the next decade.

Geophysical activity is down from 8,240 crew months in 1955 to barely half that total in 1968. Exploration drilling is down from a high of 16,207 wells in 1956 to 9,000 in 1968. As the inevitable result, development drilling has dropped from a high of 42,000 wells in 1956 to 22,000.

How will this activity trend affect future oil and gas users?

This can best be answered with a comparison. During each of the peak years of 1955 and 1956, U.S. consumers used only 2.5 billion barrels of oil and 10 trillion cubic feet of natural gas. In 1968, with exploration at critically low levels, domestic producers provided 3.3 billion barrels of oil and 19.3 trillion cubic feet of natural gas, up 32% and 93% respectively.

It is well known that the U.S. reserves to production ratios (years' supply) for oil and gas have been steadily declining for several years. Thus, from here on out the U.S. reserves position can be expected to deteriorate even more rapidly than in the past.

It will take several Prudhoe Bay discoveries to reverse the trend. Remember, 10 billion barrels of domestic crude will be used up in less than three years at projected production rates. Remember also that those rates will be at least 30% higher in 10 years. It is estimated that 55-60 billion barrels of oil and 300-350 trillion cubic feet of gas will have to be discovered during the next decade to maintain a satisfactory reserves to production ratio.

Why is exploration activity at such low levels?

Mainly because of short-sighted government and management policies. Also, mergers and purchases by large companies, drying up of risk capital and the extremely high cost of operations without a proportionate increase in crude and gas prices, have reduced the ranks of the small independent producers from more than 42,000 to less than 10,000 within 15 years.

During the peak discovery years, and, believe it or not, since the discovery at Titusville in 1859,

the independents found 85% of the new oil and gas reserves in this country. I am sure that this ratio has dropped, but the independents are still finding most of the reserves.

What do you mean by short-sighted government and management policies?

Only a few years back risk capital for drilling exploratory or wildcat wells was available through several sources, especially from people with tax dollars to risk. The pressure of over-production, imports, unnecessary drilling of highly expensive wells, inflationary costs, prices that have not compensated for inflation, more and more stifling government controls and harassment, plus lower and lower allowables, have dried up much of this money.

If adverse tax laws are passed which affect the petroleum industry, I doubt that there will be any risk capital left for wildcat exploration. This will mean the sure but slow extinction of thousands of independents—but more so, it will mean a greater dependence upon foreign sources for our petroleum requirements which could be disastrous to this country within a short period of time.

A current enigma of the oil industry—one I am sure will continue for some time—is that many of the large companies spend most of their exploration money in offshore and foreign areas, and the independents are desperately trying to find money to drill their own onshore prospects as well as the onshore prospects which the majors desire to farm out.

These short-sighted policies, compounded by the delay to put into practice new domestic exploration concepts, have caused a noted decrease in the incentive for majors and independents to conduct a vigorous exploration program.

How can exploration be increased?

The downward trend will be reversed only when government and management start to base policies of today on the long range needs of the future. Tax and price incentives must be provided to stimulate drilling of at least 25,000 wildcats per year, nearly triple the current rate.

But, even greater incentives will not be enough to increase the exploratory effort. There also must be progressive exploratory thinking.

During the past decade, management and explorationists in some large firms have adopted a passive attitude toward exploration. This has led to a belief that to locate large deposits of petroleum one has to spend a fortune offshore or outside the United States where exploration areas are virgin, where structures are huge, reserves are large and costs relatively small in relation to reserves found.

As a result, the search for onshore petroleum within our own borders has been neglected. There still are huge reserves to be found onshore.

How can geologists help?

Those responsible for exploration programs cannot sit back any longer and coast along in the rut of yesteryear's exploration methods. The drop in exploratory effort in this country is in part due to their passive and submissive attitude.

To find the new giant reserves of the future, geologist must replace the unenthusiastic and yielding attitude of the past decade with bold and progressive thinking associated with a strong courage of conviction and determination. Equally bold and faithful backing of this kind of thinking by management is a must.

Geologists will have to reassert themselves and revert to the best tool in their possession: brain power. They must once again become dedicated geologists. They must once again employ bold geological deduction and imagination.

And above all, geologists must restrain themselves from depending too much on the "magic black electronic box" and other such equipment.

There is an art to finding oil and gas. Geologists and geophysicists can supply that art, and they must if successful exploration for the hidden and subtle traps is to materialize.

What new developments in exploration thinking do you foresee?

First, I see the emergence of a new kind of geologist who no longer has a one-track mind. He will be aware of what is happening in today's new technology, the ever-changing economic conditions, new political concepts, intense fuel competition, world petroleum outlook and world markets. But above all, the new geologist will learn what significance all these things have for his industry, his company, and his own future as an explorationist.

Since modern exploratory odds are no longer conducive to the "sixth sense" approach every means will be used to reduce the risks.

This means a concentrated study of all available information on a more knowledgeable basis. Thus, greater use will be made of outstanding geologists to coordinate geological thinking with that of the geophysicist, petroleum engineer, landman, scout and other petro-professional involved with the exploration team.

This will require the petroleum geologist to maintain an attitude of creative imagination in forming new concepts concerning stratigraphic traps, unconformities, relic deltaic areas, deep-seated structures, sedimentation, geophysical and geochemical interpretation, paleontology and stratigraphy.

More creative imagination will be applied to basins and areas which are inadequately explored, such as the entire eastern seaboard from Maine to the Florida Keys.

Where do small producers fit into your picture of tomorrow?

The independent wildcatters and producers will become better and more aggressive business men and oilmen, astute economists, and above all, be either creative geoscientists, or employ or become associated with such scientists. If they don't, they will fold!

Will more independents become involved in offshore operations?

Admittedly, independents can't compete with the majors in bidding, exploring and drilling for offshore oil and gas. But, as far as I know, offshore will never become a serious threat to land prospects in volume of discoveries.

No one company can get all of the available leases in the tidelands, and those that do acquire many large blocks of acreage are the biggest gamblers the petroleum world has ever known. They can make a "killing" or they can come close to bankruptcy. Knowing this, only the biggest with the greatest cash reserves are able to cope with the big water gamble. Then, on most occasions, they do it in combination of companies to spread out the risks and losses.

More independents can be expected to form groups to seek gas and oil reserves, both offshore and onshore. Individuals and groups alike will assume a more aggressive policy in drilling new areas, in encouraging the drilling of prospects worked out by new geological exploration concepts, and in working with the majors more than ever before to increase exploration activity.

There is no question in my mind that the independents need the majors and the majors need the independents.

With proper incentives, where would you increase exploration activity?

If exploration is to succeed in finding new reserves for the future, geologists and management will have to place a greater emphasis on the search for subtle traps with large accumulations. The requirements to find these large reservoirs include focusing of exploratory thinking on the geologic conditions under which such traps and accumulations form, plus the purposeful and deliberate drilling of more stratigraphic and paleogeomorphic wildcat tests.

Prior to Prudhoe Bay, 306 giant fields had been found in this country—259 oil and 47 gas. The number of giant fields credited to each of the exploratory methods are: (1) surface evidence and surface geology, 94.5 fields; (2) random drilling, 33.5 fields; (3) subsurface geology, 59 fields; (4) geophysics, 119 fields.

Thus, most of the giant field discoveries have resulted from exploration directed purposely toward finding and exploiting the structural trap. In some places this search was successful in finding, usually unintentionally, the subtle stratigraphic or paleogeomorphic traps.

Although only a few of these subtle traps have been found to date, mostly by accident, they appear fairly often in the discovery records throughout the years. This suggests that many more such traps must occur in yet-to-be-determined areas.

If this conclusion is valid, future exploration success for our large onshore reserves lies in a search purposely directed toward the subtle and obscure traps. These traps must receive attention because obvious subsurface structural features are increasingly more difficult to find, simply because there are increasingly fewer to find.

Oil Daily
November 16, 1970

An Eminent Oil Hunter Explains HOW WASHINGTON CAN SOLVE THE ENERGY CRUNCH
by Michel T. Halbouty

Today there is a relatively mild energy crisis in this country. People are inconvenienced, especially along the Eastern Seaboard by brownouts, lack of adequate heat, air conditioning and other conveniences we have accepted as the necessities of life under our standard of living.

This is probably only a precursor of what is going to happen. In some areas gas is not available. Business expansion has slowed down. For the first time in the history of this country the people are finding normal progress limited.

All of this because there is not sufficient energy available to meet the public needs. It is the beginning of a condition which can only worsen unless proper steps are taken to reverse the situation.

The solution to this unusual national problem can be found in a highly accelerated program of exploration. But such a program is economically impossible under present government restrictions and in the face of diminishing incentives in the areas of taxes and prices.

In the public interest, it is most important that the federal and state governments take necessary action to inspire explorers—especially independents—to search for more oil and gas in this country and to go far enough to lure retired wildcatters back into the field.

This is the only way the energy crisis can be headed off. The industry has done everything it can do under existing circumstances. In Texas the state has responded admirably to the crisis, as it has always done. This is especially true of the Texas Railroad Commission.

Probably the most important single thing the government can do is convince the general public that there is sufficient oil and gas in this country to supply its needs for many years to come if the incentives are present for explorers. Many of the necessary tax incentives have been eliminated this year by the government. For years, the incentives to explore for natural gas have been non-existant due to the ridiculous price ceiling placed on gas by the Federal Power Commission and the absence of any semblance of sanctity to gas supply contracts.

Since about the middle of the year incentives such as an equitable depletion provision, intangible charge offs for drilling and other tax laws passed in the public interest by wiser congresses in the past (when they were needed far less than now) have been whittled away by the present congress.

At no time in the history of this young republic could such action have been taken when it would have been more harmful to the public interest.

There has been a conspiracy (apparently well organized) for the past two decades to "get the oil industry," and it has succeeded. The composition of this conspiracy has included demagogues in Congress, dupes in the media, self-styled intellectuals in the academic field, irresponsible economists and analysts seeking headlines and their presence on television. Even the addled-brained section of the entertainment world has participated. The public has been the victim of these types. Now the public is paying the piper because the people are unaware of the interdependence of the industry and the public.

And while all of this has been happening, weak leadership in Washington, in some of the state legislatures and public utility commissions, have failed to take decisive, if unpopular, action to prevent a shortage of energy in the public interest.

I recall back in the fifties when the Natural Gas Bill, to free producers from FPC controls, was under investigation before the United States Senate.

At one point, the chairman of the investigating committee asked Paul Kaiser of the El Paso Natural Gas Company, a witness for the proponents of the bill, what he thought should be done, Mr. Kaiser said that was up to the Congress.

But, asked the chairman, didn't Mr. Kaiser want a gas bill to be passed?

In his typical forthright manner, Mr. Kaiser replied that passing or not passing legislation was the business of Congress. He said his business was finding, producing and transporting natural gas. But, he added, if producers were not freed from utility-type price control, he would hate to be in the shoes of the members of congress responsible when the chicken finally came home to roost in the form of energy shortages.

Well, the chickens have come home to roost.

Here are some things that might be done by our government to alleviate the serious and critical situation which now exists:

Tax incentives to wildcatters might be restored and even improved.

A national fuels policy under a qualified commission might be adopted.

Control of producer prices in natural gas might be eliminated.

The oil industry might be relieved of its role as whipping boy. A positive program of telling the facts about the importance of the energy industry to the public could be started at once.

Washington could stop playing politics with the industry.

Relations with Canada and the rest of this hemisphere could be improved and maintained in regards to energy supply.

Gas and oil pipeline construction could be encouraged.

The law of supply and demand could be bolstered.

Conservation, especially field unitization, could be encouraged through the Interstate Oil Compact Commission. Threats to dissolve this great organization should cease.

Bibliography of Publications

Michel T. Halbouty started publication of papers and other material with his master's thesis on the *Geology of Atascosa County* at Texas A&M University in 1931.

The following bibliography includes 175 of his published papers and is presented in this volume in order to give the interested reader an idea of the scope of Mr. Halbouty's thinking on a wide range of subjects, both technical and non-technical.

It will be noted that the volume of papers started rising precipitously in the late 50's as his stature mounted in the industry. Since 1968 he has been forced to limit the acceptance of the many invitations to speak due to the heavy pressure of his own personally run independent oil and gas operations and his extensive banking and other interests. However, he is still ardently engaged in writing papers and books on both scientific and non-scientific subjects, all of which will be published as they are completed.

1. 1931a. Geology Of Atascosa County, Texas. Master's Thesis, Texas A&M University.

2. 1931b. "Petrographic Characteristics Of Some Eocene Sands From Southwest Texas." (With John T. Lonsdale and M. S. Metz) *Jour. Sed. Pet.*, Vol. 1, No. 2, pp. 73-81, November.

3. 1932a. "Vicksburg Formation In Deep Test, Acadia Parish, Louisiana. *A.A.P.G. Bull.*, Vol. 16, No. 6, pp. 609-619, June.

References to abbreviations

A.A.P.G. Bull.	—American Association of Petroleum Geologists' Bulletin
A.I.P.G.	—American Institute of Professional Geologists
A.P.I.	—American Petroleum Institute
G.C.A.G.S.	—Gulf Coast Association of Geological Societies
H.G.S. Bull.	—Houston Geological Society Bulletin
Ind. Pet. Monthly	—Independent Petroleum Monthly
Jour. of Pet. Tech. Bull.	—Journal of Petroleum Technology Bulletin
Jour. of Sed. Pet.	—Journal of Sedimentary Petrology
Pet. Dev. & Tech. Trans. of A.I.M.E.	—Petroleum Development & Technology Transactions of the American Institute of Mining and Metallurgical Engineering
S.P.E.	—Society of Petroleum Engineering of A.I.M.E.

4. 1932b. "High Island Dome, Galveston County, Texas." *A.A.P.G. Bull.*, Vol. 16, No. 7, pp. 701-702, July.

5. 1935a. "Conservation Of Colloidal Material In Native Drilling Muds." *The Petroleum Engineer*, p. 60, April.

6. 1935b. "Geology And Geophysics Of Southeast Flank Of Jennings Dome, Acadia Parish, Louisiana, With Special Reference To Overhang." *A.A.P.G. Bull.*, Vol. 19, pp. 1308-1329, September.

7. 1936a. "Unusual Boiler Feed Hook-Up,—Entire Unit May Be Carried From One Location To Another Without Dismantling." *The Oil Weekly*, pp. 33-34, February 3.

8. 1936b. "Geology, Chemistry And Petroleum Engineering Play Important Parts In Drilling Mud Control." Part 1, *The Oil Weekly*, Vol. 80, No. 13, pp. 19-20, March 9.

9. 1936c. "Arrangement Of Economical Circulating Mud System Essential To Proper Control." Part 2, *The Oil Weekly*, Vol. 81, No. 3, pp. 36-38, March 30.

10. 1936d. "Economic Use Of Mud Materials In Rotary Fluid Control." *The Oil Weekly*, Vol. 81, No. 4, pp. 30-32, April 6.

11. 1936e. "Geology And Geophysics Showing Cap Rock And Salt Overhang Of High Island Dome, Galveston County, Texas." *A.A.P.G. Bull.*, Vol. 20, No. 5, pp. 560-611, May.

12. 1936f. "Mud Treatment For Heaving Shales." *The World Petroleum*, pp. 268-273, May.

13. 1936g. "Petrographic And Physical Characteristics Of Sands From Seven Gulf Coast Producing Horizons." *The Oil Weekly:* Part 1, November 23, "Introduction;" Part 2, November 30, "Laboratory Procedure;" Part 3, December 7, "Texture Results;" Part 4, December 14, "Shape Results;" Part 5, December 21, "Mineral Study Results;" Part 6, December 28, "Permeability Results."

14. 1937a. "Petrographic And Physical Characteristics Of Sands From Seven Gulf Coast Producing Horizons." Gulf Publishing Co., Houston, March 15.

15. 1937b. "Use Of Viscosimeter In Determining Drilling Mud Viscosity And Gel Strength." *The Oil Weekly*, February 15.

16. 1937c. "Geology And Economic Significance Of The Anahuac Oil Field, Texas" (With J. Brian Eby). *The World Petroleum*, Vol. 8, No. 4, pp. 46-55, April.

17. 1937d. "Spindletop Oil Field, Jefferson County, Texas" (With J. Brian Eby). *A.A.P.G. Bull.*, Vol. 21, No. 4, pp. 475-490, April. (Same as #32)

18. 1937e. "Geology And Economic Significance Of Hastings Field, Brazoria County, Texas." *The World Petroleum*, Vol. 8. No. 9, pp. 36-51, September.

19. 1938a. "La Fitte—World's Deepest Major Field." *The World Petroleum*, Vol. 9, No. 5, pp. 44-48, May.

20. 1938b. "Probable Undiscovered Stratigraphic Traps Of The Gulf Coast." *The World Petroleum*, Vol. 9, No. 6, pp. 27-39, June.

21. 1938c. "Characteristics, Methods Of Combating And Economic Importance Of Heaving Shales" (W/Nicholas A. Kaldenbach). *The Oil Weekly:* Part I, Vol. 9, No. 7, pp. 17-26, October 24; Part II, Vol. 9, No. 8, pp. 42-54, October 31.

22. 1938d. "Oil And Gas Development Of South Texas During 1937." *Pet. Dev. & Tech. Trans, of A.I.M.E.*, Vol. 127, pp. 552-579, February.

23. 1939a. "Geology And Economic Significance Of Barbers Hill." *The World Petroleum*, Vol. 10, No. 1, pp. 40-55, January.

24. 1939b. "Oil And Gas Development Of South Texas During 1938." *Pet. Dev. & Tech. Trans, of A.I.M.E.*, Vol. 132, pp. 453-493, February.

25. 1939c. "Story Of Texas Oil Industry Fascinating." A review of C. A. Warner's book *Texas Oil and Gas Since 1543. The Houston Post*, May, 1939.

26. 1939d. "Temperatures As Affecting Oil Well Drilling And Production." Part I: "Temperature Effects on Oil Well Drilling" *The Oil Weekly*, Vol. 96, No. 2, pp. 10-16, December 18. Part II: "Temperature Affecting Crude Oil Production." *The Oil Weekly*, Vol. 96, No. 3, pp. 15-19, December 25.

27. 1940a. "Temperatures As Affecting Oil Well Drilling And Production." Presented at the Institute of Physics, New York in November, 1939, and published by them in book entitled *Symposium* on Temperatures, pp. 1039-1057.

28. 1940b. "Oil And Gas Development Of South Texas During 1939." *Pet. Dev. & Tech. Trans. of A.I.M.E.*, Vol. 136, pp. 458-498, March.

29. 1940c. "Sedimentation" (With Houston Geological Society Group). *A.A.P.G. Bull.*, Vol. 24, No. 2, pp. 374-376, February.

30. 1941a. "Hawkins Field Valuable Addition To Nation's Reserves." *The World Petroleum*, pp. 24-26, February.

31. 1941b. "Oil And Gas Development Of South Texas During 1940." *Pet. Dev. & Tech. Trans. of A.I.M.E.*, Vol. 142, pp. 476-504, February.

32. 1941c. "The Spindletop Oil Field, Jefferson County, Texas" (With J. Dbrian Eby). *O I L*, p. 24, November.

33. 1941d. "Geology Of The Hitchcock Field, Galveston County, Texas—Showing Stratigraphic Accumulation And Structure" (With Benjamin T. Simmons). *A.A.P.G.'s* "Stratigraphic Type Oil Fields", a Symposium, pp. 641-660, December.

34. 1941e. "Oil And Gas Stratigraphic Reservoirs In The University Oil Field, East Baton Rouge Parish, Louisiana." *A.A.P.G.'s.* "Stratigraphic Type Oil Fields," a Symposium, pp. 208-236, December.

35. 1941f. "Progress In Oil Exploration Has Been Steady Since Discovery Of Spindletop." *The Houston Post*, Section 4, p. 2, December 20.

36. 1942a. "U. S. Reserves Show Slight Increase In 1941." *The World Petroleum*, Vol. 13, pp. 36-37, January.

37. 1942b. "Oil And Gas Development In South Texas During 1941" (With James J. Halbouty). *Pet. Dev. & Tech. Trans. of A.I.M.E.*, Vol. 146, pp. 475-508, March.

Note: Entered military service in February, 1942. Separated from service in September, 1945.

38. 1947a. "Unconformities To Play Major Role In Arkansas—North Louisiana Discoveries" (With George C. Hardin, Jr.). *The Oil Weekly*. In three parts, March 31, April 7, and April 14.

39. 1947b. "Trends In Petroleum Geology Of The Gulf Coast" (With George C. Hardin, Jr.). *The Oil and Gas Journal*, Vol. 46, No. 4, pp. 136-141, 194-196, May 31.

40. 1950a. "Types Of Hydrocarbon Accumulation And Geology Of The South Liberty Salt Dome, Liberty County, Texas" (With George C. Hardin, Jr.). Abstract, Transactions of the 1950 Annual Meeting of AAPG-SEPM-SEG, Chicago, April 24-27.

41. 1950b. "Types Of Hydrocarbon Accumulation And Geology Of The South Liberty Salt Dome, Liberty County, Texas" (With George C. Hardin, Jr.). *A.A.P.G. Bull.*, Vol. 35, No. 9, pp. 1939-1977, September.

42.   1952. *Spindletop* (With James A. Clark). First Printing, Random House, New York, September.

43.   1953. "Spindletop's Second Fifty Years" (with James A. Clark). *The Texas Preview*, pp 26-28, January.

44.   1954a. "New Exploration Possibilities on Piercment Type Salt Domes Established by Thrust Fault at Boling Salt Dome, Wharton County, Texas" (With Geo. C. Hardin, Jr.). *A.A.P.G. Bull.*, Vol 38, pp. 1725-1740, August.

45.   1954b. "Thrust Faults on Salt Domes" With George C. Hardin, Jr.). A reply to Theodore A. Link's Discussion. *A.A.P.G. Bull.*, Vol. 38, No. 12, pp. 2566-2567, December.

46.   1954c. "Salt Dome Geology May Enter New Phase" (With George C. Hardin, Jr.). *The Oil and Gas Journal*, Vol. 53, No. 26, pp. 93-98, November 1.

47.   1955a. "Factors Affecting the Quantity of Oil Accumulation Around Some Texas Gulf Coast Piercement Type Salt Domes" (With George C. Hardin, Jr.). *A.A.P.G. Bull.*, Vol. 39, No. 5, pp. 697-711, May.

48.   1955b. "Significance of Salt Dome Geology in Past and Future Oil Exploration" (With George C. Hardin, Jr.). *The Oil Forum*, Special Oil Finders Issue, pp. 129-131, 152, April.

49.   1955c. "New Geological Studies Result in Discoveries of Large Gas and Oil Reserves from Salt Dome Structures in the Texas-Louisiana Gulf Coast" (With George C. Hardin, Jr.). Presented at the Fourth World Petroleum Congress, Rome, Italy. *Papers*, Sec. 1, pp. 83-101, June 10.

50.   1955d. "Sixty-Four Chances to Find New Gulf Coast Oil" (With George C. Hardin, Jr.). *The Oil and Gas Journal*, Vol. 54, No. 23, pp. 321-324, October 10.

51.   1956a. "Why Some Geologists and Geophysicists Don't Mix." *The Oil and Gas Journal*, Vol. 54, No. 31, pp. 148-150, January 9.

52.   1956b. "Genesis of the Salt Domes of the Gulf Coastal Plain" (With George C. Hardin, Jr.). *A.A.P.G. Bull.*, Vol. 40, No. 4, pp. 737-746, April.

53.   1957. "Geological and Engineering Thinking in the Gulf Coast of Texas and Louisiana—Past, Present and Future." (1) *Texas Oil Journal*, pp. 18, 19 & 26 May. (2) *The Ind. Pet. Monthly*, pp. 30-32 & 39, May. (3) *Journal of Petroleum Technology*, pp. 19 & 20, May.

54. 1958a. A Statement in reply to W. L. Clayton's "What Price Oil?" (1) *The Ind. Pet. Monthly*, April, 1958. (2) *O I L*, pp. 9 & 11, April, 1958.

55. 1958b. "Geological Prospects for Discoveries Brighter Than Ever." *World Oil*, Gulf Coast Issue, Von. 146, No. 7, pp. 102-3, 127-128, June.

56. 1958c. "Alaska—Its Oil Potentialities." *Petroleum Week*, Vol. 7, No. 12, pp. 24-26, September 19.

57. 1958d. "An Independent's Blueprint for Survival." (1) *World Oil*, pp. 103-106, November. (2) *The Ind. Pet. Monthly*, Vol. XXIX, No. 8, pp. 26-27, 58-60, December.

58. 1959a. "Why—Alaska?" ("Why Independents Should Tackle Alaska.") *The Oil and Gas Journal*, Vol. 57, No. 12, pp. 116-119, March 16.

59. 1959b. "A Geological Appraisal of Present and Future Exploration Techniques on Salt Domes of the Gulf Region of the United States" (With George C. Hardin, Jr.). (1) Presented at Fifth World Petroleum Congress, New York. Paper #5, Sec. 1, pp. 1-13, June. (2) *O I L*, Vol. 19, No. 8, pp. 33-42, August.

60. 1959c. "Exploration Techniques on Salt Domes of the Gulf Region of the United States." (With George C. Hardin, Jr.—Abridged version of #59). *The Oil and Gas Journal*, Vol. 57, No. 24, pp. 134-137, June.

61. 1959d. "A Review of Geological Concepts and Economic Significance of Salt Domes in the Gulf Coast Region." Abstract, *Houston Geological Society Bull.*, Vol. 2, No. 2, October.

62. 1959e. "Mandatory Pooling Advocated." *O I L*, p. 6, December.

63. 1960a. "Petroleum Conservation—Total or Partial?" *The Houston Post*, Section III, p. 3, April 24.

64. 1960b. "You Can't Bury Your Head in the Sand." *Drilling*, pp. 66-67, April.

65. 1960c. "Need for Strengthening Conservation Program." *Rocky Mountain Oil & Gas Association* program, Denver, Colorado, October 21.

66. 1960d. "The Effects of Excessive Foreign Imports on Domestic Exploration As Related to the Independent Producers." Program of the Joint AAPG, SEPM, & SEG Meeting, Los Angeles, Calif., November 3.

67. 1960e. Prepare Now to Drill 92,000 Wells A Year." *Drilling*, pp. 75-96, December.

68. 1961a. "One Step Toward Survival." (1) Published in Convention Report Issue, Independent Oil of the Oklahoma Independent Petroleum Association, Vol. 6, No. 2, February. (2) *O I L*, Vol. XI, No. 2, p. 7, February.

69. 1961b. "History and Forecast of Academic and Employment Relationships in the Geological Profession." Abstract, *H.G.S. Bull.*, Vol. 4, No. 2, October.

70. 1961c. "Gulf Coast Salt Domes Show Arctic Island Possibilities" (With George C. Hardin Jr.). *Oilweek*, pp. 31-41, October 2.

71. 1961d. "Port Acres and Port Arthur Fields, Jefferson County, Texas" (With Thos. D. Barber). G.C.A.G.S. Transactions, San Antonio meeting, Vol. XI, pp. 225-234, October.

72. 1962a. "Port Acres and Port Arthur Fields, Jefferson County, Texas" (With Thos. D. Barber). H.G.S. 1962 Volume *Typical Oil and Gas Fields of Southeast Texas*, pp. 169-173.

73. 1962b. "If They Had No Fear, Why Should We?" *Jour. of Pet. Tech.*, A.I.M.E., Vol 14, No. 8, pp. 821-824, August.

74. 1962c. "Independents to Survive Stronger, Wiser —" *Ind. Pet. Monthly*, December.

75. 1962d. "South Liberty Field, Liberty County, Texas" H.G.S. 1962 Volume *Typical Oil and Gas Fields of Southeast Texas*, pp. 200-206.

76. 1962e. "Nash Salt Dome, Fort Bend and Brazoria Counties, Texas" (With George C. Hardin, Jr.). H.G.S. 1962 Volume *Typical Oil and Gas Fields of Southeast Texas*, pp. 134-137.

77. 1962f. "Present Trends in Well Spacing and Possible Effects of Normanna and Port Acres Decisions." Annual Report, 1962, National Institute for Petroleum Landmen, Southwestern Legal Foundation, Dallas, Texas, pp. 117-141; Also in same volume "Seminar on Well Spacing and Compulsory Unitization", pp. 401-437.

78. 1963a. "How Unnecessary Wells are Hurting the Oil Industry, the People of Texas, and the Reasons and Benefits for Pooling Legislation." *The Tipro Reporter*, Vol. 15, No. 1, pp. 17-24, February-March.

79. 1963b. "The Industry's Stake in Proper Well Spacing" *Bulletin of The Rocky Mountain Petroleum Economics Institute*, Boulder, Colo., June 17-21.

80. 1963c. "The Petroleum Professional's Obligation in Public Affairs." International Oil Scouts Association Annual, Vol. 4, No. 9, pp. 13-15, September.

81. 1964a. "The Responsibility of Geologists and Petroleum Engineers in Meeting Exploration Demands in the Future" (With Thos. D. Barber) (Condensed). O I L, pp. 15-19, January.

82. 1964b. "Responsibility of Petro-Professionals." *The Landman* (Publication of the American Association of Petroleum Landmen), Vol. IX, No. 3, pp. 4-7, 64-70, February.

83. 1964c. "New Uses To Widen Petroleum's Value" (The Petroleum Industry in the Year 2000 A.D.). *The Houston Post*, Special Edition, Part 1, p. 12, February 9.

84. 1964d. "The Responsibility of Geologists and Petroleum Engineers in Meeting Exploration Demands in the Future" (With Thos. D. Barber) Complete paper. *Jour. of Pet. Tech. of A.I.M.E.* pp. 239-243, March.

85. 1964e. "Independents Holding Key to Oil in Twenty-First Century." *Ind. Pet. Monthly*, pp. 50-51, April.

86. 1964f. "Responsibility of the Petroleum Professional to Participate in Public Affairs" (A revision of Paper #80 with many changes). *A.A.P.G. Bull.*, Vol. 48, No. 5, pp. 723-726, May.

87. 1964g. "Can't Count Out Independents" Taken from "The Relation of the Independent to the Future of the Petroleum Industry"). *The Ind. Pet. Monthly*, p. 16, October.

88. 1964h. "A Forecast of Domestic Petroleum Demands for the Next Two Decades." (1) Preprint for 35th Annual California Regional Fall Meeting of SPE of AIME, Los Angeles, Calif., November 6. (2) O I L, pp. 10 and 24, December.

89. 1965a. Possibilities Along One Edge of a Basin: "Stratigraphic Discoveries Highly Probable on Basin Flank of the San Marcos Arch." Abstract, Program of Southwestern Federation of Geological Societies, pp. 11-12, January 27-29.

90. 1965b. Can We Meet U. S. Demands of the Next Twenty Years?" *Drilling Magazine*, Vol. 26, No. 4, pp. 39-42, February.

91. 1965c. "Bold Thinking is Key to Giant Reserves." A Statement, *The Oil and Gas Journal*, p. 88, August 16.

92. 1965d. "Geology—for Human Needs." Proceedings of the 1st Annual Meeting of the Texas Section of the A.I.P.G., San Antonio, Texas, pp. 4-12, September 17-18.

93. 1965e. "If They Had No Fear, Why Should We?" *The S.P.E. Journal*, Fall Issue, published by SPE of AIME, p. 4. (A revision of paper #73 with many changes oriented toward college students.)

94. 1965f. "By Year 2000: 'Find or Import' a Lot." *The Standard Times, San Angelo, Texas*, Oil Edition, October 10. (See Papers #82 and #84.)

95. 1965g. "Economics—the New Dimension in Geological Thinking." Abstract, *News Letter*, Shreveport Geological Society, Vol. 4, No. 2, October.

96. 1965h. "Maximum Brain Power: New Exploration Breakthrough." *A.A.P.G. Bull.*, Vol. 49, No. 10, pp. 1597-1600, October.

97. 1965i. "Petroleum Geologists Must See the Big Picture." *The Oil and Gas Journal*, Vol. —, No. — pp. 147-148, November.

98. 1965j. "Economics—the New Dimension in Geological Thinking." (Abstract), *NOGS LOG* (News Letter of New Orleans Geological Society), Vol. 6. No. 1, November.

99. 1965k. "Geology—for Human Needs" (A revision of #92). *The GEOTIMES*, Vol. 11, No. 4, pp. 14-17, September.

100. 1965l. "Economics—the New Dimension in Geological Thinking" (An Abstract). *H.G.S. Bull.*, Vol. 8, No. 4, p. 19, December.

101. 1966a. "Geological and Engineering Concepts and Economic Significance of Salt Domes in the Gulf Coast Region" Transactions of The New York Academy of Sciences, Series II, Vol. 28, No. 3, pp. 378-386, January.

102. 1966b. "Stratigraphic-Trap Possibilities in Upper Jurassic Rocks, San Marcos Arch, Texas" (Complete paper). *A.A.P.G. Bull.*, Vol. 50, No. 1, pp. 3-24, January.

103. 1966c. "The Role of the Independent in Modern Exploration." Published in Southwestern Legal Foundation's *Exploration and Economics of the Petroleum Industry*, Vol. 4, pp. 163-175, March.

104. 1966d. "Alaska, America's New Oil Frontier" *Petroleum Management*, "Areas of Promise" issue. Vol. 38, No. 5, pp. 95-97, May.

105. 1966e. "Economics—the New Dimension in Geological Thinking" *A.A.P.G. Bull.*, Vol. 50, No. 5, pp. 830-845, May.

106. 1966f. "Geology—for Human Needs" (A revision of #99.) *The Oil and Gas Journal*—Extra for IPE Meeting, pp. 20-23, May 16.

107. 1966g. "The Independent: His Role in Modern and Future Exploration." *Ind. Pet. Monthly,* under title "Independent Oilman is Not Vanishing Breed", Vol. 37, No. 2, p. 11, June.

108. 1966h. "Geology—for Human Needs" (A revision of #99 with many changes). *Town Hall* (Los Angeles), Vol. 28, No. 32, August.

109. 1966i. "Needed: Exploration Ingenuity" (Condensed paper). (1) *Nickle's Daily Oil Bulletin* Thursday, September 15 (2) Program of 16th Annual Mtg. of Rocky Mountain Section of A.A.P.G., Oct. 23-27, Abstract.

110. 1966j. "The Independent: His Role in Modern and Future Exploration." Proceedings of the Second Annual Meeting of the Texas Section of A.I.P.G., Abilene, Texas. September 9-10. (See #107 and #112)

111. "Conservation and the Public Interest." Abstract in Program and full paper in the Transactions of the West Texas Geological Society's Symposium on "Economics and the Petroleum Geologists", Midland, Texas, Publication No. 66-53m 10-15, October.

112. 1966l. "The Independent: His Role in Modern and Future Exploration." *The Shale Shaker,* Oklahoma City Geological Society, Vol. 17, No. 3, pp. 46-49, November.

113. 1966m. "Needed: Exploration Ingenuity" *The Oil and Gas Journal,* Vol. 64, No. 46, pp. 232-237, November 14.

114. 1966n. "Needed: Exploration Ingenuity" (A revision of #109 and #113 and oriented toward Canada). *The Journal of the Canadian Society of Exploration Geophysicists,* Vol. 2, No. 1, December.

115. 1967a. "Our Profession's Challenge and Responsibility" *A.A.P.G. Bull.,* Vol. 51, No. 1, pp. 124-125, January.

116. 1967b. "Needed: Exploration Ingenuity in Geological and Geophysical Coordination" (A revision of #113). *Geophysics,* Vol. XXXII, No. 1, pp. 12-16, February.

117. 1967c. "Economics—the Essential Requirement in Exploration." Abstract, Program of the Southwestern Federation of Geological Societies and Regional A.A.P.G. Meeting, Hobbs, N. M., February 1-2.

118. 1967d. "Creativity—the Basic Need in Future Exploration." Abstract, Bulletin of the Corpus Christi Geological Society, Vol. VII, No. 7, March.

119. 1967e. "The Heritage of Petroleum Explorers" *The Explorers Journal*, Vol. XLV, No. 1, pp. 59-62, March.

120. 1967f. "Drought of Geologists Bringing Serious Consequences" (The A.A.P.G. and S.E.G. presidents' views on earth-scientist shortage). *The Oil and Gas Journal*, Vol. 65, No. 15, pp. 116-118, April 10

121. 1967g. "Geology—For Human Needs" (A revision of #92 oriented toward the teaching profession). *The Journal of Geological Education*, Vol. XV, No. 2, pp. 80-82, April.

122. 1967h. "The Middle East Crisis." (1) *The Western Oil Reporter*, Vol. 24, No. 7, July. (2) *Oil, pp.* 12-13, July.

123. 1967i. "Heritage of the Petroleum Geologist." *A. A. P. G. Bull.* Vol. 51, No. 7, pp. 1179-1184, July.

124. 1967k. "The Recent Crude Oil Price Adjustments." *The Tulsa World*, Section 3, p. 4, August 6.

125. 1967l. "The Middle East Oil." (1) Newsletter of the Rocky Mountain Association of Geologists, Denver, August. (2) *The Oil and Gas Journal*, Vol. 65, No. 35, pp. 12 & 15 under "They Say," August 28.

126. 1967m. *Salt Domes—Gulf Region, United States and Mexico.* Gulf Publishing Co., Houston, September.

127. 1967n. "Needed: Greater Teamwork Between Disciplines." (1) Abstract, *Jour. of Petr. Tech.*, p. 1164, September. (2) *SPE Paper No. 1875*, Preprint, 42nd Annual Fall Meeting of the Society of Petroleum Engineers of A.I.M.E., Houston, October 1-4. (See No. 142.)

128. 1967o. "Shape Up Or Get Shipped Out." (1) Abstract, Program of 2nd Bi-Annual A.A.P.G.—Mid-Continent Regional Meeting, Wichita, Kansas, September 27-29. (2) Abstract, *A.A.P.G. Bulletin*, Association Round Table, Vol. 51, No. 10, p. 2173, October. (See No. 146.)

129. 1967p. "Oil Need Next 20 Years Tops Production To Date." Taken from: "New Philosophy Needed for Future Petroleum Exploration." *San Angelo Standard-Times*, Oil Edition, October 8.

130. 1967q. "Hidden Trends and Features." Transactions of 17th Annual Meeting of G.C.A.G.S., San Antonio, Vol. XVII, October.

131. 1967r. "The Urgent Need of Effective Communication Between the Oil Industry and the Public." *The Oil Daily*, pp. 17 & 20. November 15.

132. 1967s. "New Exploration Ideas Needed to Locate the 'Unfound' Traps." *The Oil Daily*, pp. 7 & 8, December 11.

133. 1967t. "Heritage and Challenge of the Petroleum Geologist." (1) *The Institute of Petroleum Review*, (London) Vol. 21, No. 252, pp. 397-402, December. (2) Abstract in *Journal of the Institute of Petroleum*, Vol. 54, No. 532, April, 1968.

134. 1967u. "Our Responsibility in Public Affairs." *The Journal of Geological Education*, Vol. XV, No. 5, pp. 205-208, December.

135. 1968a. "Economic and Geologic Aspects of Search for Gas in Texas Gulf Coast." Natural Gases of North America, A Symposium, A.A.P.G., Memoir 9, Vol. 1, pp. 177-186. (On Library Shelf, #333.)

136. 1968b. "Old Ocean Field, Brazoria and Matagorda Counties, Texas." Natural Gases of North America, A Symposium, A.A.P.G., Memoir 9, Vol. 1, pp. 194-199. (On Library Shelf, #333.)

137. 1968c. "Port Acres and Port Arthur Gas-Condensate Fields, Jefferson County, Texas" (With George C. Hardin, Jr. and Thos. D. Barber.) Natural Gases of North America, A Symposium, A.A.P.G., Memoir 9, Vol. 1, pp. 234-239. (On Library Shelf, #333.)

138. 1968d. "El Petroleo de Oriente Medio es el Producto Mas Caro de EE. UU." (Published in Madrid, Spain.) *Petroleo, Petrolquimica y Gas, Oilgas*, No. 3, pp. 17 & 18, March.

139. 1968e. "Our Responsibility in Public Affairs." *Bulletin of the Corpus Christi Geological Society*, Vol. VIII, No. 8, pp. 6-16, April.

140. 1968f. "The Supply and Demand of Geologists." *GeoScience News*, Vol. 1, No. 4, pp. 12-14, March-April.

141. 1968g. "Petroleum and the People." (A condensation of paper delivered before the General Luncheon of Town Hall, Los Angeles. Complete paper in Lecture File). *The Town Hall Journal*, Vol. 30, No. 17, pp. 109-111, April 23.

142. 1968h. "Needed: Greater Teamwork Between Disciplines." *The Jour. of Petr. Tech. Bull.* pp. 555-558, June. (See File No. 127 for S.P.E. reprints).

143. 1968i. "Petroleum" (A contribution). *American Educator Encyclopedia*, Tangley Oaks Educational Center, Lake Bluff, Ill., Vol. 12, P.Q.R, pp. 156-169, 1968. (Contributors listed in Vol. 1, A, p. XVIII).

144. 1968j. "Rock Structures: Diapirism and Diapirs." A book review. *Science,* Vol. 160, No. 3833, p. 1217, June 14.

145. 1968k. "Giant Oil and Gas Fields, in United States." *A.A.P.G. Bull.,* Vol. 52, No. 7, pp. 1102-1151, July.

146. 1968l. "Shape Up or Get Shipped Out." *A.A.P.B. Bull.,* Vol. 52, No. 9, pp. 1633-1637, September.

147. 1968m. "Petroleum—Civilization's Life Blood." *Bulletin of South Texas Geological Society,* San Antonio, Texas, Vol. IX, No. 2, October.

148. 1968n. "The Future of the Domestic Oil and Gas Industry." Symposium on Petroleum Economics and Valuation, 1968, pp. 61-64, Dallas Section, S.P.E. of A.I.M.E., March 5.

149. 1968o. "The Influence of International Factors on Domestic Exploration." Proceedings of the Southwestern Legal Foundation's *Exploration and Economics of the Petroleum Industry,* Vol. 6, pp. 25-44, Dallas, March 6.

150. 1968p. "The Impact of Natural Resources on Society." Proceedings of the 4th Annual Meeting of the Texas Section of A.I.P.G., Austin, Texas, pp. 7-15, September 12-13.

151. 1968q. "Shale Oil—Will It Ever Be A Reality?" *Quarterly of the Colorado School of Mines,* Fifth Symposium on Oil Shale, Vol. 63, No. 4, pp. 127-134, October.

152. 1968r. "What Now—Geologists, Geophysicists?" Abstract, *Bulletin of the Houston Geological Society,* Vol. 11, No. 4, p. 10, December.

153. 1969a. "Hidden Trends and Subtle Traps in Gulf Coast." *A.A.P.G. Bull.,* Vol. 53, No. 1, pp. 3-29, January.

154. 1969b. "The Future of the Domestic Oil and Gas Industry." (1) *Jour. of Petr. Tech. Bull.,* pp. 149-152, February. (2) *The Tipro Reporter "Viewpoints,"* pp. 13 & 35, Spring 1969 edition.

155. 1969c. "Needed: Greater Teamwork Between Disciplines." Abstract, *Institute of Petroleum Abstracts* (London), March. (See #142 for complete paper).

156. 1969d. "Needed: More Wildcatting to Increase Reserves." Interview with Don Lambert of Gulf Publishing Co. for Special Exploration Report). *World Oil,* Vol. 168, No. 5, April.

157. 1969e. "What Are We Going To Do About Petroleum Image!?" *The Oil Daily,* No. 4588, pp.m 5 and 6, September 26.

158. 1969f. "What Are We Going To Do About It!?" (1) *The Drilling Contractor,* Vol. XXV, No. 6, pp. 41-44 & 46, September-October. (2) *The California World Oil,* Vol. 62, No. 19, pp. 1-3, October 15. (3) *O I L,* pp. 7 and 8, 33 and 34, November-December.

159. 1970a. "Import Controls: How Drastic Changes Would Affect the Explorationists." *H.G.S. Bull.,* Vol. 12, No. 7, pp. 4-6, March. *H.G.S. Bull.,* Vol. 12, No. 8, pp. 6-7, April. Comments under "Follow-Up" items.

160. 1970b. "Mr. Scripps Said It." (1) *Congressional Record,* No. S9816 June 25. (2) *The Landman* (Bull. of A.A.P.L.) Vol. XV, No. 8, pp. 26-36, July. (3) *Vital Speeches of the Day,* Vol. XXXVL, No. 22, pp. 688-692, September 1. (4) *Shale Shaker,* Vol. 21, No. 5, pp. 111-115, January, 1971.

161. 1970c. "World War III—Is Under Way." *Drilling—DCW,* pp. 35-37, October.

162. 1970d. "The Exploration Geologist in the Seventies." Transactions of the 20th Annual Meeting of G.C.A.G.S., Shreveport, Louisiana, Vol. XX, October.

163. 1970e. "How Washington Can Solve the Energy Crisis." *The Oil Daily,* pp. 1-2, No. 4874, November 16.

164. 1970f. "Geology of Giant Petroleum Fields." (Special Editor). Memoir 14, A.A.P.G., November.

165. 1970g. Foreword to "Geology of Giant Petroleum Fields." Memoir 14, A.A.P.G., pp. vii-viii, November.

166. 1970h. Introduction to "Geology of Giant Petroleum Fields." Memoir 14, A.A.P.G., pp. 1-7, November.

167. 1970i. "Giant Oil and Gas Fields in United States." Geology of Giant Petroleum Fields, Memoir 14, A.A.P.G., pp. 91-127, November.

168. 1970j. "World's Giant Oil and Gas Fields, Geologic Factors Affecting Their Formation, and Basin Classification." Geology of Giant Petroleum Fields, Memoir 14, A.A.P.G., pp. 502-555, November. Part I: "Giant Oil and Gas Fields", pp. 502-528 (With A. A. Meyerhoff, Robert E. King, Robert H. Dott, Sr., H. Douglas Klemme, and Theodore Shabad), pp. 502-528. Part II: "Factors Affecting Formation of Giant Oil and Gas Fields, and Basin Classification", pp. 528-555. (With Robert E. King, H. Douglas Klemme, Robert H. Dott, Sr. and A. A. Meyerhoff).

169. 1971a. "Economics Without Which - - !" Abstract, Program of the Southwest Section of A.A.P.G., Thirteenth Annual Meeting, Abilene, Texas, February 7-9, 1971.

170. 1971b. "Rationale for Deliberate Pursuit of Stratigraphic and Paleogeomorphic Traps." (1) Abstract, *A.A.P.G. Bull.*, Vol. 55, No. 2, p. 341, February. (2) Abstract, Program of A.A.P.G. 56th Annual Meeting, Houston, Texas, March 28-31, 1971.

171. 1971c. "Geology and Environmental Factors Affecting Giant Fields." (With A. A. Meyerhoff and Robert H. Dott, Sr.). (1) Abstract, *A.A.P.G. Bull.*, Vol. 55, No. 2, p. 341, February. (2) Abstract, Program of A.A.P.G. 56th Annual Meeting, Houston, Texas, March 28-31, 1971.

172. 1971d. "Natural Gas." *McGraw-Hill Encyclopedia of Science and Technology,* Third Edition, pp. 6-8.

173. 1971e. "A Commentary On and a Review of the National Petroleum Council Report Future Petroleum Provinces of the United States." Preprint, printed by the Division of Production, American Petroleum Institute; Paper No. 360-1-F. Presented to the First Annual Meeting of the Division of Production, American Petroleum Institute, Los Angeles, California, May 5.

174. 1971f. "Mineral Economics Symposium: Introduction." *A.A.P.G. Bull.*, Vol. 55, No. 6, p. 771, June.

175. 1971g. "The Environment: The Earth and Beyond." Proceedings of the Fifth Annual Convention, Texas Section of A.I.P.G., Midland, Texas, pp. 31-37, August 14-15, 1969.